EDWIN CHADWICK AND
THE PUBLIC HEALTH MOVEMENT
1832–1854

EDWIN CHADWICK
AND THE PUBLIC
HEALTH MOVEMENT
1832-1854

R. A. LEWIS

Lecturer in History,
University College of North Wales, Bangor

LONGMANS, GREEN AND CO
LONDON ❖ NEW YORK ❖ TORONTO

LONGMANS, GREEN AND CO LTD
6 & 7 CLIFFORD STREET LONDON WI
ALSO AT MELBOURNE AND CAPE TOWN
LONGMANS, GREEN AND CO INC
55 FIFTH AVENUE NEW YORK 3
LONGMANS, GREEN AND CO
215 VICTORIA STREET TORONTO I
ORIENT LONGMANS LTD
BOMBAY CALCUTTA MADRAS

First published 1952

PRINTED IN GREAT BRITAIN
BY WESTERN PRINTING SERVICES LTD., BRISTOL

TO
MY MOTHER AND FATHER

PREFACE

It is a pleasure to record my thanks to the many people who have helped me in the writing of this book. I am indebted particularly to Professor J. A. Hawgood and Professor W. H. B. Court, both of the University of Birmingham, for much advice and encouragement while I was preparing the Ph.D. thesis of which this is a revised and shortened version; to the Librarian of University College, London, for permission to work on the Chadwick papers, and to his staff for their ready assistance over many weeks; to the staffs of the Record Room, County Hall, Westminster, the British Museum Reading Room and Department of Manuscripts, and the Public Record Office; to Professor S. E. Finer, of the University College of North Staffordshire, for some suggestive comments; and to my colleagues, Mr. D. A. Rees, who read part of the proofs, and Dr. J. Alun Thomas, who read the whole.

Finally, my thanks are due in special measure to the Press Board of the University of Wales for their generous contribution towards the costs of publication.

Bangor,   R.A.L.
May 1952

CONTENTS

PART ONE

THE PUBLIC HEALTH CAMPAIGN, 1832–1848

PART TWO

THE GENERAL BOARD OF HEALTH, 1848–1854

PART ONE

THE PUBLIC HEALTH CAMPAIGN

1832 – 1848

B

CHAPTER I

SOMERSET HOUSE

FEW men have done so much for their fellow-countrymen as Edwin Chadwick, and received in return so little thanks. The neglect is partly the result of ignorance, and he shares it with other civil servants of the first rank, such as Charles Trevelyan and James Stephen, whose great public work is shrouded in the silence and anonymity of the service. To the historian of the nineteenth century Chadwick is a driving force whose presence is rather deduced from its effects than observed in action. But Chadwick's reputation suffers from another cause: a hatred of the man and his work, widespread in his day, and colouring even now the impressions of him formed by a later generation. From prejudice and half-knowledge has grown the Chadwick legend—of a stiff and arrogant figure, doctrinaire in ideas, ruthless in methods, whose eternal monument is the Poor Law Bastille. With his fertile schemes for extending the frontier of State intervention he embodies the imperial ambition of the civil service. He is the suspected channel of foreign ideas, derived from German absolutism and French centralisation, alien transplantings into the free soil of the British constitution. He is, in short, the very type of the bureaucrat, whose ideal government is a vast Panopticon, where every individual lives and works under the austerely benevolent eye of the State official, the spontaneous activities of each directed by a controlling intelligence to some distant social end.

There is some basis to this legend, as to every other. It cannot be denied that Chadwick possessed certain qualities of character which during his lifetime isolated him behind a hedge of antipathy and distrust. He was a bore, a really outstanding specimen of bore in an age when the species flourished. He was too keenly aware of his own merits; while, on the other hand, he had no patience with fools, and his definition of a fool was a very wide

3

one, taking in, as it did, nearly everybody who disagreed with him. With a wholesome suspicion of power wielded by others he managed to combine a boundless confidence in the benefits of power in his own strong hands, and every scheme drawn up by Edwin Chadwick seemed to contain a provision at some point for giving more power to Edwin Chadwick. All this must be granted; but it would be unjust to write off the hostility he aroused as no more than the necessary reflex of his personal faults. If he was for so long one of the most hated men in the country, it was far less because he was overbearing and ambitious than because his investigations had left starkly displayed the tainted sources of many respectable fortunes. He stirred up a great deal of mud, and it is a tribute not a reproach that so much of it was thrown back at him by his critics. Other men were more in the public eye, commanded greater respect, and certainly inspired deeper affection, but no man, not even Lord Shaftesbury, has more solid achievements in the field of social reform to his credit. The career of Edwin Chadwick may well serve as the classical illustration of a historical truth too often neglected, that the shaping of events may often owe less to the Parliamentary gestures of the statesman than to the advice and activity of some obscurely influential figure, unnamed and unpraised, in a Government office.

Edwin Chadwick was born on 24 January 1800 in the village of Longsight, near Manchester. His grandfather, "good old Andrew Chadwick," founded the first Sunday school in Lancashire, and was the oldest Methodist in England at his death in 1815 at the age of ninety-three.[1] His father, James Chadwick, a man of some scientific and artistic ability, is said to have given lessons in botany and music to John Dalton; an active Radical, he knew Tom Paine and was a friend of the abolitionist, Edward Rushton. He edited the *Manchester Gazette*, and later kept the *Statesman* alive during the imprisonment of its editor, David Lovell. Edwin's mother we know only by his recollection of her as a "sanitarian *pur et simple*." It is certain that his sympathies and understanding were conditioned by a home in which the distress of the lower classes and the means of relieving it were earnestly discussed, but his mind took no direct impress from the Nonconformist and

[1] Alice Boardman to E. C., n.d. (*c.* 1878).

popular Radical influences amongst which he was raised. James Chadwick could not have read with any pleasure his son's gibes at Radical demagogues, while "good old Andrew" would have been horrified to hear his grandson rank the Dissenting chapel with the beershop and the Trade Union as the triple corruptions of the poor.[1]

From the village school at Longsight, Chadwick went to Dr. Wordsworth's boarding-school at Stockport, but at the age of ten he came to London, where he was sent to private tutors for instruction in the classics and in languages—French, Italian, and Spanish. At fourteen or fifteen he was put into an attorney's office. We may judge that his formal education was fragmentary, and his self-planned studies severely technical and utilitarian. For a career in the public service, he would undoubtedly have said, his equipment was none the worse for that. What was literature after all but the study of idlers who read for amusement, and history but "one great field of cram, of reliance on memory, and of dodging?" As for the classics, if they were brought out as new productions and sold in Holywell Street, the authors and booksellers would be prosecuted by the Society for the Suppression of Vice.[2] He had the deepest contempt for the aristocratic notion that no ideas of value could be expected from anybody who "had never been at either university, written a nonsense verse, or scanned a line of Horace."[3]

[1] Details of Chadwick's early life are meagre. His father emigrated to America about 1837 with the younger members of his family by a second marriage. The nature of the relations between Edwin and his family may be judged from the following letter, written towards the end of 1852 when it was clear that the General Board of Health was nearing its end:

"Under the circumstances I wish you to warn those whom it may concern of the uncertainty of the continuance of any income from me;—the only thing which has ever seemed to me to concern them. Except from Julia and yourself, and from my brother James, almost the only letters I have received from any one member of my family, since I arrived at man's estate, any other than spunging applications cries [of] Give, Give; never a personal civility, a message or an act that shewed sympathy for my labours, or couched with any view to give me pleasure, nothing but indirect or direct pauper importunities." (E. C. to Andrew Boardman.)

[2] "On the Subject Matters and Methods of Competitive Examinations for the Public Service," paper to the British Association, in *Journal of the Society of Arts*, vol. x, p. 725, 6 October 1862. *Subjects for Competitive Examination*, pamphlet, 1890.

[3] "On Life Assurances," *Westminster Review*, February 1828, vol. ix, p. 407.

Chadwick was admitted to the Society of the Inner Temple in 1823, and, while continuing his reading for the Bar, earned a slender living as reporter to the *Morning Herald*. By 1825 he was on good terms with the brilliant group of younger Utilitarians, and was frequently invited to dinner at J. S. Mill's to meet George Grote, J. Eyton Tooke, James Roebuck, and John Graham. He debated morals and metaphysics in a discussion class at Grote's; he heard John Austin lecture at the new College in Gower Street; daily he encountered the seminal ideas of Benthamism, and Utilitarian theory gave direction and vigour to his thought. Of equal significance for the future, he met Dr. Southwood Smith and Dr. Neil Arnott, and at University College he became familiar with current medical doctrine by discussions with students of the best medical school in Europe.[1] In politics and religion alike, he began to apply the same test, judging all activities by the volume of social benefit resulting from them. He turned his back on Wesleyan Longsight and professed himself a member of the Church of England—the church of "Jeremy Taylor, of Bishop Berkeley, of Paley"[2]—because in his experience Anglican priests, with their savings banks and clothing clubs, did more practical good amongst the poor than the Dissenters or the Roman Catholics. In the political sphere he watched with sceptical detachment the clash of parties and the manœuvrings for Parliamentary majorities. "I am a zealous advocate of all social improvements," he declared, "and am therefore an ally of any people by whom improvements would be made."[3] In the public health campaign a few years later he sought his friends in both camps, looking to paternal Tory principles to restrain the anarchic tendencies of Radical individualists, and to Radical irreverence to loosen the bonds of Tory traditionalism.

The struggle for recognition in the hard schools of journalism and the law marked him for life with the self-consciousness and truculence of the man who owes everything to his own exertions—

---

[1] "From discussions with them I derived a strong conviction of the superior importance of the study (as a science) of the means of preventing disease, and I was the better enabled to perceive some of the important relations of the facts, partially expressed by vital statistics, which were brought before me in my public investigations." (E. C. to Dr. R. Willis, 31 July 1844.)

[2] E. C. to Dr. Buckland, 17 January 1844.

[3] E. C. to Edward Gulson, July 1837.

the self-made man, proud of his creation but sensitively aware of its imperfections. In Fleet Street and the Inner Temple he learned habits of tremendous industry and methods of investigation which were later to serve him in good stead; and with them he acquired a cocksureness of manner which, coupled with a native arrogance, set people's teeth on edge. At thirty his aim in life was not yet settled, and his abilities, sharpened by application and a hard and varied upbringing, were awaiting their opportunity. He had been called to the Bar and was making a name in the Courts. Albany Fonblanque had appointed him sub-editor of the *Examiner*, from whose columns a raking fire was directed at the Lords, the Church, the magistracy, and the ineptitudes of the Wellington ministry, from a popular Radical angle with which Chadwick was not always in sympathy. He had caught the eye of Bentham and Francis Place with a couple of excellent articles on French Medical Charities and Preventive Police, which he had contributed to Blanco White's *London Review*, a ponderous quarterly which foundered after two issues. Before a Commons Committee he had defended his view that the primary object of a police force was the prevention of crime, the detection and apprehension of the guilty being of subordinate importance. He had been prominent in drawing up petitions and Bills for Joseph Hume and Edward Bulwer in their attack on the Stamp Duties or "Taxes on Knowledge," a subject which—he asserts—had been first broached in Parliament as "Mr. Chadwick's question."[1]

Early in 1831 he met Jeremy Bentham and accepted an invitation to become his secretary. "A queer old Hermit, half gone in dotage, sinking through it into the grave,"[2] haunted by gloomy dreams and the dread of blindness, the philosopher was still hard at work on his drafts and codifications. Many men of influence and ability had hurried from Queen Square, their minds illumined by some bright project for putting the world in order; but Bentham regarded few of them with more esteem than this stern disciple of his old age. The gentle recluse, devising the widest schemes of benevolence that the philanthropist could propose in the guise of the most hard-headed self-interest that the

[1] MS. notes, n.d., on his own career.
[2] Bentham to D. O'Connell, 15 February 1827; *Collected Works*, ed. Bowring, vol. xi, p. 2.

economist could desire, tapped some deep spring of feeling in
Chadwick which rarely, if ever, broke the surface in later years.
"Bentham was his ideal, his guiding star, and had called forth all
the tenderness of his nature," writes Chadwick's daughter. "He
could not bear the most innocent joke about Bentham's pecu-
liarities."[1] But Chadwick could not become the echo of another,
however venerated. When Bentham offered him an annuity if he
would undertake to devote his life to preaching the doctrines of
Felicitarianism, he refused the offer, though it must have had its
attractions for a struggling lawyer. He always made it clear that
his respect for Bentham did not imply a blind acceptance of
Bentham's doctrine. He was exasperated by those who believed
that his administrative ideas were drawn from the philosopher,
and would point out sharply that writings he had published before
those of Bentham showed the independence of his own views—
especially on sanitary questions.

Turning the pages of the *Constitutional Code*, Bentham's last and
most ambitious work, it is not difficult to detect the extent of
Chadwick's debt to him; nor is it possible to find a better illustration of the difference between the methods and achievements of
the two men. Chadwick, who was no political philosopher, took
his theory ready-made and unexamined from Bentham. At the
beginning of the *Constitutional Code* Bentham lays down three
fundamental principles. The first defines the object of the
legislator, which is to secure the greatest happiness of the greatest
number; the second states that in individuals "self-regard is
predominant," or "self-preference has place everywhere." The
business of the legislator is to reconcile the first principle with the
second, to build the structure of society upon a psychology of
atomic individualism. This is effected by the third of Bentham's
principles, the "means-prescribing, or junction-of-interest-pre-
scribing principle," according to which the laws and administration of the community should be consciously planned to ensure
that in pursuing his self-regarding activities the individual must
promote the welfare of his fellows.[2] The *Constitutional Code* is thus
a beautifully constructed mechanism of checks and incentives for
the organisation of a mob of conflicting egoisms. Here is the

[1] Marion Chadwick to Mrs. Aubrey Richardson, 24 October 1928.
[2] *Constitutional Code; Collected Works*, vol. ix, pp. 5–8.

theory implicit in Chadwick's administrative reforms, the justification for endowing the State with indefinitely extensible powers to ensure that the interests of the individual and the ends of society shall be identified—the justification for aggressive Government action to protect factory children and railway labourers; to supply a legal minimum of relief for the able-bodied pauper and institutional care for the sick, orphaned, and aged; to put under public regulation the supply of water and the burial of the dead; to cleanse parishes and municipalities of corruption and central departments of nepotism and patronage; to destroy, adapt, create institutions as the principle of utility might dictate. Here also are the blueprints for the Utilitarian State—the new Ministries for Health, Education, Justice, Indigence Relief, and Interior Communication; the administrative areas prescribed by technical necessities not historical sentiment; the officials selected for their tried and proved "appropriate aptitudes." Here are the powerful central departments, supervising, initiating, and inspecting, publishing regular reports on their activities, collecting statistics and information from the localities, vigilant for every opportunity to exercise their "melioration-suggestive" functions.

In its astonishing prescience, its inexorable detail, and its neat joinery of efficient means to useful ends, the *Constitutional Code* is the most sustained and fruitful effort of the practical imagination in the literature of government. But that it is a work of the imagination should not be forgotten. It is limited by what Bentham could see and hear from Queen Square. It is limited by the emotional prepossessions of a philosophical recluse of upper middle class origins, comfortable in his means and his habits, remarkably equable in temperament, who seems to have felt no stronger passion than a kind of intellectual irritability at the twisted logic of his opponents. The observation and experience of one man, even a man of genius, form too narrow a basis for the massive edifice Bentham built upon them. A philosopher at his desk could erect on paper his construction of pure intellect, building course by course from *a priori* foundations. He could postulate a Health Minister, ranking in importance before even the Finance Minister, and endowed with whatever powers his philosopher-creator might wish to give him, from the supervision of medical officers of the Army, Navy, and Indigence Relief departments to the maintenance of hospitals and the inspection of prisons, schools, and Poor Law establishments. This ideal Minister would, of course, be charged with a comprehensive range of minutely defined duties—an "aqua-procurative" function; a "malaria-obviating" function; a "health-regarding-evidence-elicitative-and-recordative" function, involving the collection of reports from local registrars, hospitals, and the establishments under the various Ministries; an "appropriate-publication" function enjoining that the "utmost publicity" be given to the activities of his department.[1] It was Chadwick's task to test these *a priori* notions against the evidence, to work upwards from the day-to-day facts of social circumstance, and to find in actual case histories the arguments to convince ratepayers and editors and Ministers of the Crown. "I may observe," he says, "that in my service I have never followed any one, not even Bentham, but have deduced my conclusions not even from Bentham's but solely from close and important collections of evidence."[2]

For twelve months Chadwick lived in Queen Square, nursing Bentham through his last illness. Before his death, Chadwick laid before him the outline of the Poor Law proposals, "and he was satisfied with the proofs I gave him."[3] In his will Bentham bequeathed to his secretary a small legacy and part of his library of jurisprudence, referring to him with affection and hoping that he would continue the grand work of codification.

In 1832 came the decisive point in his career. Nassau Senior, knowing him from his contributions to Blanco White's quarterly as an unusually well-informed student of social problems, invited him to assist the Royal Commission which had just begun its inquiry into the Poor Laws. Senior had the ear of the Government, and his invitation opened to Chadwick the doors of Whitehall. It was no civil service fledgling, docile, well-bred, and ignorant, however, that Senior thus introduced, but an assertive, rather crude, lawyer-journalist, with habits of mind already fixed, who for years had been elaborating theories of positive Government action and was eager for the opportunity to put them into practice. From the first he was an unwelcome and critical alien.

[1] *Constitutional Code; Collected Works*, vol. ix, pp. 443–5.
[2] *On the Evils of Disunity in Central and Local Administration* (1885), p. 2, footnote.
[3] E. C. to H. D. Macleod, 19 January 1860.

"All those who like Lord Melbourne are for letting things 'shake right,' as he expressed it, all those who in the sight of any amount of evil, use the half informed economists' cry of *Laissez faire*, set me down as mad."[1] Patronage, which filled the public service with the random selections of favour or influence, had bred a race of timid, *fainéant* officials, who looked with deep uneasiness upon investigations into social evils which must lead to activity on their part. They took the machinery nearest to hand and followed the advice which promised least trouble, clinging to old forms and worn routines to avoid the labour of inventing and mastering new. "Why can't you leave it alone?" Lord Melbourne would ask querulously when a restless subordinate suggested that something should be done.[2] To the advocates of "leave it alone" Chadwick was a dangerous eccentric. He was wild, unsafe, visionary, revolutionary even, this man with his ingenuity in devising novel administrative machinery, his expositions of the preventability of disease and crime, and his irreverent scorn for the oligarchic doctrine that the most important qualities of a man are his name and his stock. Above all, these Government servants, Ministers and departmental heads alike, were alarmed by Chadwick's faith in Government. Everybody knew that "Government does everything badly." From the beginning Chadwick, the first great civil servant with a professional sense of the dignity and proper functions of the public service, set himself to remove that slur. He was none too tactful about it. "Sir," he remarked with a truly Johnsonian grandeur to young Lyon Playfair, "the Devil was expelled from heaven because he objected to centralisation, and all those who object to centralisation oppose it on devilish grounds!"[3]

Laissez faire in economics was the obverse of Melbourne's "leave it alone" in government, and Chadwick's advocacy of positive Government action was logically combined with a rejection of the orthodox economic theories of the day. When he began his Poor Law inquiry economic science was a remote, deductive, Ricardian structure, proceeding from premiss to conclusion with the inevitable progress of a geometrical proof.

[1] E. C. to the Rev. Sidney Godolphin Osborne, 16 April 1847.
[2] MS. fragment, n.d.
[3] W. Reid, *Memoirs and Correspondence of Lyon Playfair* (1899), p. 64.

He first abandoned the method, and then found himself abandoning the principles and the deductions from them. There were, he told the Political Economy Club, two schools of economists: the "hypothesists," who reasoned deductively from unverified or imperfectly verified hypotheses which they called principles; and the "school of facts," who preferred to make inductions from the facts, incomplete though these might be. Unattractive and laborious as the latter was, it was the method he favoured. Working with hypothetical cases offered the advantages of ease and simplicity, and they could readily be shaped to fit any system the manipulator pleased; but the practice was open to the grave objection "that we are apt to imagine and to use conjunctions of circumstances which never do occur as assumed and from them to deduce consequences which never do happen as deduced, and never will so happen." The theorist might, for example, "aggravate human misery by deducing it upon hypothesis to be irremovable," the result being "to mischievously misdirect human attention: to excite false alarms, to give extreme pain."[1]

This is the note sounded time and again by Chadwick—the scorn for statesmen and administrators who continually arrived at practical decisions in incredible ignorance of the grounds on which they could safely be made; the insistence that legislation must be founded on an ample induction, an inquiry safeguarded as in a scientific investigation by every security for the attainment of objective truth. The proper place for the economist or administrator, who was preparing the ground for legislative action, was in the street and workshop; the proper method was to get first-hand acquaintance with the problems and persons to be dealt with, not to view them dimly through a mist of words and pre-conceptions. What Chadwick thought of an investigating body which sat round a table in London and listened to paper evidence and the representations of selected witnesses, he revealed in a pungent letter to the chairman of a Royal Commission which had been trespassing without due deference in a field he regarded with a proprietary eye. "You have been dependent upon what others bring before you. The merit of my procedure for investigation is, that I have the least of such dependence. I do not only

---

[1] "Population Question. Two schools of political economy: the geometrical reasoners and the reasoners from facts," MS. draft, c. June 1845.

the work of an attorney but the work of an attorney's clerk. I have gone to see the places myself . . .: and I have cross-examined the witnesses there on the spot."[1] The procedure he favoured was that of an open inquiry by a commission of experts, circulating detailed questionnaires and conducting local inquiries by itinerant investigators. This method had two advantages. First, by such inquiries the curious compound of conjecture, prejudice, and arbitrary assumption which went by the name of political and economic theory would be replaced by a body of tested knowledge, based on experiment, accurate observation, and verifiable evidence. Secondly, there would no longer be justification for the dangerous inaction of Government, which was the result partly of an honest bewilderment about the nature of the evils and the means of remedy, partly of apprehension about the public attitude to any proposals that might be made. A full and explanatory report from the commission would supply all the facts necessary for the framing of legislation and the conduct of Parliamentary debate; while the public inquiry, giving opportunity for all parties to be heard and all objections to receive their due weight, would ensure that the will of the country had been consulted—and instructed also, since the education of opinion by the inquiry was as important as the exploration of the facts.[2]

The value of Chadwick's influence in the field of social investigation during the twenty-two years of his official career can hardly be over-estimated. His method was not original. John Howard had made the round of the prisons with measuring tape, weighing scales, and notebook, and had refused to take any statements on hearsay, seeking to confirm everything by cross-questioning keepers, turnkeys, and prisoners; Bentham had laid it down that legislation is "an affair of observation and calculation," and that it should be based, not as hitherto "upon the quicksands of prejudice and instinct," but upon "the immovable basis of sensations and experience"[3]; the Poor Law inquiry of 1832–4 was conducted, probably at Lord Brougham's suggestion, by itinerant commissioners, as was also the inquiry of the Municipal

[1] E. C. to Lord Bramwell (Chairman of the Royal Commission on Metropolitan Sewage Discharge, 1884–5), 3 March 1885.
[2] Cf. *A paper on the chief methods of preparation for Legislation . . . read at a special meeting of the Society for Promoting Amendment of the Law*, 1859, *passim*.
[3] *Theory of Legislation*, ed. C. K. Ogden (1931), pp. 10, 102.

Corporations Commission of 1835. But the full development of
the method, and in particular its use as a weapon to combat the
opposition of doctrinaires and hostile interests, is peculiarly
Chadwick's achievement. In addition to the models afforded by
his own unequalled series of reports, he was ready with guidance
to other investigations, such as the Children's Employment Commission of 1840. And, under the General Board of Health, the
procedure of preliminary inquiry in the locality was used by
Chadwick's Inspectors to clear the ground for the application of
the Public Health Act.

For Chadwick everybody had his story, his facts, his fragment of
experience, with lessons to instruct the acute and sympathetic
investigator. The working-class housewife could tell him of her
market purchases, the quick succession of her confinements, her
ineffectual attempts to keep her house clean without water and
maintain the health of her family in the midst of damp and filth.
The young criminal in the prison cell could describe how he fell to
the temptations of the flash-house. The gravedigger had stories of
the horrors of the churchyards, and the slaughterer in Clare Market
could suggest how disease might be spread by nasty feeding. Even
the journeyman mason with his ample whiskers could give support
to the idea that a beard was not only an addition to manly beauty
but also had a utilitarian value as a protection against dust.
Chadwick talked to them all, and what they told him went down
in his notes or his memory, to reappear in some report as buttress
to an argument, or as a clinching illustration in a speech or letter.
He let them speak for themselves in copious extracts, and his
favourite method in the descriptive portions of his reports was to
present his facts in the words of his informants, knitting their
accounts together with a few remarks of explanation and comment. There was usually, however, an admixture, more or less
preponderant, of Edwin Chadwick in that evidence. He took a
stand on the facts very quickly, sometimes too quickly; he soon
made up his mind what he wanted to find out, and he used both
the rein and the spur in guiding his witnesses towards a conclusion
he already had clearly in mind. It was not for nothing that he
had read for the Bar. The ideal of scientific objectivity which he
set before the social investigator was not easy for any man to
attain; for Chadwick himself, with his training and temperament,

it was doubly difficult. Charles Darwin had an excellent habit of making an immediate note of every fact he encountered which seemed at variance with his own theories; because, he said, he was sure to remember those facts which supported his case, but was likely to overlook those facts he would like to forget. Had Chadwick done the same he might have trod more cautiously on debatable ground, and lost something of that dogmatic self-assurance which at times irritated his best friends.

Revolutionary conclusions emerged from this close examination of the facts. Every one of his inquiries, says Chadwick, had the result of reversing the principles which the Government, the economists, and the general public had adopted, and on which they were prepared to legislate; and the findings, he adds, were most of them new to himself as well as his colleagues.[1] In controversy this close acquaintance with the facts gave him the moral and intellectual ascendancy of the man who had been and seen for himself. "John Stuart Mill always deferred to me on any question I had examined because as he said, I always got my information first hand, whilst he could only get it second hand or from books."[2] He would ask acquaintances round to his house at Stanhope Gate for a "little sanitary chat," and over breakfast or an early dinner would submit them to his "inquisitorial thumb-screw," as one visitor described it with rueful admiration.[3] Not that the flow of information and experience went all one way; he gave better than he got; and he was always ready with advice to the Chairman of the Board of Guardians who wanted to tighten up the administration of his Union or the enlightened land-owner who was thinking of putting up some improved cottages for his farm labourers. If you were in doubt about the right depth to lay tiles for drainage, or wanted the name of a man who would plan a farm or a cemetery on the most approved models, or were at a loss for a set of clauses for a Bill or some telling figures for a speech, Chadwick could be depended upon to help. If he did not know, he could always put his hand on somebody who did. "You know all the clever fellows and who can do everything

[1] "Representative Reform; jottings down of a letter on a commission," MS., n.d. (c. 1859).
[2] E. C. to Lord Bramwell, 3 March 1885.
[3] George Sumner to E. C., n.d.

better than anybody else," wrote James Morrison, in difficulties with his Railway Committee.[1] "Whenever I see a stupidity going on, I think of you, of course as you can imagine," said a German economist, "because you are the man to bring the proper remedium."[2] Altogether, as J. S. Mill remarked, there was nobody quite like Chadwick for being practically useful.[3]

To the Commissioners, engaged in unearthing the abuses of the old Poor Law system, Chadwick was presently indispensable; and his colleagues, uneasily turning over the fragmentary and inadequate schemes so far devised, listened with relief to a voice which spoke with so confident a note of authority. The most influential figure on the Commission was the urbane Oxford professor, Nassau Senior, the Maynard Keynes of his day, to whom the Government looked as the leading interpreter of the science of Ricardo and Malthus. When Chadwick joined the inquiry, Senior had not conceived any practicable way of offering relief to able-bodied paupers which would not bring all the demoralisation of Speenhamland in its train, and in consequence, as a draft of 1831 reveals, he could see no remedy short of a heroic surgical operation to cut away in its entirety the corruption of the allowance system.[4] Nor had he formulated any suggestions as to the machinery of administration. By September 1832, however, Senior was urging on the Government the introduction of the workhouse test; and in a letter to the Lord Chancellor in January 1833 he outlined proposals for a central Commission of three, a body of itinerant inspectors, paid overseers, and compulsory unions of parishes.[5] In brief, Senior had capitulated to Chadwick's arguments that a legal provision of relief to the able-bodied paupers was necessary, and that it could be given in a form which would neither undermine the character of the recipient nor sap the position of the independent labourer; and, further, he had adopted unreservedly Chadwick's administrative scheme. Chadwick's energy and self-assurance, his bold prescription of remedies, and the weight of evidence he had assembled with

[1] James Morrison to E. C., 22 March 1845.
[2] T. Garnier to E. C., n.d.   [3] J. S. Mill to E. C., 1846.
[4] M. Bowley, *Nassau Senior and Classical Economics* (1937), p. 317.
[5] Ibid., pp. 317, 319.

extraordinary rapidity, had all worked with the utmost success on Nassau Senior, who possessed, as Dr. Bowley has shown, a flexibility of outlook which belies his reputation as a doctrinaire of the *laissez faire* persuasion. Chadwick was now asked to prepare the heads of a Bill, based on the principles he had suggested.

From the outset he was in revolt against the principles on which philanthropists and economists had hitherto based their attitude to pauperism. He rejected out of hand the thesis of the evangelicals, voiced eloquently by Dr. Chalmers, that all statutory systems of relief were pernicious, and that public doles should be replaced by the alms of the charitable. He rejected with equal scorn the sentimental paternalism of the country Justices, who did not doubt that the agricultural labourer "must be poor," and must live in perpetual dependence on the parish rates. But his main battle lay with the "hypothesists." To them the whole inquiry appeared superfluous, since it was obvious that the cause of pauperism was the growth of population beyond the means for its support. From their *a priori* law of population, they went on to deduce that the labour market was saturated, and the paupers had been squeezed out by the competition of their fellow workers. Look at the facts, retorted Chadwick, and observe that they in no way bear out this grim picture of a population pressing right up to the margin of subsistence, and in their struggles pushing the less fortunate over that margin into starvation and misery. From talks with aged labourers in the country parishes he learned that within the span of their experience their conditions had greatly improved; their real wages had risen and were still rising, and their expectation of life was longer now than ever before. It was true that in some areas dangerous congestions of pauperism existed, but, viewing the country as a whole, there was no general surplus above the average demand for employment throughout the year.

As he put it, the existing mass of pauperism was not a disease attacking the very structure of society, but merely a disorder of its functions, which could be corrected by a proper regimen. If the attractions of relief were lessened by cutting it to subsistence level and accompanying it by an irksome discipline; if it were made impossible for farmers to get cheap labour at the public expense; if the area of the labour market were widened by tearing down the

C

fences of the Settlement laws, and by encouraging the emigration of labourers from the heavily pauperised South to the
industrial North—if this were done, asserted Chadwick, all
those apparently surplus labourers would be rapidly absorbed
into productive employment.[1] There remained those who
were too young or too old for work, or who were unemployed
through sickness or some temporary dislocation of the industrial machinery. For their benefit he proposed that, under
the control of the new Union authorities, "the rudimentary
charities of a civilised community"[2] should be legalised and given
the strength and efficiency of large-scale organisation. In view of
the later lapse into the horrors of the General Mixed Workhouse,
it should be emphasised that he recommended not a single penal
establishment, but a series of specialised institutions, in which the
various classes of paupers—the old and impotent, the children,
the able-bodied females, and the able-bodied males—might be
separated for differential treatment.

Nor would he have stopped there. Great, half-formed plans,
for Government action to an extent never before contemplated by
practical statesmen, flitted through his mind as he worked over
the evidence. Repression alone could not solve the problem.
Preventive measures were necessary—a system of elementary
education for working-class children, and sanitary regulations to
relieve the burden of excessive sickness and premature widowhood
and orphanage. Chadwick asked for more time to consider these
measures; but Lord Melbourne (under the impression, Chadwick
observed, that a few weeks were sufficient to work out the principles of a revolution in the largest branch of public administration)
kept sending word that he could not understand why the report
was being delayed. Between the impatience of the politicians and
the contentiousness of the Commissioners, Chadwick's scheme was

---

[1] Chadwick, who met Malthus at the Political Economy Club, asserts that
he had begun to modify his opinions on over-population before he died (E. C.
to Macvey Napier, 15 June 1836; Macvey Napier Papers, B.M. Add. MSS.
34,617, f. 458). There is a quite incorrect impression that Chadwick was a
disciple of Malthus; Dr. Gilbert Slater, for example, describes him as "eager
for the Malthusian principles of the Royal Commission" (*A Century of Municipal
Progress* (1935), p. 339). Chadwick, in fact, lost no opportunity to combat
Malthusian doctrine, both in Poor Law and sanitary questions.

[2] "Notes on the retirement of Mr. Nicholls from the Poor Law Board,"
MS., n.d.

bungled. Only parts of his ambitious project found their way into the report and were later passed into law.[1] Unaccompanied by the supplementary preventive measures, the new law took on harsher, more unsympathetic lineaments than he had intended; the omissions, he believed, were a major cause of the irritation which the Act of 1834 aroused, and much of his energy in the following years was devoted to the attempt to supply them.

One fact consoled him. The regulating machinery he had devised was to be erected and set in motion. The Union would be a more effective and economical unit of administration than the parish; though he had misgivings about entrusting it to a committee of amateurs, "annual, unskilled and practically irresponsible,"[2] instead of the paid experts he had originally suggested. More promising still was the central department, from which a vigorous and well-informed Commissioner—and who more vigorous than the man who had dominated the Poor Law inquiry, or better informed than the principal architect of the new system?—could plan to push forward the frontiers of beneficent State control. Confidently Chadwick awaited his reward from a grateful Government.

A Commissionership at £2,000 a year, however, could not well be bestowed on one who had no social standing and no claims to distinction save his knowledge and ability.[3] Thus, despite Senior's recommendation that his name should be the first to be considered for one of the three vacancies, it was as a secretary and a subordinate that Chadwick went to Somerset House. He saw the danger at once. Already, with those inflexible notions of his, he had crossed swords with various members of the Commission of Inquiry. In a secretary such contrariness would be unseemly. Senior assured his incensed friend, however, that he would be looked upon rather as a confidential adviser than as a mere clerk with no right or opportunity of expressing an opinion, "rather as a

[1] In the Report the abuses of the old system were described by Nassau Senior, while to Chadwick was assigned the exposition of the remedial measures, with the important exceptions of the sections dealing with Bastardy, Settlement, and Emigration, which were drafted by his collaborator (E. C. to Edward Gulson, July 1837).

[2] E. C. to S. G. Osborne, 22 August 1844.

[3] "I must speak frankly, your Station in Society was not such as would have made it fit that you should be appointed one of the Commissioners" (Lord Spencer (Althorp) to E. C., 8 May 1841).

fourth Commissioner than as a Secretary."[1] Fortified by this assurance, Chadwick took up his position with a very superior view of the scope of his duties.

It is understandable that he should eye the three Commissioners with a natural resentment, which deepened when he assessed their characters and their fitness for the work in hand. J. G. Shaw-Lefevre was certainly, he thought, "a gentlemanly person of engaging manners;"[2] "but about as fit to act for the poor law as a delicate girl would be to assist in performing an operation."[3] Member of a Whig family, Senior Wrangler and Fellow of Trinity, a brilliant linguist with first-hand knowledge of Europe, Shaw-Lefevre had enjoyed all the advantages of birth, education and patronage that had been denied to Chadwick. He got on well with the Secretary, as he got on well with everybody else; but Chadwick mistrusted amiability which too easily softened into compliance, and in his eyes social qualities did not make up for lack of special knowledge, and the stiffening that came from the conviction that one was holding firm to right principles. George Nicholls, the manager of a Birmingham bank and a former East India captain, he regarded with more respect. Nicholls had reformed his own parish of Southwell on principles which foreshadowed those laid down in the Poor Law Report, but his experience was limited to the parish and parochial machinery. Earnest and humourless (attending a performance of *Don Giovanni* on one occasion, he was heard to murmur "What a shocking state of society!"[4]) he had a profound and narrow faith in the benefits of the workhouse test.

With Shaw-Lefevre and Nicholls Chadwick remained on good terms, despite their differences. The guiding spirit of the Commission, however, was a voluble, positive Welshman, Thomas Frankland Lewis, for twenty-two years a Tory M.P., with some experience in minor ministerial appointments, who entered Somerset House "with an express warning from Lord Melbourne against theory and speculation."[5] In him Chadwick saw personified the do-nothing traditions of the old Government service.

[1] Nassau Senior to E. C., 5 February 1837.
[2] E. C. to Lord Liverpool, 14 October 1841.   [3] MS. fragment, n.d.
[4] Memoir of George Nicholls by H. G. Willink, prefixed to Nicholls' *History of the English Poor Law* (1898 edition), vol. i, p. lxxii.
[5] E. C. to J. H. Burton, 3 June 1844.

How could he carry out the new ideas, demanded Chadwick, this man who was a disciple of Ricardo and Malthus, and who had drafted the report of Sturges Bourne's Committee, which proclaimed him a disbeliever in "compulsory contribution for the indigent"? They hated and distrusted each other on sight. Chadwick, with good reason, thought it futile to expect the introduction of comprehensive institutional provision for the paupers, or any other aggressive action planned to deal with the wider problems of destitution, from one who felt in his heart that these were matters with which Government should not meddle. Lewis, for his part, at once showed that he intended to give no elevated status to this dangerous, unpractical visionary. There would be no unofficial Fourth Commissioners while Frankland Lewis ruled at Somerset House. When Chadwick expressed an opinion at the Board, it was received frigidly as though a clerk had broken in on the discussion. At one of the earliest meetings Lewis requested him to withdraw while the Commissioners deliberated. As he left, Chadwick protested that by the terms of the Act, the Commissioners were bound to keep a record of their proceedings, and the proper recording officer was their Secretary.[1] For a subordinate it sounded an arrogant claim; but it was the only ground on which Chadwick could assert a right to be present while the Commissioners discussed and framed their policies; and he had no intention of surrendering into the inactive hands of Frankland Lewis the administrative weapon which he had forged, and with which he had planned to assail so many social evils. From this time onward there poured in to the Government a steady stream of protests and remonstrances from the disaffected Secretary, complaints of the way in which his chiefs were executing the law, and claims for promotion in recognition of his superior merit and grasp of the subject.

Meanwhile, for good or ill, the new Poor Law was now connected indissolubly in the public mind with the name of Edwin Chadwick. As he complained bitterly to Lord Spencer, while all the Ministers seemed unaware of his services, the agitators against the measure identified the Commission with himself.[2] The favourite phrase of the editor of the *Northern Liberator*, he

[1] E. C. to Lord Spencer, 8 May 1841.
[2] E. C. to Lord Spencer, 25 April 1838.

heard, was that Chadwick ought to be forthwith gibbeted, while in some parts of Yorkshire the mob swore never to be "Chadwicked," as they termed being married under the new Registration Act.[1] It became the most hated name in England as the odium of the Poor Law Bastilles increased. On the other hand, amongst those whose duty it was to enforce the Act in the localities, it was widely believed that "the Secretary was everything and the Commissioners mere cyphers." Much of the correspondence was addressed to him personally as if his superiors did not exist. When deputations of Guardians waited on the Board, they would ignore the Commissioners and address their remarks to Chadwick, a situation so embarrassing that eventually he ceased to attend when deputations were present. Sometimes, after seeing the Commissioners, they refused to leave until they had stated their case to Chadwick; as they did not always inform him that they had seen the Commissioners first, they occasionally got contradictory advice. Such incidents did nothing to lessen the tension between Chadwick and the Commissioners. They imputed to him a spirit of insubordination, an overbearing ambition, and a rigidity of outlook that no experience could soften; while, for his part, Chadwick saw in every departure from the line he had marked out in the Poor Law Report jealousy of himself and a determination to cripple the measure which was his creation. Hence, as Chadwick describes, to circumvent their watchful animosity he was compelled to disguise the suggestions which he thought it necessary to make. His method was to coach the Assistant Commissioners, and put them forward to voice his ideas. "On one occasion when I had given some suggestions as to regulations to a young Assistant Commissioner on a subject referred to him, and when he brought them forward and read them at the Board, there was a brightening of countenances, and strong and immediate praise to him for the ability of the suggestion. When he unwittingly and ingenuously declared that the praise was not due to him but to the Secretary sitting at the bottom of the table, there was such a change in the expression of the countenances to sour blank, and the scene was so ludicrous that I could scarcely refrain from laughing outright."[2]

---

[1] E. C. to Russell, 1 February 1838; to Lord Spencer, 25 April 1838.
[2] "Notes of personal paper," MS., n.d., probably 1847.

Meanwhile, Chadwick found it hard to credit that so excellent a law was as unpopular as *The Times* and the agitators made out. How could the charge of harshness be maintained? Were not wages highest and the condition of the workers most improved where the measure had been most fully carried out, and depression greatest and discontent most widespread where the rates were heaviest and least had been done to abolish the old practices? Complete satisfaction with the Act and—only thinly veiled—with himself as the author of it runs through Chadwick's survey in the *Edinburgh Review* for July 1836 of the first eighteen months' working of the Poor Law Commission.[1] In the southern districts paupers had been thrown off the rates in droves, and the "surplus" labour had been absorbed as he had predicted; in twenty-two counties, comprising 187 Unions, the expenditure on relief had fallen by 43½ per cent. In the winter of 1836, however, the Commissioners turned their attention to the industrial districts, and Chadwick's complacency was blown upon by a bleak wind of failure and hostility from the north. Bad harvests, severe winters, influenza, extensive unemployment in the textile industry, the resistance of the working classes, all combined to rout the Poor Law Commissioners. It had been a serious error in tactics, he believed, to deal with the southern counties first; the new system should have been introduced into the northern towns in the first year, while trade was still good and the agitators were otherwise engaged. But not the slightest doubt entered his mind that if the workhouse test had been introduced before depression hit the industrial workers, and if it had been administered with rigid honesty and efficiency, it would have taken the strain of any burden likely to be cast upon it, and would have withstood even the impact of widespread and prolonged unemployment.

Thus it was to the administrative weaknesses of the Commission and the local authorities that Chadwick pointed in explanation of the swelling figures for poor relief. Worst blunder of all had been to appoint Commissioners who were half-hearted at best in their adherence to the principles of the Act, and who shaped their policy with a fearful eye on *The Times* and the agitators. Frankland Lewis had now retired, but his spirit continued to rule in Somerset House, for he was succeeded by his son,

[1] *Edinburgh Review*, July 1836, vol. lxiii, pp. 487–537.

George Cornewall Lewis, who inherited his father's feud. As strong-willed as his father, George Lewis possessed considerably more ability. He was, says Bagehot, "too prosaic, too anxiously safe, too suspicious of everything showy";[1] but on these qualities he had built up a reputation with the Whigs as a practical man of business with aims and motives which any other practical man of business could readily comprehend. Unemotional himself, and distrustful of feeling in others, he could not understand Chadwick's fierce enthusiasms; and he turned a cold eye on Chadwick's theories of Government action. "The relation between himself and the secretary," remarked a writer in the *Westminster Review*, who was clearly indebted to Chadwick for his information, "was that of an ill-assorted marriage of a Catholic husband and a Protestant wife; the wife somewhat the cleverer of the two, but with no privilege beyond the use of her tongue."[2]

So for a dozen years the conflict of wills went on at Somerset House. Chadwick was unsafe and unpractical, the Lewises told their Whig friends, he wanted to go too fast, and his proposals were inhuman in their severity. The Commissioners were pusillanimous, retorted Chadwick, they countenanced practices which were flatly opposed to the principles of 1834, they employed office methods which were arbitrary and inefficient and, in fact, illegal. Over the question of outdoor relief to the able-bodied Chadwick fought innumerable skirmishes and four major battles. The last and greatest battle he fought and lost in 1841; and as a result of it even his infrequent attendances at the meetings of his chiefs came to an abrupt end. He thought seriously for a time of accepting an offer from Lord Normanby to place him in some other Government department—as counsel to the Home Office he could supervise the execution of two other measures he had fathered, the Factory Act and the County Constabulary Act. Since 1839, however, he had been engaged on the sanitary inquiry, and he was beginning to realise that it was the biggest and most important of his career. He stayed to see it through.

It is fortunate for Chadwick that his reputation does not rest entirely upon this chapter of his career. Had he been in command

[1] W. Bagehot, *Biographical Studies* (1881), p. 207.
[2] "Patronage of Commissions," *Westminster Review*, October 1846, vol. xvi, p. 229; probably by W. E. Hickson.

at Somerset House from 1836 to 1841, that unquestioning confidence of his in the possibility, even the expediency, of cutting off all forms of outdoor relief to the able-bodied might well have brought the whole Poor Law edifice crashing about his ears. The "supineness" of the Commissioners at least averted that danger. One unexamined theoretical assumption and one large practical miscalculation had between them made nonsense of Chadwick's Poor Law scheme. The assumption was Chadwick's excessive faith in the elasticity of the economic system, and in its capacity to absorb the impact not merely of casual day-to-day unemployment, but even of the hard-core unemployment which emerges when an industry goes into decline, and the recurrent mass unemployment which is due to fluctuations in trade and is the heaviest burden of all. Believing that the demand for labour might shift but did not fall away in total sum, he seriously over-estimated the facility with which a labourer thrown out of work in one trade could find alternative occupation in another. The rest followed logically. If there are jobs for all, then the ablebodied man who is without one for any length of time must be either unwilling to work or of such a character that no employer would engage him. In short, he was likely to be a bad lot: an idler, a wastrel, a trickster, an inefficient worker, or a black-listed Trade Unionist. To submit him to the discipline and frugal diet of the workhouse was as much in his own interests as in those of the community at large. Only by those reformatory influences could his moral fibre be sufficiently strengthened to support the strain of independent existence; only so could the honest labourer be spared the demoralising spectacle of a man who had not worked enjoying every day of the week the luxuries of meat, white bread, and strong ale.

For one whose boast it was that his proposals were based unshakably on the facts, Chadwick showed a peculiar insensitivity to the evidence when he visited the handloom weavers of Bolton and Macclesfield in 1840; and for one who claimed to trace back pauperism to its roots, he remained singularly incurious about the extent and nature of the various types of unemployment. While his theory was thus insecurely erected on an assumption as uncritical as any made by the "hypothesists" he so despised, his practical recommendations were also vitiated from the start by a fundamental miscalculation—that, having read his reports, the

Government would be stimulated with something of his vision and his enthusiasm for large administrative schemes. Where were the teachers, the nurses, the asylum attendants, and all the other specialists demanded by the policy of "aggregate in order to segregate"? To find and train them, and to establish and equip the various residential institutions for instructing the young, tending the old, and curing the sick, made a call upon the resources and the active goodwill of the Government for which there was no precedent. Neither the Poor Law Commissioners nor the Whig Ministers had any heart for so ambitious a programme. They chose instead to do as little as they dared, and that as cheaply as they could. On the grounds of economy and simplicity, they created a hermaphrodite administrative monster, uniting in a single body one institution whose purpose was deterrence, with another institution, or series of institutions, whose professed objects were treatment and instruction. In so doing they made it impossible to divide the "involuntary" sheep from the "voluntary" goats; all alike, the aged and infirm, the orphans, the widows, the vagrants, the able-bodied unemployed, bore the same stigma and were subjected to the same discipline.

To do justice to Chadwick, therefore, it is essential to realise that his dispute with the Commissioners over their policy of indulgence—a dispute in which his errors of judgment and obtuseness of feeling reveal him in the worst possible light—was only one aspect of a wider conflict of principle. The Webbs have made it their major criticism of the Poor Law Commissioners that they did not view pauperism in the context of destitution, and therefore neglected the causes which led to the perpetual recruitment of the pauper host.[1] This criticism, valid as it is against the Commissioners, cannot be levelled with anything like the same force against their Secretary. For, as we have seen, Chadwick in 1834 was already elaborating measures designed to cut at the roots of pauperism. He never believed, with Frankland Lewis, that pauperism was part of a divine or natural ordering of society, and that—as the Malthusian revelation ran—great numbers of mankind were doomed to live on the margins of misery, only relieved by the casual charity of their betters. To the faith in "God" or "Nature," which issued in a policy of administrative inertia

[1] *English Poor Law History*, Part II, vol. i, pp. 160–1.

(Melbourne's "letting things shake right") and a complacent acceptance of things as they are, he opposed a faith in Government as a contrivance of the human will, which might be used aggressively to minimise the volume of pain and maximise the volume of pleasure. Limited as he was in the range of his intelligence and sympathies, and inept as he showed himself in the calculation of political expediencies, he stands out as one of the very few men in the State departments of his time who held firmly to the belief that it was the essential business of Government to take thought for the welfare of the people—and, having thought, to act.

As he told Sir George Grey in 1847, he had from the first urged the segregation for specialised institutional treatment of the various classes of paupers, the sick, the blind, the idiots, the lunatics. But these were "collections of sores" which treatment could only alleviate; and "the contemplation of these wrecks of humanity continually forced upon me the consideration whether nothing effectual could be wrought for prevention. At every opportunity, I have made exertions to explore the various contributory sources or causes of Pauperism and the practicable means of prevention. . . . It was frequently only necessary to go a few links or a few steps back beyond the range of popular discussion and legislation, when we are brought upon causes which upon due investigation are found to be preventible and generally with large pecuniary economy." With the most notable of these inquiries, the sanitary investigation, this study deals at length. But there were others, some fruitful, some—through lack of time, shortage of money, and the scepticism of the Commissioners— abortive. He devised a scheme of industrial schools intended to train pauper children for productive employment. He conducted, to give a further example, a private investigation into the causes of the appalling number of deaths and injuries among the labourers engaged in constructing the new railway system with which England was equipping herself in the 1840's; and, since George Lewis could not be persuaded that this fell within the scope of the Poor Law Department, he printed and circulated at his own expense a report containing his recommendations.

For six more years after his revolt in 1841 Chadwick remained at Somerset House in this anomalous position, not strong enough to overthrow the Commissioners, too powerful to be dismissed by them. The bulk of the Poor Law work had passed from his hands into those of the Assistant Secretary, George Coode. "Your differences with Mr. Lewis were so notorious in the office," commented E. C. Tufnell, one of the Assistant Commissioners, "that I remember once mentioning to Mr. Coode that I wondered why you were not dismissed or could stay at your post. His reply was, that though you did next to nothing as Poor Law Secretary, you were so useful to the Government in conducting the Sanitary inquiry and other matters, that you fully earned your salary, and were one of the hardest worked public servants that he ever knew."[1] Thus, one good result emerged from that unhappy tangle of crossed wills—he was left very much to himself to work out the principles of his preventive administration. It was fortunate indeed for the public health movement that Chadwick did not make his escape in the summer of 1841.

[1] E. C. Tufnell to E. C., 1847.

CHAPTER II

THE "SANITARY IDEA"

CANNING once observed that there was nothing he so much dreaded as facts and figures; repeating this to Lord Brougham, Chadwick added that in truth there was nothing which ought to have been dreaded more than such figures as were then available—"wretchedly imperfect figures, giving only half facts, leading to wrong or wild conclusions."[1] At the turn of the century there had been keen debate whether the population of England was increasing or decreasing, and elaborate theories about the future of society had been spun with vast ingenuity from the few known facts. Error and bias were inevitable where judgment and not measurement was the guide. Fear of Roman Catholics was enhanced because their exact strength was unknown; jealousy of cheap Irish labour could grow because its proportions were not clearly seen; and—to quote one of Chadwick's examples—the pessimistic school of social moralists were encouraged in their gloom by Patrick Colquhoun's fantastic estimate that there were 50,000 prostitutes in the capital, which meant one for every three or four males in the London of his day.[2] Political arithmetic was making a slow progress, however, trimming the outlines of fluffy generalisations, replacing crude guesswork by verifiable information, defining the lineaments of society every year in sharper outline. Finlaison had taken the first English census in 1801 (fifty years before, Parliament had rejected an idea which infringed the liberty of the subject and was likely to bring about a plague or

[1] E. C. to Lord Brougham, 28 February 1856.
[2] *Constabulary Report*, p. 15 (*P.P.* 1839, vol. xix, p. 1). Even in 1844 South-wood Smith could write to Chadwick (19 January 1844): "It is notorious that during the last year fever has been ravaging many localities in the provinces and in the large towns, but no one can form any conjecture as to the real extent of the evil, though this is a matter which the public and the legislature have a deep interest in knowing."

other public disaster); actuaries, worried about the validity of
their life tables on which the solvency of the insurance companies
depended, had begun to work out the theory of vital statistics; in
1832 the Board of Trade had set up a Statistical Department,
introducing an outside expert, G. R. Porter, to superintend it; in
1833 the Statistical Section of the British Association had been
established, to be followed promptly by the foundation of Statistical Societies in London, Manchester, and Bristol. More and more
the appeal to facts and figures strengthened the hand of the
reformers. John Howard, touring the gaols in 1774, had been the
first to use the statistical method as an instrument to diagnose the
character and assess the gravity of social disease. John Rickman's
census of 1831, showing the population and wealth of the manufacturing districts, had its influence on the Reform Bill debates.[1]

In this development, which before the century was out was to
make the central departments vast factories for the production of
blue-books, Chadwick played a decisive part. He possessed no
mathematical ability, and the subtleties of statistical analysis were
beyond him,[2] but he realised that the first step towards controlling
social evils was to measure them. Finding his advance everywhere
blocked by entrenched interests, he soon perceived the blasting
power of fact. His first work of note, the essay on "Life Assurances" in the *Westminster Review* (1828), was an exposure of the
misleading picture of social conditions presented by the out-of-
date life tables of the insurance companies, and a plea for
Government action to institute a complete registration of births,
marriages, and deaths, the "first stages of the process of forming a
legitimate theory" being "diligent investigation and the sagacious
comparison of a variety of phenomena."[3]

Eight years later the Whig Government introduced a Registration Bill, intended primarily as a measure for the relief of Non-
conformists from that remnant of Anglican privilege, the Church
registration of births, marriages, and deaths. Chadwick seized
upon the Government's little measure, which lacked any scientific
attributes, either medical or economic, and gave it a new power

---

[1] J. Rickman to E. C., 5 June 1840.
[2] See Sir A. Newsholme, *Elements of Vital Statistics* (1889), p. 112, for examples
of his statistical blunders.
[3] *Westminster Review*, February 1828, vol. ix, p. 417.

and a new direction. He obtained the provision that when a death was registered its cause should also be indicated, so ensuring that the record should furnish not merely the roll-call of the dead, but the diagnosis by which the communal efforts of preventive medicine might be directed.[1]

In the debate Lord Ellenborough carried a suggestion that the measure should be put into effect by the new Poor Law Unions, on the grounds, as he later explained to Chadwick, that the Government's first proposal would have distributed throughout the country "a strong Battalion of Whig Attornies to act as Party Agents at the Public Expense."[2] There was "great wailing about the lost Battalion,"[3] and the wailers looked on Chadwick as the cause of their bereavement. He always believed that Lord Melbourne's bearing towards himself became less cordial after this incident. But Ellenborough's proposal was, in fact, made without consulting Chadwick.[4] Once it was put forward, Chadwick's one concern was to insulate the Poor Law Guardians against the jobbery and intrigue which the creation of new offices always bred; and at his suggestion the appointment of the local registrars was made subject to the approval of the Registrar-General. Nor did the measure increase his popularity with the Church. The poor curate, with his £70 or £100 a year, looked eagerly for the "godsends" of the smallest fees; moreover, the clergyman who recorded the marriages of the middle classes was frequently invited to the wedding dinner afterwards, and "to a poor clergyman a feast is something."[5] But it was their baptismal fees which were hit most of all. "The labouring classes have a notion that if their children die without being properly named the proper Angels will not know by what names they may be called to heaven by. But if the child be named and registered by any public officer that will do as well; the child is named and that is enough: they don't see why they should go and pay the parson when they can get it done for nothing by going to the Registrar. The inferior clergy have preached various sorts of doctrine against this belief, but still their baptismal fees have diminished and they

[1] 6 & 7 Will. IV, c. 86.
[2] Lord Ellenborough to E. C., 27 October 1841.   [3] Ibid.
[4] The Webbs (*English Poor Law History*, Part II, vol. i, p. 118) echo the Whig rank and file in asserting that the idea was due to Chadwick.
[5] E. C. to Lord ? (probably Russell), 8 January 1841.

preach vigorously against the Government from which it eman-
ates."[1] It was a curious episode, and as a result of it Chadwick's
reputation suffered on two counts, as an enemy of the Church for
sponsoring the Bill, and an enemy of the Government for de-
priving them of some five hundred appointments.

The new department was established at a time when a large
proportion of Government offices was directed to the outdoor
relief of the upper classes, and granted by Ministers to those
bearing the family name, or, perhaps, merely the family features.
The first Registrar-General was T. H. Lister, who was distinguished as a three-decker novelist, but had the additional
qualification of being Lord John Russell's brother-in-law. He
was succeeded by a cavalry officer, the brother of Sir James
Graham. "Neither gentleman understood anything of medical
and sanitary statistics and never perhaps wrote a line of the reports
on them."[2] But Chadwick succeeded in persuading Lister to
appoint as his assistant a young doctor, William Farr, who, in the
course of an unorthodox and unsystematic medical training, had
picked up a knowledge of vital statistics; and Farr set to work,
contentedly and profitably, to introduce order and method into
the facts, and illuminate with their aid some of the darker problems
of society.

There was no personal friendship between the two, and
Chadwick, who at times was as imperious with figures as with men,
inevitably came into conflict with the quiet clerk at the Register
Office. Farr ventured to question in the *Lancet* some tables which
Chadwick had drawn up to show that in those prisons where the
diet was richest the amount of sickness was greatest, tables of
which he was very proud, and which tended to demonstrate what
was not as obvious as it might be to the queasy stomachs of the
working classes—that the most economical feeding was also the
most humanitarian. This piece of perverseness Chadwick overlooked. But next he found in the Registrar-General's returns a
number of deaths from starvation. This implied that there were
people who preferred to die quietly in the street rather than enter
one of the Poor Law Bastilles. Chadwick therefore published an
attack on Farr's figures, together with animadversions on his

---

[1] E. C. to Lord ? (probably Russell), 8 January 1841.
[2] E. C. to Duke of Northumberland, 27 December 1878.

integrity, in the *Official Circular*, and showed that only two or three per cent of the cases registered as deaths from privation were in fact deaths from lack of food, and those were either accidental or suicidal.[1] This coolness continued between the two men, so differently constituted and working by so different ways to the same end. He paid no attention to Farr's "animosities or petty jealousies," Chadwick told a friend in 1844, "but I am sorry to say that it is not the only instance in which on looking into some covert from whence an insidious attack on my labours has proceeded I have found some one behind to whom I have rendered some special service."[2]

The article on Life Assurances, which reveals Chadwick's early interest in statistics, shows also that at twenty-eight he had already formulated the theory which underlies his public health work, the broad but sufficient principle that the length and healthiness of life are determined by the circumstances in which it is lived. He quotes with approval the conclusion of Villermé, the French medical statistician, that "the gradations of wealth, or the means of providing comforts, may almost be taken as the scale of mortality," and urges that an investigation into the conditions of the working classes would be an "invaluable acquisition to science, and would direct the public exertions in removing those circumstances which shorten life, and in promoting those under which it is found to attain its greatest duration."[3] A few years later, when he was preparing his report on London and Berkshire for the Royal Commission on the Poor Law, he observed how some unhealthy neighbourhoods were notorious as sources of pauperism. The beadles of Newington, for example, being ordered one very severe winter to pay particular attention to the sick outdoor poor, had gone at once without the need of any inquiry to a certain group of courts—just as a gamekeeper might go to a well-stocked preserve—and had returned with two coach-loads of fever victims.[4]

This was the seed which was to bear so plentiful a crop in later years, but it did not germinate until 1838, when Chadwick, now

---

[1] E. C. to Dr. Laycock, 13 April 1844.   [2] Ibid.

[3] *Westminster Review*, February 1828, vol. ix, pp. 413, 385.

[4] *Extracts from the Information received by H.M.'s Commissioners, as to the Administration and Operation of the Poor Laws*, 1833, p. 310.

D

Secretary of the Poor Law Commission, was permitted to enter upon a course of inquiry which his superiors thought of little importance, save in one respect—that it kept him quiet. Through-out the intervening years he had sat in Somerset House, at the centre of the Poor Law web, receiving from day to day the reports of Guardians and relieving officers and workhouse surgeons with their constantly reiterated lesson that disease filled the workhouses and insanitary conditions bred disease. "For some reason, which . . . he never understood, the sanitary idea became dominant in his mind, and he became impressed with the conviction that if sanitation were carried out in its completeness, disease, which was the cause of all death before the appointed time, would itself die."[1]

To the relieving officer at the parish pay table and the parish surgeon on his rounds in the lower districts of London the con-nection between the fever nests and the mounting poor rates was obvious enough. Reasoning that there could be no end to the outlay of money in relieving individual cases of fever until the cause which produced the malady was removed, the Union authorities in some places indicted the landlords for nuisance, defraying the expense of prosecution from the poor rates. In doing so they came into conflict with the auditors, under orders to strike out and disallow all charges not expressly authorised by statute. The disputants took their argument to Chadwick, who saw at once that it offered an opportunity to introduce into the practice of the Poor Law Commission some of the principles of preventive administration which he had tried unsuccessfully to insert into the Act of 1834.

In 1838 the steady annual stream of typhus cases swelled suddenly to flood proportions. Altogether 13,972 cases of fever, 1,281 of them fatal, were reported in London during the year, 9,228 being contributed by certain districts, and in particular Whitechapel, Bethnal Green, Lambeth, St. George the Martyr, Stepney, Holborn, and St. George in the East. Chadwick called the attention of the Commissioners to the preventable nature of a large proportion of the fever cases, and recommended a special investigation by three well-known medical observers, Drs.

[1] Obituary of Chadwick, *Lancet*, 12 July 1890 (the writer is reporting a conversation with Chadwick).

Arnott, Kay, and Southwood Smith. No better choice could have been made. Dr. Neil Arnott, a friend of Bentham and J. S. Mill, at whose house Chadwick had made his acquaintance, had written a celebrated work on physics, and was a recognised authority on the warming and ventilation of houses. Dr. Kay (later Kay-Shuttleworth) brought to the inquiry the experience of a dispensary physician in the Irish quarter of Manchester, which, as he says, burned into him the conviction that it was futile to look to charity and medical skill alone to deal with social evils.[1] With an appetite for work which rivalled that of Chadwick, he possessed also something of his self-confidence and restless energy; and, exerting the same heroic strength of will and purpose, a few years later, as Secretary to the Committee of Council on Education, he was to drive himself into a break-down grappling with difficulties not unlike those which surrounded Chadwick at Somerset House. It is well to remember that Chadwick was not the only permanent official of the time to engage in disputes about his status, to arouse hostility from powerful sections of public opinion, and to encounter the charge that he was making a department of State the instrument of his own views and ambitions. With the third member of the medical inquiry, Chadwick's career was to be more intimately linked. Southwood Smith, physician to the London Fever Hospital, was another Benthamite (Bentham had left him his body for dissection and he had pronounced an oration over the philosopher's corpse at the Webb Street School of Anatomy); and as the author of a standard *Treatise on Fever* was shortly to become the chief medical theorist of the sanitary reformers. The heart of the gentle doctor, however, was a great deal sounder than his epidemiological views, and the simplicity and integrity of his character won over for the cause many who were repelled by Chadwick's demoniac reputation. All who met him—including even the cantankerous Toulmin Smith—acknowledged his love of his fellow men, which warmed the sympathies more than Chadwick's hard dry passion for efficiency. There was need for both men in the public health movement, which must touch the conscience as well as persuade the reason if the Peels and Grahams were to be brought to act.

In May 1838 the three set off on an exploratory tour, Arnott

[1] F. Smith, *Life of Kay-Shuttleworth* (1923), p. 14.

and Kay to Wapping, Ratcliff Highway, and Stepney, Southwood Smith to Whitechapel and Bethnal Green. How far, they inquired, were the conditions in which the poor lived due to the habits of the poor themselves, how far were they "voluntary," to use the favourite word of the Poor Law theorists? Very little, the Union medical officers replied. True, the poor drank too much; they neglected vaccination; they were reluctant to enter a hospital when they were attacked by contagious disease; they did not wash their persons, their clothes, or their houses often enough; they crowded noisomely together in dwelling-houses and lodging-houses. But it was not by these "personal habits" of the poor, as the investigators termed them, that their lives were most powerfully moulded. They were surrounded by filth, accumulated in cesspools and privies and stagnant surface drains; they breathed the exhalations of undrained marsh land, graveyards, and slaughter-houses; they had no choice but to live in narrow alleys and close courts. The investigators concluded that there were some evils which could not be avoided by any exercise of prudence on the part of the poor, and which were independent of their personal habits. They were removable, however, by the intelligent arrangements of public authorities: by a system of sewers, a plentiful water supply, an effective service of scavengers, by control of building, and regulations against overcrowding and noxious trades. Powers should, therefore, be given to Poor Law Guardians to cleanse ditches and pools, to inspect lodging-houses, to indict nuisances, and to carry out generally the functions of a public health authority—functions for which, as a locally elected body, charged with duties relating to the poor, and commanding the services of paid officers, they were particularly fitted.

It was not the first time that medical men had investigated the sanitary condition of the towns—Currie at Liverpool, Ferriar at Manchester, Haygarth at Chester, had done valuable pioneer work in this direction at the end of the eighteenth century—but it was the first time that a Government department had directed such an inquiry with a view to action. The reports were forwarded to the Home Secretary, Lord John Russell, on 14 May 1838, under cover of an official letter from the Commissioners, recommending as a temporary measure that the Guardians should be empowered to indict the parties responsible for nuisances.[1] Thus, within four years of its establishment the new Poor Law Commission was expanding in a way which threatened to burst its statutory limits. The underlying theory of the Act of 1834, that most pauperism was "voluntary," the result of moral defects such as idleness, intemperance, and improvidence, was breaking down before the logic of the facts; and if the diagnosis was incorrect, it followed that the course of remedy must be altered. A case might be made out for invoking pains and penalties to scourge "voluntary" paupers out of their fecklessness; but once let it appear that the main causes of pauperism were not personal but social, that the pauper was usually the end-product of social processes over which he had no more control than he had over the weather, then a punitive treatment of paupers was no more just and sensible than a punitive treatment of lunatics, whom an earlier age had considered in some way responsible for their condition. Deterrence and alleviation, the remedies of 1834, must give way to an inquiry into causes, and the elaboration of wide schemes of reform aimed at prevention. Under Chadwick's influence a department founded to regulate relief to the poor was assuming, reluctantly, functions which reached out to embrace the duties and interests of all classes. It had already given birth to a Registration Act, under which for the first time the facts of national ill-health and premature mortality were being assembled. It was presently[2] to offer to vaccinate at the public expense the children, not of paupers only, but of anyone who cared to bring them to the Union surgeon. If Chadwick had his way it would also become a department of education and a department of public health, unless the Government should segregate these functions before they swamped the Poor Law Commissioners.

The letter to Russell produced no immediate effect. In their next report the Commissioners underlined its argument by publishing a description by Southwood Smith of the fever epidemic in the metropolitan Unions.[3] The Hill Coolies that year received from the Whigs attention and abundant sympathy, Chadwick observed drily, but nothing was done for the helpless

---

[1] *Fourth Annual Report*, 1838, pp. 93–151.
[2] By the Vaccination Acts, 3 & 4 Vict., c. 29; 4 & 5 Vict., c. 32.
[3] *Fifth Annual Report*, 1839, pp. 160–71.

population of the great towns.[1] Eventually, in August 1839, the Bishop of London, who coupled the experience of a London parish priest to his episcopal authority and influence, addressed the Lords on the text of Southwood Smith's report, and moved that an inquiry be made into the sanitary conditions of the labouring classes. No money was voted, no arrangements made to facilitiate the investigation; a curt note communicated the resolution of the House to the Poor Law Commissioners.[2] As Chadwick commented, "the inquiry seems to have been barely tolerated."[3]

The investigation thus begun in 1839 was not completed until 1842. Shortage of money, the indifference of Chadwick's superiors, a change of Government, but most of all the intrinsic complexity of the subject, all combined to drag out the inquiry. "No money is allowed the Board for the compensation of professional men of eminence and only honorary service can be asked," he warned Dr. Hodgson, Peel's physician, requesting him to superintend an inquiry in Birmingham.[4] Yet Parliament was considering a proposal to settle an annual allowance of £30,000 on the Queen's Consort! "The grant of £30,000 for the purposes of a general system of education by which several hundreds of thousands of children in various ways could derive benefit, was fiercely resisted," Chadwick wrote in disgust. "The grant of the same sum of money for the benefit of this one young man will be granted with adulations of virtues which he has yet had no opportunity of displaying."[5] The deficiency of means Chadwick made up by his own untiring activity. A set of inquiries, based on the conclusions of the *Fever Report* of 1838, was directed to the Assistant Poor Law Commissioners and the Union medical officers in all parts of England, Wales, and Scotland.[6] The replies to these questions were supplemented by material collected by Chadwick in personal interview or correspondence with surveyors, builders, prison governors, lawyers, police officials, with anyone whose position

[1] "Notes on Lord Normanby's speech," MS., 1844.

[2] "Memoranda of answers to the imputations of blame in respect to alleged delay to adopt sanitary measures," MS., 13 July 1844.

[3] "Notes on Lord Normanby's speech," MS., 1844.

[4] E. C. to Dr. Hodgson, 13 November 1839.

[5] "Memoranda. For consideration in respect to the young Prince Albert's proposed allowance to be as considerable as that to the old Princes Royal," MS., n.d.

[6] The terms of reference were widened to include Scotland in January 1840.

brought the facts beneath his constant observation. In addition, in obedience to his own canons of research by which the investigator was adjured not to rest content with the testimony of others, however well informed and intelligent they might be, Chadwick himself made a number of excursions to the provinces.[1]

The inquiry had been in progress eighteen months when a well-intentioned but impatient Member of Parliament, Robert Aglionby Slaney, obtained a Select Committee on the Health of Towns.[2] He "must be doing something in it," snorted Chadwick, who resented the trespass.[3] Chadwick had already squeezed dry Slaney's principal witnesses, and he saw nothing in the recommendations but "off hand and easy generalities, which could be reduced to little practice."[4] The Report of Slaney's Committee, however, though of no great value in itself, prodded the Government into a show of action. Casting about for popular measures as the Home Secretary of the weak and failing Whig Ministry, Lord Normanby suddenly seized upon the sanitary question, and in 1841 introduced three Bills, "for the improvement of certain boroughs," "for regulating buildings in large towns," and "for the better drainage of large towns and villages." Chadwick's annoyance at this step, though it was sharpened by affronted *amour propre*, is understandable.. His own investigation was still in progress; the results of the local inquiries were still coming in; and his general report was as yet a series of massive fragments. The Home Secretary now imposed a ban on the continuance of the inquiry, and when Chadwick got a friend in the Lords to ask for the production of the local reports the request was refused point blank. "A manifest determination was evinced to give the labours in the Poor Law department the go by, on this subject. The government was determined to have the exclusive merit."[5] However, Normanby's ill-constructed Bills, concocted, as Chadwick judged, by Home Office lawyers and palace architects, fell to pieces in Committee. The wreckage was bequeathed to the Tories, in whose hands it remained for three years more an impending threat to the progress of true reform. Chadwick, while

---

[1] See, for example, the description of his inspection, in the company of Neil Arnott, Sheriff Alison, and a police superintendent, of the district of Glasgow lying between Argyll Street and the river (*Sanitary Report*, p. 24).

[2] *P.P.* 1840, vol. xi, p. 277.

[3] "Notes on Lord Normanby's speech," MS., 1844.   [4] Ibid.   [5] Ibid.

pursuing his own inquiries, fought simultaneously a running battle against the principles of these Bills, which embodied technical recommendations out of step with the best contemporary developments, and revealed a timid anxiety to avoid any large-scale administrative experiments.

The downfall of the Whigs in September 1841, when Lord Melbourne thankfully surrendered the government and the deficit to Sir Robert Peel, brought a double benefit to the public health movement. First, out of a robust belief in the virtues of the measures he had introduced, Lord Normanby discovered in opposition a fervent enthusiasm for sanitary reform, together with an immense indignation at Tory tardiness; and he later proved a valuable ally to Ashley and Southwood Smith in the Health of Towns Association. Secondly, Chadwick was given permission to finish his report, which he was firmly convinced would never have appeared if the Melbourne Government had retained office. Towards the end of 1841 he was instructed to complete it so that it might be put into circulation before the next meeting of Parliament.

Another six months elapsed, however, the 1842 session approached its close, and still the report had not appeared. The Commissioners concurred cautiously with Chadwick's draft, but urged him to prune some of the stronger passages. The report was originally printed with the Commissioners' names appended but George Lewis opposed its adoption on the ground that it was calculated to give offence to Commissioners of Sewers and similar authorities. Before it could appear Chadwick had to undertake to bear personally any odium it might arouse. "It contains a great deal of good matter," George Lewis remarked to George Grote, with an air of giving the devil his due, "and, on the whole, I prefer it to anything else he has written. We shall present it shortly as *his* report, without making ourselves responsible for it."[1]

The elements of the problem which confronted Chadwick in 1842 are simple to grasp. In the years from 1740 to 1820 the age-

[1] G. C. Lewis to G. Grote, 13 March 1842 (*Letters of Sir George Cornewall Lewis,* ed. Sir G. F. Lewis (1870), p. 119).

long balance between birth rate and death rate, between human
fecundity and the adversities and accidents of human environment, had been upset decisively by a steep fall in the death rate.
Humanitarian activity, advances in empirical medical knowledge,
a more abundant food supply, the rising level of urban wages,
the work of Improvement Commissioners and joint stock companies, all these together had brought down the death rate of
Londoners in 1811 to 26 per thousand—little more than half
the estimated figure for 1750. But after 1820 there was no great
fall in the death rate till the seventies; and the difference between
a crude death rate of 23 per thousand in the middle decades
of the century and one of 18 per thousand at its end is a rough
measure of the toll of slum housing, inefficient sewerage, and
impure water supplies in the raw industrial towns. Year by year
the great towns continued to grow, partly by a natural increase,
but even more by the influx of immigrant workers whom the
expanding industries attracted across the St. George's Channel
and from the rural areas of England and Wales, till by 1851 half
the population was urban. To the administrative difficulties
raised by this unprecedented growth and concentration of the
population very little hard thinking had been directed by the
departments of State before the publication of the *Sanitary Report*;
and the engineers who had produced the railway locomotive and
the steamship had neglected to apply the same technical skill to
the complex problems of human aggregation. The building
encyclopædias of the time could be searched in vain for the word
"ventilation." Great modern mansions in Belgravia reeked with
exhalations from defective house drains. Perhaps not one home
in a whole street of middle-class residences possessed a bath.[1]
When Lyon Playfair examined the condition of Buckingham
Palace, he found it so bad that the Government did not dare to
publish his report.[2] While the middle and upper classes lived in
such splendid squalor, the lower classes seemed in danger of being
engulfed and poisoned by their own excretions.

The localising of "zymotic" or infectious diseases in the narrow courts and alleys of the poor had been frequently noted by
those eighteenth-century physicians whose broad sympathies or

[1] E. C. to F. O. Ward, 7 October 1849.
[2] *Memoirs and Correspondence of Lyon Playfair*, ed. W. Reid (1899), p. 94.

straitened means drove them to practise in the lower quarters of the towns. This observation—that outbreaks of fever were correlated with insanitary conditions—gave rise to the characteristic medical theory of the public health reformers. According to this "pythogenic" theory, disease was caused by an "unknown something in the atmosphere" acting upon the gases from animal and vegetable decomposition, given off, for example, by a midden, a stagnant sewer, an overcrowded churchyard, a slaughter-house or a tanner's yard. Any of these, in combination with the epidemic influence, might produce, by a kind of spontaneous generation, an outbreak of typhus, or perhaps—since this promiscuity of filth brought forth an uncertain progeny—of typhoid or cholera. Certain corollaries followed from the theory. First, the transmission of disease by contagion was a fallacy, and quarantine therefore an archaic survival from less enlightened days; Southwood Smith showed his faith in this conclusion by taking his granddaughter with him when he walked the fever wards.[1] Secondly, impure air and the reek of filth, not the privations of poverty, formed the predisposing circumstances which favoured the spread of disease, the chief sufferers being not paupers but independent labourers, artisans, and small shopkeepers, who were not destitute of food and clothing. Nor was it usually the weak and sickly who fell victims, for a large proportion were in the prime of life, at the height of their productive powers, and with dependent families, who, on the death of their parents, must be cast upon the rates. The comfortable belief was thus discredited that the unfit and superfluous, the paupers and the weaklings, were beneficently cut off by nature; and if the political economist was wrong, so was the philanthropist, who thought that fever was caused by destitution, and could be combated by grants of money, fuel, and blankets.

That disease was traceable to specific infections had been demonstrated clearly enough during the eighteenth century, and the pythogenic theory could be sustained only by ignoring some very obstinate facts, to which Chadwick closed his eyes to the end of his life. At the time of the "Great Stink" of 1858, for example, when the stench of the polluted Thames closed the law courts, emptied the river steamers, and assumed the proportions of a

[1] C. L. Lewes, *Dr. Southwood Smith* (1899), p. 77.

national calamity second only to the Indian Mutiny, the sanitarians gloomily prophesied pestilence on an enormous scale; the
death rate for the year was, in fact, below the average, and there
was a notable diminution in the amount of fever, diarrhœa, and
dysentery.[1] To counter a disease, however, it is not essential to
know its causal agent. Leprosy, the "sweating sickness," plague,
typhus, cholera, and typhoid, were all uprooted from England
before their generating bacteria were detected. They retreated
because the environmental conditions which favoured their
advance were vanishing, for, from the point of view of preventive
action, the soil in which a disease flourishes is no less important
than the seed from which it springs. For a movement which
aimed at clearing up the dark corners of the towns it was the
soundest of doctrine to teach that man could make himself secure
from pestilence only by directing intelligence and determination
to the removal of its localising conditions. Thus, radically wrong
as the pythogenic theory proved to be, it was given plausibility by
its demonstrable effectiveness in practice; and it may well serve as
an instance of those "fruitful errors" which in the history of
thought, as Vaihinger reminds us, have so frequently produced
sound practice out of false theory.[2]

In the light of this medical doctrine Chadwick turned to the
examination of the returns from the local Registrars which by the
end of 1839 were pouring in from 553 districts, giving for the first
time in history a reliable and comprehensive picture of the causes
of national ill-health and mortality. In the first year, 1838, for
which returns were made, he found that the deaths in England
and Wales from zymotic diseases numbered 56,461. It was as if
the whole county of Westmorland or Huntingdon "were entirely
depopulated annually, and were only occupied again by the
growth of a new and feeble population living under the fears of a
similar visitation."[3] From typhus alone the yearly slaughter was
double the casualties suffered by the allied armies at Waterloo.
The "Fever Bill" footed every year by the nation, in the form of
charges for medical attendance, for the support of widows and

---

[1] For a description of this historic stink see William Budd, *Typhoid Fever*
(1874), pp. 141–2.
[2] H. Vaihinger, *The Philosophy of "As If,"* (2nd ed. 1935), pp. 45–6.
[3] *Sanitary Report*, p. 3; *P.P.* 1842, vol. xxvi, p. 1 (House of Lords).

orphans, for labour lost by sickness, for the shortening of the average working life by premature mortality, was an immense and growing burden.

The lesson of Chadwick's report was that the great mass of this mortality and sickness was preventable. He demonstrated this by a simple but conclusive device, which came as near as practicable to experimental verification in a field where laboratory methods of control and observation were out of the question. He took the average age at death for various classes of the community, inhabiting different quarters of the towns, so revealing at a glance the disparities concealed beneath the general averages for the country.[1]

District	Gentry and professional classes	Tradesmen	Labourers
Derby	49	38	21
Bolton	34	23	18
Leeds	44	27	19
Truro	40	33	28
Bethnal Green	45	26	16
Whitechapel	45	27	22
Strand Union	43	33	24
Kensington	44	29	26

The age at death of the individual was thus shown to bear a direct relation to his rank in society. Now the circumstances of the labouring classes differed in two main respects from those of the gentry; they enjoyed a smaller income, and they inhabited dirtier districts, dirtier streets, and dirtier houses. Which of these two factors, income or environment, was responsible for the different expectation of life of the two classes? It was proved—to Chadwick's satisfaction—that the labouring classes received on the average a real income sufficient to keep them well above the level of starvation;[2] the greater mortality from which they suffered must therefore be ascribed to the physical conditions amongst which

[1] *Sanitary Report*, pp. 154–61.   [2] See below, p. 65.

they lived, and he illustrated this conclusion by "Sanitary Maps" of Bethnal Green and Liverpool, which showed the black crosses of death crowding thickly in the foulest and most overcrowded districts. It followed that if those physical conditions could be improved, there would be a corresponding improvement in the statistics of sickness and death.

Fever, then, was not the result of destitution; on the contrary, destitution usually came on the heels of fever, and "the poor's rolls were the pedigrees of generations of families thus pauperised." Of the 112,000 orphans and 43,000 widows receiving poor relief in 1840, Chadwick estimated that 100,000 orphans and 27,000 widows had been reduced to dependence by the death of their breadwinner from some sort of zymotic disease, arising from causes which were known and removable.[1] These pauper orphans and widows were a legitimate concern of the Poor Law Commission. Chadwick, however, looking beyond the walls of the workhouse, went on to demonstrate that preventable disease had economic and moral effects upon society at large far more serious than the additional burden it cast upon the ratepayers. Economically it represented a heavy annual drain upon the country's most valuable capital, its strongest and most experienced workers. During the Napoleonic wars Bethnal Green and Spitalfields had raised a regiment of volunteers, but in 1840 the recruiting officers would find it difficult to get together a grenadier company from the same districts; yet the wealth of the nation was ultimately dependent upon the bodily strength of the British worker, so superior to that of the foreigner that English navvies had been imported to build Continental railways.

But the moral effects were the gravest of all. It was often alleged that the misery of the poor was chiefly the result of their own intemperate habits. They had few or no pleasures to wean them from intemperance, replied Chadwick, and gin offered the readiest release from the depressing conditions which hemmed them in.[2] "Seeing the apparent uncertainty of the morrow, the

---

[1] *Sanitary Report.*, pp. 190–2.
[2] In 1834 he had urged the Select Committee on Intemperance (*P.P.* 1834, vol. viii, p. 315) to consider "whether sober habits might not be efficiently promoted indirectly by the formation of cricket grounds, of public walks; horticultural gardens in the neighbourhoods of the smaller provincial towns, and by the institution of zoological repositories in the neighbourhood of the larger

inhabitants really take no heed of it, and abandon themselves with the recklessness and avidity of common soldiers in a war to whatever gross enjoyment comes within their reach."[1] Cleanliness and decency were impossible for the family which occupied a single room in a house unprovided with water or a privy. Overcrowding led to bastardy and incest, and forced the children on to the streets as thieves, beggars, and prostitutes. The evidence was overwhelming "how strongly circumstances that are governable govern the habits of the population,"[2] how filth and overcrowding acted as "physical barriers to improvement" against which "moral agencies have but a remote chance of success."[3]

Besides crime and vice, there were other products of the slums which the statesman and the employer had good reason to fear. Zymotic disease, which doomed so many workers to premature death and thinned the ranks of the higher age-groups, left behind "a population that is young, inexperienced, ignorant, credulous, irritable, passionate, and dangerous, having a perpetual tendency to moral as well as physical deterioration."[4] It was raw youths like this who were so easily deceived by "anarchical fallacies" and flocked in thousands to the Manchester torchlight meetings; and such "mere boys" formed the majority at Trade Union meetings, from which their more responsible elders, with sounder views on the relationship between capital and labour, tended to stay away in disgust. Thus, just as fever sometimes broke from its reservation in the poorer quarters and crept out to ravage the broad squares and streets of the West End, so the social diseases of Trade Unionism and Chartism might be born amidst the neglected inhabitants of the slums, and emerge to threaten the established order. Chadwick drew his respectable hearers to the edge of the pit, and bade them observe the monsters they were breeding beneath their feet.

This was the first great service of his Report—to dispel by the hard light of its revelations the darkness of ignorance which hid from bourgeois eyes the domestic condition of the workers. The

---

towns; and by the free admission of persons decently dressed to them on Sunday, after the morning service . . . an over-strict and Judaical observance of the Sabbath (being) equally prejudicial to true religion and temperance." (Q. 325.)

[1] *Sanitary Report*, p. 131.   [2] Ibid., p. 44.   [3] Ibid., p. 134.   [4] Ibid., p. 203.

lanes and alleys of the poor, "Little Ireland," the wynds of Edinburgh and Glasgow, the rookeries of St. Giles's, Villiers Square, and Golden Square, were as remote from the experience and imagination of the great majority of the middle and upper classes as some Punjab village or South African kraal. After 1842, however, there could be no excuse for ignorance, though interest might still continue to find arguments for inaction. In the language of eyewitnesses Chadwick gave descriptions of removable causes of disease, to be found not only in the industrial cities, but even in the small country towns and villages, which the sentimental delighted to paint as the homes of rustic comfort and rude agricultural health. The most damning evidence came from the Medical Officers of the Poor Law Unions, almost the only members of the professional or middle classes whose duties brought them into close contact with the lower classes in their houses. Thus, the Medical Officer of the Liverpool Union reported: "In consequence of finding that not less than 63 cases of fever had occurred in one year in Union-court Banastre street (containing 12 houses), I visited the court in order to ascertain, if possible, their origin, and I found the whole court inundated with fluid filth which had oozed through the walls from two adjoining ash-pits or cesspools, and which had no means of escape in consequence of the court being below the level of the street, and having no drain. The court was owned by two different landlords, one of whom had offered to construct a drain provided the other would join him in the expense; but this offer having been refused, the court had remained for two or three years in the state in which I saw it; and I was informed by one of the inhabitants that the fever was constantly recurring there. The house nearest the ash-pit had been untenanted for nearly three years in consequence of the filthy matter oozing up through the floor, and the occupiers of the adjoining houses were unable to take their meals without previously closing the doors and windows. Another court in North-street, consisting of only four small houses I found in a somewhat similar condition, the air being contaminated by the emanations from two filthy ruinous privies, a large open ash-pit, and a stratum of semi-fluid abomination covering the whole surface of the court."[1]

[1] *Sanitary Report*, p. 31.

It was true, as Ashley observed, that "one whiff of Cowyard, Blue Anchor, or Baker's Court, outweighs ten pages of letter-press";[1] but all that print could do to shock and shame was done by Chadwick in the most powerful assault upon the sensibility of the ruling classes that had ever been attempted. All pointed to the same general conclusions: that the health and comfort of civilised man, urban man, depended upon arrangements for bringing his water supply into the towns and taking his wastes out, and for ensuring to each individual his due share of light and air; that in nineteenth-century Britain those arrangements were grossly inadequate; and that their inadequacy must be ascribed not so much to lack of knowledge as to a failure to apply such knowledge as was readily available. It was not the intractability of brute physical facts which formed the main obstacle to the cleansing of the towns, but the plain human stupidities of in-difference, self-satisfaction, lethargy, and stubborn habit; it was not that the problem was too difficult, but that the mental effort directed towards its solution was too puny.

In drainage, water supply, ventilation, in all the essentials of urban life, the existing practice was far below the existing science. Methods of drainage exhibited the crudest empiricism, an ignorance of elementary hydraulics, and a conservatism which was blind to the benefits of the simplest improvements. Street sewers were immense brick caverns, flat-bottomed and flat-sided, washed only by a feeble trickle of water. Built on the hypothesis that they would accumulate deposit, they were made of brick so that they might be the more readily opened; and at intervals of five or ten years the streets would be excavated and men would scoop up the deposit in pails, raise it by windlass to the road surface, and leave it there in noisome heaps to be collected by the scavenger's carts. House drains were also made of brick, and in construction were no better than extended cesspools, fitted rather to retain deposit than to carry it away; and it was usual to lay down for a single house a drain with capacity sufficient to remove the refuse of a thousand. Rarely in the design of sewers and house drains was there any recognition of the elementary principle of hydraulics which forms the basis for the modern system of water-carriage, that by concentrating the flow of water in a smooth

---

[1] E. Hodder, *Life and Work of the Seventh Earl of Shaftesbury* (1886), vol. i, p. 361.

circular channel its scouring power may be increased. Only in a few middle-class houses had the water-closet replaced the cesspool or the privy midden; and in London its introduction was obstructed by the Commissions of Sewers, who imposed an illegal fee on any householder who sought permission to drain his house into the public sewer. Moreover, there were profits to be made out of filth which would be threatened if it were removed by the expeditious water-closet. Vast dumps of ashes, night-soil, rotting vegetables, straw, dung, refuse of all kinds, in thousands of tons occupying hundreds of cubic yards, the sweepings of the streets, the offal of the slaughter-houses, and the contents of the public privies, were built up in the midst of densely populated districts as the stock-in-trade of dealers who retailed it to farmers by the cart- and the barge-load.[1] In London, however, no refuse, except coal ashes, cinders, and dust, which were used in the making of bricks, paid half the expense of cartage, and transport costs limited the use and deposit of the refuse within a radius of three miles beyond the line of the district post. The charge for emptying cesspools averaged £1, and in metropolitan parishes remote from the agricultural areas this expense, to people who were usually in debt at the end of each week, acted as a complete barrier to cleanliness. Thus, as the great towns expanded and their centres grew ever more distant from the country districts, as the numbers of their inhabitants increased and the volume of their wastes increased in proportion, the burden became too heavy for the small scavenging contractors, and the traditional methods of sewage disposal were breaking down. The result was the steady secretion of filth in basements and backyards.

In street paving and the arrangements for surface cleansing, Chadwick found the same waste and the same want of science. A road-sweeping machine had been invented (by Whitworth), but the parish authorities clung to the old methods of hand-labour which provided employment for their paupers. When paving was laid down, the primary object was, not to facilitate cleanliness,

---

[1] The famous dunghill of Market Street, Greenock, described in the *Sanitary Report*, pp. 46–7, which the Webbs considered "the climax of horrors" (*Statutory Authorities*, p. 339), was rivalled in many other towns; cf. the "Ash Yard" of Gaywood, Norfolk, which was estimated to contain some 2,025 tons of refuse. (W. Lee, *Report to the General Board of Health on Gaywood*, April 1850, pp. 9–10).

E

but to expedite the flow of cart and carriage traffic, and it was therefore usually confined to the main streets. Of 687 streets inspected in Manchester, 248 were unpaved, 112 ill ventilated, and 352 contained stagnant pools and heaps of refuse and ordure. Yet the street cleansing of Manchester cost £5,000 a year; for which sum the first-class streets and the large thoroughfares were cleansed once a week, the second-class once a fortnight, and the third-class once a month—leaving untouched the courts and alleys where the poor lived, and where cleansing was required daily. Against any extension of the street cleansing services was raised the cry of immediate expense. In London an annual bill of £40,000 was incurred; but, as Chadwick pointed out, two-thirds of this was accounted for by the cost of cartage, which would become unnecessary if the sewers were properly adapted to carry away refuse. So far were local authorities from realising that the sewers offered the most rapid and economical means for the removal of refuse and mud from the road surface that in some towns the use of the sewers for this purpose was expressly forbidden under penalties in the local Improvement Act.

But the gravest deficiency of all, since it was the key to most sanitary improvements, was the shortage of water, not only for house cleaning and sewerage, but even for drinking, washing, and cooking. The water companies had got into the habit of intermittent supply at a time when their mains were made of hollowed elm-trunks, not strong enough to withstand the pressure of a constant supply. Though cast-iron mains were now in use, they still clung to their old practices, and, fearing the expense of new plant, were prepared to argue that a constant supply was technically impossible. In London the companies supplied their tenants on three days of each week for two or three hours at a time. With a show of generosity they had erected public fountains and stand-pipes in the streets and courts, where the poor might help themselves without charge, and around these, when the water was running, the inhabitants gathered to catch their supply in pails, fish-kettles, casks, cans, and even soup-plates. Yet, as Chadwick showed, every house could have a constant supply for twopence a week, so that the time of even the lowest paid labourer was wastefully employed in fetching and carrying water.[1] An efficient

[1] Even in middle-class districts the register of the cistern was watched with

sand-filter had been introduced by James Simpson, the engineer to the Chelsea Water Works, in 1829, but more than half the metropolitan supply still passed untreated from the river to the consumer. It was hardly surprising that during the cholera epidemic of 1831–2, the poor in some districts were convinced that the water had been poisoned to destroy them by a Malthusian-minded Government. In general, throughout the country, the well, the ditch, the river which served also as the main sewer of the town, were the sources from which urban populations drew their water; and few towns had yet had the enterprise to look further afield for more abundant and purer supplies, which the technical advances of the age had made it possible to pipe and pump to them from upland gathering-grounds.

Finally, Chadwick demonstrated how the immense expansion of the population had offered bounties to the shrewdness of the speculative builder and the "ignorance, cupidity, or negligence of landlords."[1] The census returns gave the impression that the number of houses had kept pace with the size of the population, but in actual fact every occupation under the same roof had been counted as a separate dwelling; and conditions in the growing towns were illustrated by Blackfriars parish, Glasgow, where in the years between 1831 and 1841 the population had increased by 40 per cent while the number of houses had remained the same.[2] The labouring classes, obliged to dwell within convenient distance of their places of work, must take whatever accommodation they could get. In the old districts of the towns they crowded, from cellar to garret, the decayed and superannuated mansions abandoned by the rich. In the new suburbs no scrap of land seemed too narrow, too damp, or too close to a public midden, to be free from the activities of the jerry-builder. Cellar dwellings, lacking drains or conveniences of any kind; back-to-back houses,

---

an anxious eye, and the household amenities expanded or narrowed from day to day with the fluctuations in supply. Cf. a letter to the *Times*, 14 July 1851: "Monday—water six inches. Cook and housemaid on short allowance. Master's bath relinquished. Tuesday—water one inch. Boiled vegetables and teas strictly forbidden. Wednesday—cistern dry; water nowhere. Thursday —the water on. Hurrah! Listen to that rushing sound. We shall drink— we shall wash—we shall bathe! Ah, in five minutes the stream ceases, and all our hopes are blighted."

[1] *Sanitary Report*, p. 7.   [2] Ibid., p. 121.

without the sweetening draught of through ventilation; closed courts, with a stand-pipe at one end and a privy at the other— every obnoxious ingenuity in the economy of land and materials that the self-interest of landlords could devise, and the necessity of tenants could be obliged to accept, was to be found in London and the great provincial towns. No attempt had been made by the Government, apart from Lord Normanby's ill-considered Bills, to deal with these evils. Openings for light and air were actually penalised by the iniquitous Window Duties.[1] The chief concern of the legislature, as revealed in the Metropolitan Building Act, had been to prevent the spread of fires by requiring the construction of party walls of a minimum thickness; and no legal obstacle existed to bar the speculative builder from running up houses with walls one brick thick on undrained sites outside the jurisdiction of that Act. Viewing the chaos of London, sprawling outwards without plan and without control, Chadwick sighed for the "great design" of Sir Christopher Wren, the rejection of which, he believed, had cost each succeeding generation a death-rate too high by one-third. Christopher Wren and Edwin Chadwick between them would have made a good job of London.

As he thus surveyed the technical deficiencies in the planning and construction of essential public services, and the universal neglect of the lessons of science in solving the problems of the towns, it became obvious to Chadwick that he must become his own engineer. No one had yet taken the principles of hydraulics out of the text-books and applied them to town drainage, nor had any one yet thought of bringing together all the practical improvements in water supply and housing that the inventive genius of the period was now making readily available. Chadwick boldly annexed to himself this vast, little-explored region. There were, indeed, at the beginning few to contest his title. The Institute of Civil Engineers had been founded as long ago as 1818, but its members were still struggling to establish recognised standards of professional competence. Before the eyes of the ablest of the profession, the railway projectors dangled the richest

[1] By 4 & 5 Will. IV, c. 54, occupiers, if they were duly assessed to Window Tax in 1835, were permitted to open as many windows as they pleased. This step was rendered nugatory by the lawyers, who proved that nobody had been duly assessed to Window Tax in 1835!

prizes that their talents could command. The engineers of the water companies were wedded to the restrictive policies of their employers. In rural districts the highway surveyors were often no more than "ditch casters" or common labourers, while in the towns they were frequently unsuccessful builders or tradesmen, few of whom were capable even of drawing. The surveyors of the metropolitan Commissions of Sewers were little better; the extent of their acquirements was suggested when one Commission advertised for a surveyor able to use a spirit level.[1] Those "wretched empirics the modern engineers!"[2] It was Chadwick's continual lament that there were "marvellously few" trustworthy men amongst them; "a more ignorant, or a more jobbing set of men, less to be trusted, as the difference of their estimates and their expenditure will shew, than the common run of men who dub themselves with the title of engineer and pretend to science I have rarely met with."[3] Nor were the architects any better, he told the students when he distributed the prizes at the Putney College for Civil Engineers; the proofs of their incompetence were displayed in "spectacle after spectacle of the ruins of fallen bridges, factories, and large buildings, in horrible deaths, and shocking mutilations occurring again and again from the like preventable causes."[4] Altogether, "in no profession, perhaps, is there so large a proportion of bold, rapacious quackery as in the professions of civil engineering and architecture."[5]

Here and there, however, he found a shining exception, a man of practical common sense and an inventive turn of mind, who had experimented with ideas of his own. Such a man, for example, was the surveyor to the Holborn Sewers Commission, John Roe, "perhaps the only officer having the experience and qualifications of a civil engineer,"[6] who since his appointment in 1820 had succeeded in introducing a number of improvements in the face of the conservatism and obtuseness of his employers. Roe had devised a system of flushing which halved the cost of cleansing the sewers; he had reduced the size of drains for short streets and

[1] *Sanitary Report*, p. 332.   [2] "Water Supply. Metropolitan," MS., n.d.
[3] E. C. to John Shuttleworth, 9 October 1844.
[4] *The Builder*, vol. cxxx, p. 362, 2 August 1845.
[5] *Papers read before the Statistical Society of Manchester on . . . Labourers engaged in the Construction and Working of Railways*, 1846, p. 23.
[6] *Sanitary Report*, p. 55.

courts from 4 ft. 6 in. x 2 ft. 6 in. to 15 in. in diameter; and,
finding that the practice of joining sewers at angles (frequently
even right angles) caused eddies and the deposit of sediment, and
obstructed the current of water, he had persuaded the Commissioners to require that curves should be formed in the sewers
with a radius of not less than twenty feet. Chadwick was delighted,
and set Roe to work on a series of experiments to ascertain the
most economical size of pipe for drains and sewers and the best
materials for their construction. The "arterial-venous system" of
town drainage, which he elaborated in the next two years, owed
much to these suggestive experiments by John Roe. Despite the
scepticism of engineers and Sewers Commissioners, Chadwick
could not see why—if drains and sewers were formed of glazed
earthenware instead of rough spongy brick, and a regular flow of
water were concentrated in these smooth circular tubes—sewers
of deposit should not cease to exist, and excreta be conveyed away
from the household by the prompt and cleanly water-closet.

The two main objections to the use of the water-closet, apart
from the cost of its installation, were that it must result in the
pollution of the rivers, and that, at the same time and by the same
process, it would permit valuable manure to run to waste. The
key to the understanding of Chadwick's engineering schemes,
which he sketched for the first time in the *Sanitary Report*, is his
effort to show that neither of these results was inevitable. As he
saw it, town and country stood in a reciprocal relation. Only too
often the country, suffering from an excess of moisture and a
shortage of manure, presented a gloomy picture of poor water-
logged land, thin crops, a population few in numbers and afflicted
by rheumatism, ague, and other illnesses produced by a damp
environment. The companion picture could be seen in the neighbouring town, its inhabitants ravaged by the zymotic diseases
caused by accumulated filth and a deficient water supply, its
houses and streets foul with the matter needed by the starved
land outside.[1] The solution was the "arterial-venous system",
with the public sewers as the arteries pumping out the rich town
guano, and the water pipes as the veins returning the excess
moisture of the countryside to the place where it was most needed.
A great annual revenue could be won by the simple expedient of

[1] *Sanitary Report*, p. 97.

removing the sources of ill-health from London's back-streets. If this income were vested in the public authorities, to whom, indeed, by law and custom it properly belonged, it would go far towards footing the bill for the other public services which were now so much neglected. The whole scheme was fascinating in its simplicity and economy.

If he must turn engineer to rescue the towns from filth, Chadwick found also that he must be equally inventive in his administrative proposals. No authorities existed whose functions had for their conscious object the maintenance and improvement of the public health. The Privy Council had been charged, under an Act of George I, to keep watch against the dangers of foreign pestilence, and an annual sum of £2,000 was voted for the National Vaccination Board. Beyond this the central Government acknowledged no responsibility for the health of the subject. Every man had a Common Law right to "air for his health, light for his profit, prospect for his pleasure," and the legal remedies of indictment might be invoked to suppress any nuisance which endangered the health or personal safety or conveniences of the citizen. "Annoyance juries," appointed by the Courts Leet, still perambulated some towns in search of public nuisances, an inquest of reluctant and ignorant tradesmen which retained its value only in the antiquarian affections of a Toulmin Smith. The public continued to suffer because no funds existed to defray the cost of prosecution by indictment, while large capital defended the most offensive nuisances.

Apart from the ancient and ineffectual remedies provided by the Common Law, the state of the public health was the unlooked for by-product of the activities of bodies with quite other aims in view; of Town Councils, for example, not yet quickened by a civic conscience and concerned mainly with the preservation of the archaic dignities and privileges of their members; of Commissions of Sewers, whose traditional function was defence against floods and surface waters, and whose works were ill-designed for the additional burden thrown upon them by the introduction oi the water-closet; of paving trusts, more concerned to ensure a smooth flow of traffic than the cleanliness of the streets. Most oi the early Local Acts, though providing for paving, lighting, cleansing, and watching, contained no powers for the drainage oi streets or houses, being framed not for sanitary purposes but for the defence of life and property and the improvement of communications. More recent Acts, containing drainage provisions, did not extend to courts which were not thoroughfares, these being looked upon as private property and so not entitled to benefit. Though Local Acts contained a multitude of clauses directed against nuisances and obstructions, these were often of little effect, since the most influential members of the Corporation or the Improvement Commission might well be the company directors whose gasworks contaminated the streams or whose chimney smoke darkened the atmosphere.

In the new suburbs of the growing towns, lying outside the jurisdiction of the Town Council or the Improvement Commissioners, frequently the only powers for drainage were afforded by the Highway Act.[1] These powers were permissive; they were clearly intended only to provide means for carrying off surface water which might obstruct the highway; and their enforcement depended upon the energy and public spirit of a body of unwilling householders, annually elected to form a Highway Board, and commanding the services of a single paid surveyor. Yet in many large towns the drains so formed were often the only available channels for conveying refuse from the household.

In the metropolis the natural drainage area was capriciously subdivided between the ancient Commissions of Sewers, each of which sat within its frontiers, jealously guarding its jurisdiction against the encroachments of the rest, and stubbornly resisting all attempts to saddle it with the sanitary burdens of a new age. When the Holborn and Finsbury Commission enlarged its sewers, the sewers of the City, which lay on a lower level and with which they communicated, proved insufficient to carry away their contents, with the result that houses on the river bank were inundated by sewer water after each fall of rain. Blind to the absurdity of draining a natural area by unconnected and partial schemes, the City Surveyor complained in an aggrieved tone that the waters of the "county" ran into the City jurisdiction, obliging the Common Council to widen its own sewers. The drainage of houses was not a function that the Commissions regarded as falling within the scope of their normal service. Any one who

[1] 5 & 6 Will. IV, c. 50.

applied to have a drain laid down from his house to the sewer was charged a guinea; this fee, which was quite illegal, was defended by one surveyor on the ground that "if they were not to resort to that measure, the sewers would be destroyed. Every one would make a hole in the sewer."[1] When the medical observers of the Poor Law Commission were conducting their investigation in 1838, the clerk to the Tower Hamlets Division told Dr. Arnott that he had heard few reports of fever in his district—yet Baker's Arms Alley, a notorious fever nest, was distant only the length of a short street from his office.[2]

While drainage, which offered no prospect of profit, was thus left as an inefficient public service in the fumbling hands of local authorities, water had become an article of trade, and in all but three or four towns was distributed by commercial companies. These had defects of their own. They directed their supplies exclusively to those houses which could pay water rates, and took no account of the important public objects of cleansing streets, flushing sewers, and fighting fires. Competition, the economists' recipe for cheap and efficient service, had given no defence to the inhabitants of the capital. The London water companies, with whom Chadwick was presently to be at open war, had soon perceived that it would be more to their profit if instead of cutting each other's throats they got together in a gentleman's agreement to cut the throats of their customers. There had been first a period of wild competition, when two or three sets of pipes were driven through the wealthier districts, and gangs of rival pipelayers fought in the streets. Then followed a reflective interval while the companies licked their wounds. And finally came a compact between the nine companies to partition London, and subject Londoners to a nine-headed monopoly.

One primary public service, water supply, therefore, had been abandoned to irresponsible and arbitrary private companies, who confined their activities within the estimated range of easy profit; two more, drainage and paving, were imperfectly executed by torpid, amateur authorities, who, in the acid words of Chadwick's famous indictment, "sit still amidst the pollution, with the resignation of Turkish fatalists, under the supposed destiny of the prevalent ignorance, sloth, and filth."[3] In all three services, a new

[1] *Sanitary Report*, p. 311.   [2] Ibid., p. 313.   [3] Ibid., p. 44.

direction, a new spirit, and a new organisation were urgently
required. It took Chadwick another two years to work out in full
the remedies he proposed to meet the situation, but we may note
briefly here the main points of the preliminary sketch given in the
Sanitary Report. He insisted, in the first place, that all arrangements
for drainage and road construction must for the sake of efficiency
and economy be brought together into a single public service.
These duties should devolve upon the existing machinery of
Commissions of Sewers, extended from the metropolis to all parts
of the country, "revised as to jurisdiction, and amended and
strengthened as to power and responsibility."[1] Secondly, the
supply of water should be entrusted to "the most eligible local
administrative body."[2] This would generally be the drainage and
cleansing authority, but at any rate it should be a public body—
water supply should be removed from private hands. Chadwick
had been greatly impressed by that most successful of early essays
in collective regulation and enterprise, the municipal gasworks of
Manchester, established under a Local Act in 1817, and managed
by an elected committee of ratepayers. Another notable example
of public enterprise was reported to him from Bath, where the
Corporation supplied more than three-quarters of the town,
in competition with four small private companies; their water
rents amounted to £3,233 2s., their expenses to no more than
£449 3s. 3d., leaving a profit of £2,783 18s. 9d., which went to the
reduction of the borough rate.[3] Chadwick had not yet fully
elaborated his theory of public utilities, but in the *Sanitary Report*,
with these practical instances from Manchester and Bath before
him, he made his first authoritative pronouncement in support of
public management. He recommended, finally, the appointment of full-time district medical officers, charged with the duty
of hunting out the physical causes of disease in the houses of the
poor. A "single securely-qualified and well-appointed responsible
officer," he considered, would be far more effective than the local
Boards of Health recently suggested by the Report of Slaney's
Select Committee.[4]

Chadwick thus revealed that in local sanitary administration
his ideal was a compact Commission, appointed by the Govern-

---

[1] *Sanitary Report*, p. 339.   [2] Ibid., p. 80.
[3] Rev. Whitwell Elvin to E. C., 11 January 1842.   [4] *Sanitary Report*, p. 356.

ment, executing or supervising public works through a competent full-time engineer, and working in co-operation with a qualified medical officer of health. As he had earlier tried to ensure that the relief of the poor should be in the hands, not of elected Guardians, but of a paid permanent official, so he now insisted that the public health was not a matter to be left to local representative bodies. Nearly ten years of day-to-day contact with the corruption and petty intrigue of vestry politicians had taught him a profound and bitter contempt for the workings of representative government. From the Poor Law Report down to this latest product of his inquisitive spirit he had been displaying in countless instances the ineptitude, the stupidity, and the greed of the men who were thrown up promiscuously by the process of election. Under this system the public service had come to be regarded principally as the means of rewarding the elector who "voted straight"; a tailor would sell his support for a legal clerkship, or the voice of an "illiterate tinman, a leading speaker at parish meetings," would be bought for a surveyorship worth £150 a year.[1] Besides the corruption it bred, representative government led to a further mischievous error—the belief that the public business could best be conducted by unpaid amateurs, elected to serve their turn as civic officers, as Highway Surveyors, Paving Trustees, Sewers Commissioners, or Town Councillors. This implied, first, that the public business offered no problems which could not be solved by any gentleman who gave to it a fraction of the attention he gave to his own affairs; secondly, that any gentleman who served in such a capacity would look for no reward other than the respect of his fellow citizens and the approval of his conscience. Both these assumptions were vigorously denied by Chadwick. Throughout his career he was combating this legacy from a leisurely, aristocratic tradition, the belief that "unpaid dilettante service is cheap service,"[2] and opposing to it the principle of administration by salaried experts; for these, being paid, could be held accountable, they possessed special aptitude for the work, and they stood above local conflicts, viewing the local scene from the impartial aspect of the wider community.

[1] *Sanitary Report*, p. 332. [2] E. C. to ? (Lord Morpeth), n.d., *c.* May 1848.

CHAPTER III

INTERMENTS REPORT, 1843

MORE copies of the *Sanitary Report* were sold by the Stationery Office than of any previous Government publication, to the great satisfaction of the reformers who believed that "its good effect would be (as much almost as by legislation) created by its private influence on society."[1] J. S. Mill, to whom Chadwick had sent the Report in proof, could not find "a single erroneous or questionable position in it, while there is the strength and largeness of practical views which are characteristic of all you do"; the style and arrangement appalled him, however, and he wished that Chadwick would learn "some of the forms of scientific exposition of which my friend Comte makes such superfluous use."[2] The Home Secretary, Sir James Graham, declined to present the report to Her Majesty, but his vigilance was circumvented by Sir James Clark, the Queen's physician, who gave a copy to Baron Stockmar, "purposely to get him to read the part on Windsor";[3] (one investigator had described the Royal Borough as incomparably the worst of all the towns he had visited). To many the astounding details came with all the force of a revelation. The medical superintendent of Arkwright's mill at Cromford, for example, despite his opportunities for observation, confessed that he had not previously been aware of the great mortality of the poor as compared with those in more easy circumstances.[4] But others were less impressed, and where they were not openly incredulous greeted the report with the defensive reactions of disgust or derision. E. C. Tufnell, one of the Assistant Poor Law Commissioners, wrote lightly, "your Report reads like one of Ainsworth's novels, and will I think furnish some good hints

[1] J. H. Burton to E. C., 29 September 1842.
[2] J. S. Mill to E. C., April 1842.
[3] Sir James Clark to E. C., 21 August 1842.
[4] T. Poyson to E. C., 29 March 1843.

60

for deepening the horrors of his next Jack Sheppard production."[1] In Paris a squeamish editor suppressed a review of the report for the *Siècle* because of its dirty subject.[2] Many others shrugged their shoulders when it was mentioned to them, Chadwick recalled later, as much to say, "It is all very fine but you see *the people* like dirt and prefer dirt, and you cannot force them to spend money against their will.'[3]

By many engineers, however, the practical value of the report was instantly recognised. At the Putney College Butler Williams began to use it at once as a text-book for his classes in civil engineering; and his students, following up Chadwick's suggestions, carried out experimental surveys of Putney and Wandsworth, and prepared the first contour map of the City of London. When William Lindley was engaged to rebuild Hamburg after the disastrous fire of 1842, he proposed to design the city's sewerage on Chadwick's principles of flushing and water carriage. The City Engineer and City Architect promptly reported against his plan, basing their objections on passages from the *Sanitary Report*, which they were convinced had been written to indict the evil effects of all sewers upon the health of the population. Not until Chadwick had sent Lindley written confirmation of his real views would the Hamburg Senate allow him to proceed with his scheme.[4]

In political circles some, like Lord Howick, were now learning with "astonishment and dismay" of the state of the towns, and were beginning to ask themselves whether "we have trusted too much in a case where it does not apply, to the maxim that men should be left to take care of their own interests," whether it would not have been better if "even at the price of some sacrifice of productive power and of national wealth, the State had earlier interfered, and had taken measures which should have opposed some check to so vast an increase of population, without some corresponding increase in the machinery for maintaining order and decency, and diffusing the blessings of education and religion."[5] Lord Normanby was already a convert; he had thought the account in the *Fever Report* of 1838 exaggerated, till

[1] E. C. Tufnell to E. C., 27 April 1842.
[2] W. E. Hickson to E. C., 20 January 1843.
[3] E. C. to Sir Henry de la Beche, 25 December 1843.
[4] William Lindley to E. C., 18 April and 13 June 1843.
[5] *Hansard*, vol. lxxiv, p. 647, 3 May 1844.

Southwood Smith conducted him on a tour of Bethnal Green and Whitechapel.[1] Ashley also, with the Doctor as guide, had been to see and smell for himself the houses in Cowyard, Blue Anchor, and Baker's Court.[2] But the Government, in the person of Sir James Graham, maintained a wary reserve. Too many interests must be disturbed, too many tenacious preconceptions abandoned, too many innovations in the scope and structure of administration accepted, for any hasty decision to be made by a Home Secretary in 1842, whether he were a Whig or a Tory. The Health of Towns Commission, described in the next chapter, gave the Government the breathing space and the strengthened arguments that they required. Thus, a few individuals, like Ashley and Normanby, were already convinced that the State must stretch out its power to avert the yearly doom of disease and death in the towns; many more, like Howick, were uneasily aware that past indifference and inactivity had produced a problem whose solution could not much longer be postponed; but by a vast inertia the ideas of most legislators continued to move in the deep grooves cut by habit and comfortable thinking. The time for legislation had not yet come.

Ignorance and interest found a colour of theory for their opposition in the teachings of that complacent school of philosophers who claimed to see in the operations of misery and disease the workings of beneficent economic laws. "That error of Mr. Malthus stands as a wall against measures of sanitary improvement," cried Chadwick in exasperation.[3] It met him at the outset of his public health campaign as it had met him ten years earlier when he began his Poor Law investigations, that fatalistic view that the pressure of population must in the nature of things lead to a large amount of unavoidable distress, that "undefined optimism" which found ground for inaction in the belief that the ravages of disease formed a natural or positive check, a "terrible corrective,"[4] to man's tendency to multiply beyond the means of subsistence. Wars and plagues, thought McCulloch, tended to place an old country in the situation of a colony: they lessened the number of inhabitants without in most cases lessening the capital which existed for their maintenance. This assertion Chadwick

---

[1] C. L. Lewes, *Dr. Southwood Smith*, pp. 69–70.
[2] Ibid., and E. Hodder, op. cit., vol. i, p. 361.
[3] E. C. to J. H. Burton, 31 July 1844.   [4] *Sanitary Report*, p. 176.

strenuously denied, in his reports and in discussions at the Political Economy Club. Such figures as he had been able to collect, from America and Europe as well as Great Britain, showed that districts where mortality was greatest had also the highest birth rate, and that the losses due to pestilence were more than made up by new births. "In one of the illdrained and illcleansed and over crowded courts where there was a heavy mortality I once observed, to one of the women living there: 'Why the undertaker is never absent from this place.' 'No, nor the midwife either,' was the reply and it was then crowded with young and puny children."[1] Nor was it true that the "corrective fates" left the capital of a country unchanged, since they swept away many workers at the height of their productive powers, diminishing the proportion of adult workers and increasing the proportion of dependent children and widows. The farmer would soon give his opinion of McCulloch's "corrective" if of the colts born on his farm he could rear only one-half, and if the average working period of those reared were reduced by disease from ten years to five![2]

Let it be granted then, said Chadwick, that the ratios of Malthus' hypothesis were as well founded as the theory of gravitation; one could admit the tendency of all stones to fall to the centre of the earth, and yet deny that in actual experience any stones actually did so fall.[3] The truth was that the belief was quite fallacious that the economic condition of the labouring classes was depressed. In that Malthusian stronghold, the Political Economy Club, he was amazed to find the impression that the wages of cotton workers were continually decreasing under the inexorable competition of excessive numbers. Another unfounded deduction of the "hypothesists"! Actually, he pointed out, an analysis of the purchasing power of the wages now paid as compared with

[1] MS. notes, n.d. Nearly half a century later Chadwick claimed that he had told Malthus at the Political Economy Club, just before his death in 1834, "the fact of the quick reproduction of human life in the high rated districts of death. He was quite astonished that this point had escaped his observation." (*National Health*, ed. B. W. Richardson, 1890, p. 313.)

[2] "Heads of Answer to J. McCulloch's positions as to pestilence being corrective of population" (MS. notes of a paper read to the Political Economy Club in June 1845). See also the detailed discussion in *Sanitary Report*, pp. 182-3, 193-5, 204-5.

[3] "Heads of Answer to J. McCulloch's positions as to pestilence being corrective of population."

those of an earlier generation proved exactly the contrary. In 1792, a Lancashire manufacturer told Chadwick in 1841, his father paid his spinners 4s. 4d. a week; he himself paid them 8s. 8d. or more—and the price of provisions was as high in 1792, and of clothing was 30 or 40 per cent higher.[1] In Stockport, Chadwick informed Sir Robert Peel in December 1843, wages had recently averaged 11s. per head for man, woman, and child, twice the amount paid in the agricultural districts. Such wages for cotton operatives were "beyond their capacity of frugal application."[2] Whenever he heard it objected that the working classes could not afford to pay for improved housing and drainage, he would point to the amount of their "self-imposed taxation" as reflected in the excise returns. On liquor, beer, tobacco, and snuff, they spent £45 or £50 millions annually, more than the whole expenditure of the Government on the administration of justice, the civil service, and the Army and Navy. The town of Bury alone, with a population of 25,000, spent £54,190 each year on beer and spirits, £2 3s. 4d. a head, enough to pay the rent and taxes for 6,770 new cottages at £8 per annum each.[3]

Fever was born of distress—so ran the easy generalisation of the politicians and economists, the corollary being that prosperity was the one cure for epidemics. The records of the fever hospitals, Chadwick replied, showed that the pestilential miasma which caused disease was governed more by the weather than by the state of the market. Liverpool and Manchester, the two most thriving cities in the country, were also the most unhealthy. It was true, of course, that the districts where the greatest mortality occurred were probably the poorest, but not invariably so. It was the physical circumstances of place which determined the mortality rate, and in the American cities, New York and Philadelphia for example, the mortality was greater even than in Dublin. So much for the argument that high wages and American democracy were the best remedies for all social evils![4]

---

[1] *Sanitary Report*, p. 188.

[2] "Memorandum on present condition of Manufacturing Districts," December 1843; *Peel Papers*, British Museum Add. MSS., vol. 40, 537, ff. 132–159.

[3] *Sanitary Report*, p. 227. Also "Draft Memoranda on the exposition of the Budget," MS. fragment, n.d.

[4] E. C. to Lord Francis Egerton, 1 October 1845.

The population theory of Malthus was Chadwick's favourite example of the unverified assumptions on which economists based their recommendations and statesmen built their policies. He was on firm ground when he asserted that the rise in average real incomes, and the concurrent increase in both population and wealth, showed that the limits of subsistence had not in fact been reached. He was right to urge against Malthus that in the Britain of his day the Nemesis of decreasing returns was held at bay by improvements in agriculture and in the technique of production, that "the labourer goes into the market as a producer, rather than as a competitor."[1] In the face of that loose complacency which, from a dread of over-population, saw good in a heavy death rate, he did right to point out, in terms that economists and industrialists could understand, that every labourer who, over and above his subsistence, produced a surplus to make it worth while to employ him, possessed a pecuniary value; that just as much as the destruction of a machine, his death was an economic loss; and that, simply from an economic point of view, the more there were of such labourers the better for the community, just as the community was all the better the more it had of productive machines in active employment.[2] Unfortunately, however, while deriding the smugness which characterised many of Malthus's followers, he adopted certain complacent doctrines of his own. He was led to argue that there was little in the circumstances of the lower classes that good drains and pure water and improved housing, combined with intelligent administrative arrangements, could not cure. Their diet was ample enough; a working woman, he maintained, to lose children and reproduce them again in such rapid succession, must be robust and well-nourished, and her physique could not be reduced and attenuated by starvation.[3] Their hours of work were not excessive; Chadwick, who drove himself hard for anything up to sixteen hours a day, probably never felt the full force of the argument for a ten-hour day; and, as he told Peel, while strikes for higher wages were common enough, he had never heard of one for shorter hours.[4] As for their

[1] E. C. to Archibald Allison, 5 August 1840.
[2] *Select Committee on Railway Labourers*, Q. 2208; *P.P.* 1846 vol. xii, p. 1.
[3] E. C. to John Wilson, 5 January 1844.
[4] E. C. to Sir Robert Peel, 16 May 1846; *Peel Papers*, British Museum Add. MSS., vol. 40,592, f. 6.

F

wages, they were actually in many cases excessive, in view of the recipients' ignorance and lack of self-control; and the excess was too often divided between the publican, the Dissenting minister, and the Trade Union agitator. It is not surprising then that between Malthus, who told them they could never be better off, and Chadwick, who told them that they were better off than they thought, the working classes could see little to choose.

The *Sanitary Report* was presented on 9 July 1842, and nearly a year was to elapse before Chadwick opened the extended inquiry under the Health of Towns Commission. The intervening months were occupied in preparing a Supplementary Report on Interments in Towns, a subject omitted from the *Sanitary Report* on account of its size and special character. A final chapter, and that the grimmest, remained to be added to his sanitary survey, and without a break he plunged single-handed into what was to prove the most disagreeable and thankless of his investigations.

The overcrowding of the graveyards was only a special aspect of the central problem of civic police which the enormous growth of the population had thrust into the unready hands of nineteenth-century administrators. As the housing accommodation of the metropolis was insufficient for the number of living Londoners, so the graveyard space was insufficient for the number of the dead. The channels of habit had been cut deep by the centuries; and even when the churchyard was hemmed in by buildings on all sides, and ten parishioners required burial where one had been buried before, the custom maintained its hold of burying in the holy ground within the walls of "God's Acre." And now, in the 218 acres of London's burial grounds, 20,000 adults and nearly 30,000 youths and children were interred each year—a million and a half bodies within the last generation. In the cemeteries of German towns—German experience afforded Chadwick the standard by which to judge English conditions—the number of interments to the acre averaged 110 each year. In the same area the London gravedigger had to find room for probably twice that number of bodies annually, and perhaps for ten, twenty, or even thirty times as many. Faced by the physical impossibility of burying more corpses than could be accommodated by the ground at his disposal, he had been driven to gross expedients. One body was scarcely laid in the soil before it was rudely disturbed to admit another. At the burial ground of the Tottenham Court Road chapel, seven or eight adults and twenty or thirty children were crowded into each grave, the whole corrupting mass being temporarily covered by a light layer of earth after each new interment. When the close-packed earth could hold no more, bodies were broken and hewn into pieces to fit them into a smaller space. In one corner of the churchyard of St. Olave and St. John in Tooley Street a pit sixteen feet deep and twelve feet square was dug for the reception of bones thrown up by the sexton's spade. Church vaults were never filled up, because the older coffins mysteriously disappeared, the bones being wheeled away in cartloads as farm manure, while the lead was stripped from the coffins and sold by the gravedigger.

For the sanitary reformers, believing that decomposing animal matter was injurious to health, the Grand Guignol horrors of the churchyards were deepened by a further fact—that an epidemic might well be started by exposing a putrid body. London's two hundred graveyards gave off incessantly the exhalations of decay, and the morbific matter, whose deadliness was shown if it got into the slightest cut, might be breathed into the lungs when it was diffused into the atmosphere. Plague, typhus, or cholera might be generated in this way amongst the overcrowded town populations, just as "dissecting-room fever" had been known to strike down the students and attendants who handled the cadavers in the medical schools. It was on this deduction from the crude pythogenic theory that Dr. G. A. Walker, "Walker of the Graveyards," based the attack on the dangers of intramural interment which he launched in 1837. In the Commons the campaign was led by W. A. Mackinnon, another of those parliamentary francs-tireurs who from time to time ranged themselves at Chadwick's side, banging away enthusiastically at some well-loved target—the soap duties, quarantine, factory smoke, or the window tax—and more often than not embarrassing him with their half-baked schemes and uncontrollable tendencies to fly off at a tangent. On 8 March 1842 Mackinnon obtained a Select Committee, the Home Secretary, Sir James Graham, admitting that some legislative

interference was "absolutely necessary."[1] By August he was
ready with the draft of a Bill to implement the findings of his
Committee; and Graham, hesitating to move against the religious
and customary prejudices and the strong sectional interests with
which the subject was hedged, turned for fuller information to
Chadwick.

Mackinnon had been concerned only to abate the dangers and
indecencies of existing burial practices by ensuring that interment
should take place at a distance from the boundaries of the town,
the arrangements being controlled by a parochial "committee of
health" under the general supervision of the diocesan or of a
Central Board in London. Chadwick at once opened up the
attack on a wider front. In a demonstration of remarkable power,
he confronted the social conscience of the law-making classes,
numbed as it was by indifference, ignorance, and the anodyne
of interest, with a picture of the working-class family, caught in a
web of custom and economic circumstance which could be broken
only by the benevolent strength of the central Government. The
grossness and muddle of the desecrated graveyards seem to have
touched something deep in Chadwick. Perhaps in no other report
of his is the criticism of unregulated private enterprise so fierce,
and the revelation, how often a man's self-interest shaped his
opinions, so ruthless. We see him probing his witnesses with sharp
questioning—the gravediggers, prematurely aged, with their
shrunken figures and cadaverous aspect, solemnly swearing to the
healthiness of their occupation; the robust keeper of a dissecting
theatre who had never suffered ill effects (though, to be sure, his
assistants did the most dangerous and dirty work, and eight of
them had died, some being dissected in the very theatre in which
they were employed);[2] the employers, shrugging away the early
deaths of their workmen, with "But they drink—they are a
drunken set"[3]; the cemetery owners adding to their profits by
"working the earth close"; the secretaries of the burial clubs
revealing the fantastic finances of their societies, the undertakers
urging a "respectable funeral," the clergymen pocketing their
fees and perquisites, "a silk scarf of three yards and a half, a silk
hatband, and black kid gloves."[4] We can feel his mounting

[1] *Hansard*, vol lxi, pp. 281–3, 8 March 1842.
[2] *Report on Interment in Towns*, p. 8.   [3] Ibid., p. 9.   [4] Ibid., p. 49.

impatience with their shifts and equivocations, and share something of the enthusiasm with which he invokes the power of
Government to tidy up the mess.

His first step was to show that in a startlingly high proportion of
cases in London and the industrial towns, one room was the sole
accommodation for the whole family. "It is their bedroom, their
kitchen, their wash-house, their sitting-room, their dining-room;
and, when they do not follow any outdoor occupation, it is
frequently their workroom and their shop. In this one room they
are born, and live, and sleep, and die amidst the other inmates."[1]
Out of 1,465 families in the inner ward of St. George's, Hanover
Square, 929 had a single room and 408 others had only two; of the
same families 623 had one bed each, another 638 only two. In
Marylebone conditions were even worse. Out of 608 families, 159
occupied part of a room, 382 had one room, and 61 had two; only
5 families had three rooms, and only 1 had four. Thus, in St.
George's about one family in eleven possessed a third room where
a corpse might be laid out; in Marylebone only one in a hundred.[2]
In the one-roomed homes of the poor the body must await burial,
while the normal life of the family went on around it, the family
eating, sleeping, working, the children playing, in close proximity
to a corpse perhaps still covered with the visible marks of disease.
It might remain there the best part of a fortnight, since for the
working classes Sunday was the one day free on which they could
bury their dead, and if a death took place in the middle of the
week, the body was frequently kept until the Sunday week, while
subscriptions were being collected. Corpses had been retained,
according to one undertaker, even after the coffins had been
tapped to let out the liquid products of decomposition, till maggots
were seen crawling about the floor and over the trestles on which
the tapped coffin was supported, till, as the body was borne away,
escaping matter ran down the shoulders of the bearers.[3] When
the cause of death was an infectious disease, the results could be
predicted. The louse, carrier of typhus, deserted the chilling
body for a warmer host, and a victim of typhus had been known
to be followed very shortly to the grave by five of his children
and two or three visitors. Chadwick summed up the inescapable
conclusion: if four out of every five working-class families had only

[1] *Report on Interment in Towns*, p. 31.   [2] Ibid., pp. 31–2.   [3] Ibid., p. 38.

one room, every one of 20,000 deaths a year in London must be accompanied by the dreadful incidents his witnesses had described; and, furthermore, in the case of every one of the 4,000 deaths from epidemic disease included in that total, the surviving relatives must be in acute danger of being struck down by the same infection.[1]

Why, he asked, picking up the next link in the sordid chain, why was burial so long delayed amongst the lower classes? The answer plumbed the depths of human habit and social custom. In the great majority of cases the reason was the high cost of dying, the lack of money to defray the expenses of interment. The greatest dread of the poor man was to be buried as a pauper, to be carried in a plain parish coffin borne by pauper bearers to the "bone-house," the last resting-place for suicides and those unfortunates whom nobody claimed as friend or relative. To avert that humiliation, and to secure respectable interment, was perhaps the most powerful motive which drove him. It was estimated that a third or a fourth of the £24,000,000 in the savings banks was earmarked for funeral expenses, and even paupers were sometimes found at their deaths to have concealed a hoard to pay for their own decent burial. Much of the business of the small-debt courts was concerned with the enforcement of undertakers' bills; and one undertaker told Chadwick that if they did not give time for payment to two-thirds of their customers, the poor would not be able to bury their dead at all.

This "pride" of the working classes, rooted in long custom and in the courage of self-respect struggling in adversity, made them the easy victims of the burial club and the undertaker. In Westminster, Marylebone, Finsbury, Tower Hamlets, and the City, there were about two hundred burial societies, organised usually by one of the small, grubbing undertakers and the publican of the tavern where the meetings were held. Membership ranged from 100 to 800 and deposits from £90 to £1,000; contributors usually paid 1½d. or 2d., and relatives received a benefit of from £5 to £10. The undertaker president profited by the funeral orders, while the publican treasurer had the members' custom (and that of the undertakers' mutes, who were notoriously heavy drinkers), and in addition the handling of the money, which he usually banked

[1] *Report on Interment in Towns*, p. 43.

with his brewer at four or five per cent interest. As a form of insurance, Chadwick demonstrated, this system was completely unsound. Actuaries showed that the premiums were far too high, that one Preston society was charging 7s. 10d., for example, for a risk covered for 3s. 9d. in the tables of an assurance company. Moreover, since it was to the interest of the undertaker president to admit bad lives, the societies frequently failed. Another weakness was the rule that all members, whatever their age, paid the same rate; many clubs in consequence were broken up by the younger men, in revolt against the excessive demands made upon them. There was some evidence, too, that multiple insurances on the lives of children, by placing "interests in operation against moral duties," acted as bounties on neglect and infanticide. A child could be buried for £1 or £1 10s.; the clubs allowed from £3 to £5 for the purpose, and the child might well be in four or five societies. Hence the common phrase in Manchester: "Aye, aye, that child will not live; it is in the burial club."[1]

By this time Chadwick was far beyond the range of previous explorers of the subject, penetrating an uncharted region that W. A. Mackinnon and "Walker of the Graveyards" had not dared to enter—and whither Sir James Graham did not attempt to follow him. He now turned to make a merciless exposure of the trade in burial. On the mortality returns of the previous three years the number of deaths in London averaged 114 a day. Competing for those 114 bodies, according to the Post Office Directory, there were 275 undertakers. In addition, however, there were at least a thousand, perhaps as many as three thousand, lesser tradesmen—drapers, tailors, publicans, carpenters, cabinet-makers, upholsterers, auctioneers—who displayed the undertaker's insignia in the hope of catching one or two orders a year. All these obtained their funeral supplies from one of the principals in the trade, and in the last analysis it was some sixty of the leading undertakers who performed the real service, the inferior agents merely interposing their unnecessary offices and stepping up the charges to allow for their own remuneration. An intense competition between a great and growing number of entrepreneurs—so the funeral trade appeared; but, in defiance of the teaching of the economists, the result was heightened prices. The

[1] *Report on Interment in Towns*, p. 64.

explanation was simple: there was no real competition, because there was no real freedom of choice by the consumer. In those hours of anxiety and grief which immediately followed a death, the relatives of the deceased could scarcely go round from one undertaker to another, comparing services and haggling over prices. When a death occurred, therefore, the burial club benefits were so much "exposed prey"[1] for the undertaker. His procedure was to find out the amount of the insurance money, whether the widow was expecting £10, £15, £20 or more, and then to arrange the funeral accordingly. Once the funeral was over, the widow could not dispute the bill without laying herself open to the charge that she begrudged proper respect for the dead. The estimates therefore never came under close scrutiny. The total cost of funerals in England and Wales in one year Chadwick calculated to be not far short of five million pounds; in London alone probably nearly a million pounds was "annually thrown into the grave."[2] The evidence showed that that figure could be cut by at least a half.

The Commons Committee of 1842, under the influence of its chief witness, the Bishop of London, had been strongly in favour of the continuance of parochial control, and Mackinnon in his Bill[3] had provided for the establishment of extramural cemeteries under the management of a parochial committee of health. Chadwick, however, expressed a lively disbelief that reform was likely from the very agency under which the present abuses had developed, and which still maintained them in the face of all protests. In Government circles it was felt that, if the parish administration had failed, the solution was to trust to the operation of natural economic forces, to that pursuit of individual profit which, as a by-product, brought about the benefit of society. Already the majority of Dissenters, who could not be admitted into consecrated ground, together with many Anglicans who were appalled by the state of the churchyards, were burying their dead in cemeteries owned by individual entrepreneurs or joint stock companies. Unfortunately, Chadwick bluntly revealed, the arrangements of the capitalists showed as little regard for health and decency as those of the parish gravediggers. More crowded

---

[1] *Report on Interment in Towns*, p. 52. [2] Ibid., p. 70.
[3] *P.P.*, 1842, vol. ii, p. 603.

even than the churchyards were the private cemeteries, usually the property of an undertaker, where, as one Congregational minister described, the soil was "saturated and blackened with human remains and fragments of the dead," and "the splash of water is heard from the graves, as the coffins descend, producing a shudder in every mourner."[1] Nor were the eight joint stock cemeteries, more recently established under Private Acts, so superior as their shareholders claimed. All but one were on sites unfitted by the clayey nature of the soil or lack of drainage for interment purposes; and to squeeze out the maximum profit the companies were burying in every acre 11,000 bodies in common graves. The main effect of the Cemetery Acts, in which neither the promoters nor the Commons Committees had thought to insert the improvements suggested by the best foreign experience, had been merely to transfer the evils from the centre of London to the periphery.

In the disposal of the dead the planless operations of English capitalists and parochial authorities lagged far behind the achievements of the benevolent absolutisms of the Continent. In English political circles, however, the administrative devices of the foreigner, if referred to at all, were usually mentioned not as examples to be emulated but as awful warnings to be avoided. It was a prejudice not shared by Chadwick, who based his recommendations for reform on a close study of Continental models, and in particular the municipal cemeteries of Frankfort and Munich and the Parisian *Service des Pompes Funèbres*. With a severe logic, conceding nothing to the vested interests in burial, he sketched a radical and comprehensive scheme, which met in turn with a well-designed remedy every abuse that he had uncovered. All interments in towns, without exception, must be prohibited. The joint stock cemeteries and the private grounds must be bought out. The churchyards must be closed, their sites being kept as open spaces for the public use. In their place national cemeteries should be established, on ground selected according to scientific principles, with suitable decorations and vegetation chosen on the best artistic advice; and these publicly owned cemeteries should be managed by officers possessing appropriate qualifications. The danger and indecency arising

[1] *Report on Interment in Towns*, p. 135.

from the prolonged retention of the corpse in the one-roomed homes of the poor should be averted by providing "reception houses" (sc. mortuaries), such as those at Frankfort and Munich, to which the body was removed by the municipal authorities on the notification of death, and where it was kept under medical inspection for three days before burial. The officers in charge of the public cemeteries should be empowered to enter into contracts for the supply of funeral services and materials, the aim being the eventual extinction of the private unregulated undertaker. By such large-scale contracts the funeral expenses of the upper and middle classes might be cut by at least two-thirds, while artisans could be buried at half the present cost; the total saving in London alone would be about £350,000 a year. Apart from the cemetery owners who were to be dispossessed, the interests of three groups were affected by the scheme—the clergy, the Dissenters, and the undertakers. The clergy should be compensated for the loss of their burial fees; the Dissenting congregations who lost their graveyards should receive an equivalent space in the public cemetery. But Chadwick could see no reason to hold out promises to the hundreds of inferior tradesmen who gave themselves the title of undertaker.

It is the most courageous, the most clear-cut, the most coherent of all his schemes; but it bears on its face the prophecy of the failure which dogged it for the eight unhappy years of its history. Chadwick had forgotten nothing. He believed that he had answered by anticipation all objections, conciliating those bodies which had legitimate interests, exposing and rebutting those whose claims could not be justified. He was soon to find that to answer an argument was not to silence an opponent. He had shown that abroad the various parts of his plan were at that very moment working effectively and to the satisfaction of the people. The problem remained of convincing English statesmen that ideas which thrived under German despotism or French centralisation could bear transplanting to the freer soil of England. He concluded his report with the appeal that the Government "should only set hands to this great work, when invested with full powers to effect it completely: for at present there appears to be no alternative between doing it well or ill."[1] A Tory Home Secretary

[1] *Report on Interments in Towns*, p. 201.

of the eighteen-forties, called upon to interfere with large masses of capital, to arbitrate between the Church and the Dissenters, to lay on Government a delicate and unaccustomed burden, might well hesitate and consider that between the two absolutes of "all or nothing," "well or ill," that Chadwick presented there stretched an infinite possible series of piecemeal improvements.

There remains to be discussed what Chadwick regarded as the pivot of the whole scheme, a proposal, however, which had an independent life of its own, and so may be considered apart from the interments problem with which it was at first inseparably linked by Chadwick. This was his suggestion that local authorities should appoint medical officers of health, to perform certain necessary duties connected with the public burial service, and in addition to carry out other measures of medical police. Here was one of the most serious gaps in the defences of the public health. For the cure of disease by tending and dosing the sick Liverpool, for example, had 50 physicians and 250 surgeons, apothecaries, and druggists; for its prevention, by investigating and removing its causes, the city employed not one medical officer. Nor did the City of London—though it spent £72,000 a year on hospitals and medical charities.

There were, it was true, the 2,327 medical officers in the Poor Law service.[1] But these were cramped and starved in their activities by the parsimony of Somerset House; they were subjected to unwholesome influences from property owners amongst the Guardians; and their miserable pay did not free them from the necessity of attending private patients, so that, as Chadwick testified, many of them "hold office merely to keep out rivals or interlopers from their field of private practice; they serve very unwillingly and are in perpetual hostility with the Boards of Guardians."[2]

[1] Chadwick's figure in a letter to Normanby, 3 February 1841. In a memorandum for Sir James Graham, G. C. Lewis put the figure for 1844 at 2,825; these were paid £130,198 in salaries and £21,244 in midwifery and surgical fees, a total of £151,442. (10 January 1846; Peel Papers, British Museum Add. MSS., vol. 40,582, f. 202).

[2] "College of Physicians reply to. Controversy with the College of Physicians and its jealousy of the first General Board of Health," MS., n.d. (c. Oct.–Dec. 1848).

In the England of the eighteen-forties, indeed, the medical profession as a whole had great need to put its house in order. Of 1,830 medical men who presented themselves to fill offices under the Poor Law Commission in 1834, 327 had not been examined in surgery, 323 had not been examined in medicine; and 233 had not been examined by any medical body at all.[1] The twin oligarchies of the Physicians and the Surgeons were less concerned to advance medical science and raise professional standards, than to assert the superiority of their members in the face of competition from "Scotch doctors," the lowly Apothecaries, and the "general practitioners" who were now being turned out in increasing numbers by the Hospital Schools. The profession was expanding rapidly, and in the absence of a public criterion of competency and a recognised course of training it abounded with opportunities for quackery, abuses of practice, and the toleration of the unqualified and the inefficient. It is little to be wondered at that in the social controversies of the time the spokesmen of medicine sometimes cut a very poor figure; that one Select Committee should severely comment on "the ignorance of some who set up for surgical practitioners";[2] and that a Minister should be able to find, when he wanted them, 43 doctors out of 48 in favour of a measure to enable children over twelve years of age to work a full day in the factories—so reversing the findings of a Royal Commission two years earlier, before which only one doctor out of 31 supported the same proposal.[3] Nevertheless, as Ashley bore witness, in the factory agitation he received more help from the medical men than from the clergy, who only too often were "cowed by capital and power."[4] And from the first, when Chadwick sent Arnott, Kay, and Southwood Smith on their tour of investigation in 1838, the doctors were the strongest supporters of the sanitary movement, from the Queen's physician, Sir James Clark, and the University professor, W. A. Guy, down to the dispensary and hospital physicians, Joseph Toynbee, Thomas Laycock, William Duncan, and the unnamed rank and file of the

[1] Speech by Sir Benjamin Hawes on Second Reading of Medical Reform Bill; *Hansard*, vol. lvii, pp. 329–33, 17 March 1841.

[2] *Select Committee on the Factory Act, P.P.*, 1841, vol. ix, p. 8.

[3] *Hansard*, vol. xxiii, pp. 739, 746, 9 May 1836.

[4] E. Hodder. *Life and Work of the Seventh Earl of Shaftesbury*, vol. ii, p. 209; vol. i, p. 346.

Union surgeons and general practitioners. "Of all the professions, the members of the medical profession are the shortest lived and the poorest," said Southwood Smith, speaking at a public meeting to raise a subscription for the family of Dr. J. R. Lynch, a brilliant young surgeon whose life had been cut short by a fever contracted in the slums.[1] Visiting patients in their one-roomed homes, and encountering some of the same hazards and discomforts, they saw the obverse of that splendid picture of power and wealth which dazzled the eyes of the majority of the ruling classes.[2]

While welcoming these allies, Chadwick was watchful of their pretensions. Medicine had its part to play in the defence of the public health, but it was not the pre-eminent rôle that most doctors would claim for it. The doctor's efforts must be strictly subordinated to those of the engineer and the administrator; and in proportion as the sanitarians were successful in eliminating the causes of disease from the environment, they would render less necessary the traditional ministrations of the medical man. In 1843 the public medical service was represented only by the Union surgeons, whose cheapness and servility were despised and resented by their fellow practitioners. Yet the publicly employed medical officers, if their status and qualifications were improved and the scope of their duties widened, could perform more valuable services to society than the private dealers in physic, concerned as these were with the effects of disease, not its causes.

Already in the *Sanitary Report* Chadwick had urged the appointment of a full-time district medical officer with superior qualifications. If burial were to become a public service, such an appointment would be essential. It would be the duty of the officer of health to inspect the corpse and note the cause of death, to give instructions where necessary for its removal to the

---

[1] *Health of Towns: Report of the Speeches of Edwin Chadwick, Esq., Dr. Southwood Smith, Richard Taylor, Esq., James Anderton, Esq., and others* (pamphlet), 1847, p. 10.

[2] "Often the family doctor mingles in the crowd of mill-people as they leave at night and greets them again in the early morning as they congregate to their toils without his having, meanwhile, pressed his pillow. By the way it is a curious sight—the swarming streets at a quarter past five of a cold stormy winter morning. Who but this poor drudge sees it? Most educated people who live on the spot don't know that the labourers, men, women, and children, rise at five, be the weather fine or foul at the sound of the bell to their work. . . ." (Dr. John Roberton to Mrs. Chadwick, 14 February 1845.)

reception house, and supply the relatives with a tariff of the prices of burial. "The ordinary service of such an officer would consist of the verification of the fact and cause of death, and its due civic registration."[1] This would appear to be a very oblique entry upon the duties of a Medical Officer of Health, as the term is now understood, but there were very strong reasons why Chadwick should stress this and other functions which in modern society are performed by the general practitioner, the registrar, and the undertaker. It was a great disappointment to Chadwick to find that the Registration Act of 1836 was failing to produce all the legal and scientific benefits he had expected. The data afforded by the existing system of recording deaths were of little value to the lawyer in determining titles to succession, to the actuary in constructing life tables, or to the doctor and administrator in seeking to ascertain the effect of occupation and locality on health and mortality. The only qualifications stipulated for the local registrars were that they should be resident in the district, solvent, and free from clashing duties. Many of them were political appointees, and so notoriously unsuited to their functions that, as Chadwick declared, it would have been better even from the party point of view to have given them "expensive outfits and to have sent them for example as justices to Sierra Leone or to the West India Islands, to any part of the Empire except to the towns where they were known."[2] Furthermore, it was not required of them to visit the house of the deceased and enter the details on the spot. The only securities against foul play lay in the suspicions of neighbours and the alertness of the parish beadle or constable. Most of the local registrars could tell of doubtful cases which had eluded these flimsy safeguards. How many children perished from overdoses of "quietness"? Chadwick wondered. How many died after being treated for croup and penumonia by unqualified practitioners, such as druggists, who were in attendance at the death of one infant out of every four? How many were murdered for the burial money? How easy, again, it was to commit a fraud, when, as at present, any person might go to the registrar's office to record a death, and when, for all the registrar knew, there might be no such death, no such body, and even no such house!

[1] *Report on Interment in Towns*, p. 159.
[2] E. C. to ? (probably Lord John Russell), 8 January 1841.

Let it be insisted, however, that the registration of death should take place on the spot and on view of the body by a qualified medical officer, and all these opportunites for fraud and secret murder would disappear. It was a sound argument, but the problem was to be solved along different lines when the attendance of the "family doctor" ceased to be a luxury out of reach of most working-class homes. Greater interest attaches to Chadwick's second main argument. A public medical officer would occupy a vantage point from which he could bring under one informed view all the causes of disease in his locality and the possible means of eradicating them. It had long been recognised that the military or naval surgeon, such as William Lind or Gilbert Blane, spoke with peculiar authority; this was because his opinions were the fruit of constant observation of the behaviour of large bodies of men, living in uniform conditions, which could be changed at will and compared for purposes of experiment. In the great towns the same opportunity occurred for observing large populations living under similar circumstances, and studying their response to a changed environment. An officer of health, assembling and scrutinising the statistics of mortality and sickness, would furnish the accurate diagnosis on which the preventive action of the administrator could be based. Briefly Chadwick sketched the essential qualities of such an officer. He would need to possess special technical qualifications; the only safe proof of a candidate's fitness, Chadwick suggested, would be evidence that he had already conducted some piece of successful research in the field of preventive medicine. His freedom of action and opinion must be protected by two essential safeguards. First, he must exercise his functions in independence of the local administrative body, since this would probably contain the chief employers, connection with whom would expose him to suspicion of partiality and undermine his influence with the lower classes. It was necessary, secondly, that he should devote the whole of his time to his public duties, since in a conflict between the demands of a private practice and of a public office, it would inevitably be the latter which would suffer.

In the Report on Interments the officer of health appears chiefly in the unusual character of a recorder of deaths and a superintendent of burials. Within less than twelve months, however, Chadwick was submitting to the Health of Towns Commission an interesting memorandum, worthy of more attention than it received, in which the appointment takes on the lineaments with which a later generation became familiar.[1] In this paper the functions of the medical officer are greatly widened and enriched. He is required to inspect his district periodically, tracing the signs of sickness among the population to their source in homes and places of work, and enforcing the law against those responsible for removable nuisances and wanton neglect. On the outbreak of an epidemic, he is to control all measures to combat it, issuing instructions to Union surgeons and relieving officers, surveyors, scavengers, police, and other public servants. He should undertake the analysis of matters sold as food or drink, taking measures to stop the sale of dangerous and unwholesome adulterations. He is to direct the arrangements for vaccination, and inspect all children who apply for certificates of age, strength, and bodily ability for labour in mines and factories. He is required, finally, to present an annual report, giving the statistics of sickness and mortality for his district, comparing it in these respects with other places, analysing the causes of each class of cases, and specifying those causes which he considered removable or preventable for the future.

In all this Chadwick anticipates intelligently the later emergence and development of the Medical Officer of Health, but it was to take nearly seventy years to establish the conditions in which that most valuable of all local officials could function, as Chadwick desired, as an impartial adviser and guardian of the public, independent of local influences, and shielded against the intimidation of threatened interests. When the proposal was first made, the leaders of the medical profession were slow to recognise its importance; and the politicians at once objected that it would be "unpopular." As one critic wrote, the powers such an officer would wield were "far too vague and arbitrary; and would be considered an infringement of the liberty of the subject, intolerable in a free country. A man's home would no longer be his castle, into which no one must penetrate without a special

---

[1] "Health of Towns Improvements. Draft Clauses for consideration in respect to the appointment and duties of Officers of Health," MS., n.d. (c. December 1844).

warrant."[1] In the swarming tenements of Whitechapel and Bethnal Green this talk of inviolate "castles" must have sounded strange, but the argument that the poor would resent having "little inquests" held in their homes weighed heavily with the sentimental middle classes, and diverted attention from the less questionable duties of the officer of health. It was unfortunate that the appointment should have first been presented as part of Chadwick's scheme for national cemeteries and a public burial service, and so shared the disfavour with which that scheme was generally regarded in Government circles. Not till 1846 did Chadwick's suggestions bear fruit, when Liverpool appointed the first Medical Officer of Health, William Duncan, under the terms of its new Local Act. And Duncan was engaged on conditions which ran completely counter to the principles laid down by Chadwick. The Corporation paid him £300 a year only, and allowed him to continue in private practice. For a year he acted merely as a weekly registrar of deaths; when it was urged that he might make reports on conditions in the city, the Corporation refused their consent, "and the reason given was *that if Dr. Duncan recommended any step it would be needful for the Committee to take it.*"[2] Fearing that this bad example might be followed by other towns, Chadwick protested energetically to the Home Secretary, and as a result in 1848 Duncan's salary was raised to £750 and he was employed on full-time health duties.

The Interments Report, containing in its sombre pages the most powerful of Chadwick's exposures of social evil and the most revolutionary of his administrative proposals, was a strange volume to emerge from a Government department in 1843. Throughout the summer its fate was in balance. In December Chadwick submitted a revised draft to Sir James Graham, assuring him that any investigator who followed the path he had trodden would find his description if anything an understatement of the evil.[3] He sent the report out at last as a Christmas and New Year gift to his friends. "It was the most difficult and the most painful of the painful investigations which I have been called upon to conduct," he told Ashley, "and unless it be

[1] Thomas Stewart Traill to Dr. W. P. Alison, 25 April 1845.
[2] Dr. J. Sutherland to E. C., 17 February 1848.
[3] E. C. to Sir James Graham, 4 December 1843.

G

followed by some better and more complete adoption of the measures than is usual, I intend that so far as I am concerned it shall be the last that I conduct."[1] The published report was not so strong as he would have wished, but—as he told Lord Lovelace—"I am as yet only a slave of the lamp (by Lord Althorp's breach of engagement with me)." "My report, your Lordship should remember," he continued, "had to undergo a jealous official ordeal before permission to print was obtained. I rejoice at having obtained leave to print so much."[2]

As Chadwick had foreseen, the report drew upon itself the hatred of the Dissenters, the cemetery companies, the undertakers, and churchmen like the Rev. Mr. Tyler, who looked like losing £800 a year if his churchyard were closed. "It warms one into impatience to see the grand plan adopted," Professor Owen had written, after seeing the first draft. "I hope you will live to see it in full operation: yours will then be—or ought to be—the most conspicuous Mausoleum in the chief National Cemetery, and a grateful people, who will only know the evils you have remedied by your descriptions in the effort to banish them, will point it out first to their children."[3] But public monuments and a nation's thanks were far from Graham's mind, when he turned over this plan which coolly proposed to sweep away important profit-making interests, which trenched upon the traditional prerogatives of the Church, and threatened to stir up a buzz of sectarian jealousies. It was soon clear that he would take no step except on the heels of a strong public opinion. But one important supporter could be counted upon; the Bishop of London favoured a scheme which would rescue the clergy from the competition of the cemetery companies with their unqualified chaplains, and his influence offered the main hope of stirring the Home Secretary into activity.

[1] E. C. to Lord Ashley, 13 December 1843.
[2] E. C. to Lord Lovelace, 1 January 1844.
[3] R. Owen to E. C., 12 February 1843.

CHAPTER IV

HEALTH OF TOWNS COMMISSION, 1843–1845

SIR JAMES GRAHAM, the Tory Home Secretary, had inherited from Lord Normanby three Bills for the drainage of towns, the improvement of boroughs, and the regulation of buildings, but he had not inherited with them also that nobleman's enthusiasm for sanitary reform. The *status quo* has rarely had a more devoted spokesman or a more skilful stonewaller than Sir James Graham. Overbearing in his manner, with a hard, limited mind, massively impenetrable to argument, he opposed all the resources of his powerful will to the social reforms of his time. He had done his best to hold back the report on the employment of women and children in the coal mines. He had—says Ashley—so terrified the Factory Inspectors that, though they shared Ashley's views on the Ten Hours Bill, they did not dare to say so.[1] But, if he resisted Ashley's "Jack Cade legislation," it was not out of a perverse obstructionism, but because, when confronted by the great social questions of the age, Graham, like Peel, was often at a genuine loss to see a practicable solution. As a deputation from the Lancashire Short Time Committees discovered in November 1841, he had "drunk too deeply at the fount of Malthusian philosophy."[2] For him the iron laws of the economic order—perpetual and unchanging since they were the expression of the ineradicable concupiscence of man—bound the working classes to a life which he summarised as "but eating, drinking, working, and dying." He walked in blinkers, seeing everywhere the limits set by his own preconceptions as the inescapable decrees of nature. It is, therefore, a measure of the effect of Chadwick's reports and of the advance made by the public health campaign that early in 1843 the Home Secretary decided to refer the question to a Royal

---

[1] E. Hodder, *Life and Work of the Seventh Earl of Shaftesbury*, vol. i, pp. 409, 418.
[2] *Manchester and Salford Advertiser*, 8 and 15 January 1842.

Commission. The sanitary question was moving into the sphere of practical politics. Reluctantly, impelled more by the pressure of opinion from behind and without than by the drive of inner conviction, a Tory Home Secretary was consenting to explore the ground with a view to ultimate legislation.

Graham's first move was to halt the progress of Normanby's Bills, which had twice passed the Lords and had reached their Second Reading in the Commons. This action, though it dismayed Ashley, met with Chadwick's heartiest approval, for the Whig measures, drafted by the experts of the Woods and Forests department without reference to the evidence collected by the sanitary inquiry, seemed more objectionable to him with every appearance they made.[1] He was equally pleased with Graham's next decision. From vestries and board rooms in every Sewers division of London the Government had heard rumblings of alarm and anger, and something weightier than the report of a single civil servant would be needed to batter down their defences. The Sewer Commissioners were, therefore, to be given a second hearing before a Royal Commission. Chadwick, having no fears for their verdict, welcomed the idea; an inquiry whether his principles of drainage were applicable to the Westminster sewers would in effect be an inquiry whether in Westminster there was any exception to the law of gravity! He intended, however, that the Royal Commission should do much more than listen to protesting surveyors. He was well aware of the limitations of the sanitary inquest on Great Britain he had conducted brilliantly through three laborious years. To those who, like Ashley and Normanby, pressed for immediate action on the conclusions of his report he replied that, while he had established the general principles which must guide legislation, he had not indicated the particular measures in which they were to be embodied.[2] The syllabus he drew up set a threefold task before the Royal Commission. It must devise the legal instruments which would ensure the efficiency of works of drainage and water

---

[1] It is clear from Chadwick's numerous memoranda on the subject that the Hammonds' description of these Bills as "drastic and revolutionary" (*Age of the Chartists*, p. 293) greatly overvalues their technical and administrative significance.

[2] "Memoranda of answers to the imputations of blame in respect to alleged delays to adopt sanitary measures," MS., 13 July 1844.

supply—for the necessary securities were so far outside the range of the old-style Local Acts that no legal draftsman could lay his hands at once upon a suitable form of clause. It must demonstrate by actual trial the practicability of the various improvements he had suggested, in particular the advantages of circular drains of tile over square drains of porous brick; and pronounce judgment on the wider questions of municipal engineering, such as the feasibility of a constant water supply. And finally, what was equally important—for it was useless to demonstrate improvements without showing how they could be paid for—it must show how, by spreading the costs over a long enough period, the burden could be fitted to the means of small property owners and working-class occupiers.[1]

It was not, on paper, an unpromising list of Commissioners. Southwood Smith was not there, though he of all men next to Chadwick had the right to be heard. But it included Neil Arnott, Lyon Playfair, the chemist, Sir Henry de la Beche, the geologist, James Smith of Deanston, the famous authority on land drainage, and the zealous Professor Owen, who once declared, "I would rather achieve the effectual trapping of the sewer-vents of London than resuscitate graphically in Natural History records the strangest of the old monsters which it has pleased God to blot out of his Creation."[2] The sanitary cause was safe with these men. Two of the engineers Chadwick had suggested, Captain Denison of the Royal Engineers, and the younger Stephenson, were also included, together with William Cubitt, the leading building contractor in the country. Chadwick had asked for a lawyer or two; these were denied him, but in their stead Graham introduced a leavening of Parliamentary members, a Scottish Duke, Buccleuch, to act as chairman, Lord Lincoln from the Woods and Forests, and the mover of the 1840 Committee, R. A. Slaney.

By some strange whim of Graham's Chadwick himself was omitted, but he discovered at once that the chief burden of the Commission rested on his shoulders. Some of the medical and engineer Commissioners drifted off into their professional affairs, while the others, willing as they were, lacked his experience and powers of investigation. So Chadwick took full command at

[1] E. C. to Sir James Graham, 15 March 1843.
[2] Professor Richard Owen to E. C., 9 September 1844.

Gwydyr House, when the Commission began its meetings there on 1 June 1843; he marshalled the witnesses, he took the notes of evidence, he prepared the resolutions, and he drafted the reports. And at the same time he was confronting jealousy and mismanagement at the Poor Law office, completing his Interments Report, replying to the cross fire of four of the metropolitan Sewers Commissions, and bombarding the Home Office with memoranda on a new Buildings Regulations Bill "most preposterously devised by the palace architects."[1] He had probably never been busier nor more happy in his life.

Under Chadwick's directions, the Commission first despatched a letter with an appendix of 62 questions to the fifty towns with the highest death rates; these included the largest manufacturing towns and the principal ports, comprising a population of three millions.[2] But he would not let them rest content with paper evidence. The towns were divided into six districts; and in the middle of July 1843 the active Commissioners set off in ones or twos on an itinerary he had drawn up for them, with a paper of his instructions in their hands, to see for themselves the conditions in the most populous areas.[3]

At the same time, at a number of provincial towns, at Liverpool, Preston, Nottingham, York, and Chorlton-upon-Medlock, where he was acquainted with energetic friends of the cause, Chadwick put them to work to report on the state of their districts.[4] Encouraging them with notes of approval, directing their attention to fruitful lines of investigation, occasionally making a sortie himself to inspect some well designed cemetery or the working of a constant supply system, Chadwick drove forward his team of doctors and engineers and politicians. When de la Beche retired discomfited from an argument at Windsor, he wrote with an unusual sprightliness to ask, "Into what geological hole have you got to hide your head? Come out and let us hear the rights of

---

[1] E. C. to A. G. Escher, 24 December 1843.

[2] *First Report of Health of Towns Commission*, vol. i, p. xi; *P.P.*, 1844, vol. xvii, p. 1.

[3] "Minutes of Proceedings of the Commissioners for inquiring into the state of large Towns," MS. (at P.R.O.), 18 July 1843.

[4] Dr. W. H. Duncan at Liverpool, the Rev. J. Clay at Preston, Thomas Hawkesley at Nottingham, Dr. T. Laycock at York, Dr. P. H. Holland at Chorlton-upon-Medlock.

it."[1] To Dr. Laycock, who was preparing a report on York, he suggested that an estimate should be made of the number of medical practitioners whose income was derived from attending cases of zymotic disease amongst self-supporting labourers. "Do not flinch," he added, "at estimating how many would be dispensed with from York or enabled to transfer their labours to the colonies or to productive industry if all sanitary measures within view were adopted! It will look impartial and be popular at the same time."[2] Of the hazards and horrors of the inquiry he gives a glimpse in a letter to the Registrar-General. "My vacation has been absorbed in visiting with Mr. Smith and Dr. Playfair the worst parts of some of the worst towns. Dr. Playfair has been knocked up by it and has been seriously ill. Mr. Smith has had a little dysentery; Sir Henry de la Beche was obliged at Bristol to stand up at the end of alleys and vomit while Dr. Playfair was investigating overflowing privies. Sir Henry was obliged to give it up. . . ."[3] Usually, however, Chadwick remained in London, examining witnesses at Gwydyr House, testing street sweeping machines and jets d'eau, collecting specimens of earthenware pipes from Glasgow and Zurich to compare with the products of the Southwark potters, and arranging experiments to determine the engineering formulæ for the construction of scientific water and drainage systems. Over the reports of the Commissioners and other expert correspondents he exercised a watchful censorship, for error crept in by the most unlikely ways. A paper on French cemeteries by W. E. Hickson, the editor of the *Westminster*, was quietly discarded after Chadwick had objected to its excessive praise of French municipalities.[4] When the great Robert Stephenson, "who is recognised as the real inventor of the locomotive engine brought forward by his father," submitted a report on water supply, Chadwick condemned it at once for its shocking ignorance of correct principles, and prevailed upon the Commissioners to reject it unanimously.[5]

To Chadwick's immense relief ("the continued labour of

---

[1] E. C. to Sir Henry de la Beche, 22 December 1843.
[2] E. C. to Dr. Laycock, 6 June 1844.
[3] E. C. to Major Graham, 7 December 1843.
[4] E. C. to J. H. Burton, 3 February 1844.
[5] E. C. to Lord Morpeth, 18 September 1848.

examining witnesses was becoming very severe"[1]) the First Report
of the Commission was published in July 1844. He had written
two-thirds of it, he told his friends.[2] However, the octavo
volumes looked very well, and he felt satisfied that his trouble
with them had been well expended.[3] The Government apparently
considered that this satisfaction should be his only reward, for he
received no acknowledgment of his services and no recompense for
the additional labour which had lengthened his hours of work from
six to sixteen. If he had employed the same time in writing for
reviews, he complained later to the Duke of Buccleuch, as Cabinet
Ministers had been known to do while in office, he would have
made more money.[4]

The First Report was brief, merely outlining in general terms the
conclusions suggested by the evidence, and apart from a few
striking passages about the state of drainage and water supply in
the provincial towns (passages which have served historians well
ever since) it made little impact upon the public consciousness.
It gained hardly a notice in the newspapers, their columns being
filled with the case of a boy who had been flogged by an Irish
magistrate.[5] The jolt given by the *Sanitary Report* to the conscience
of the ruling classes was not to be easily repeated.

There was a strong impression, voiced by Normanby in the
Lords, that nothing new had been brought out by the inquiry.
It was true, Chadwick agreed, that the medical witnesses did little
more than corroborate the earlier testimony;[6] but the evidence on
water supply, the key to all sanitary improvements, he believed—
with some justice—would revolutionise that branch of engineering,
and he counted his examination of Thomas Hawksley, the
engineer of the Trent Water Works, as the most important he had
ever taken.[7] Many of the conclusions on technical and administrative matters had in fact been glanced at in the *Sanitary Report*; but
these were precisely the parts of the report which had made least

[1] E. C. to Thomas Hawksley, 9 July 1844.
[2] E. C. to J. H. Burton, 31 July 1844; to Macvey Napier, 12 October 1844
(Macvey Napier Papers, B.M. Add. MSS., 34, 624, f. 629).
[3] E. C. to Thomas Hawksley, 1 September 1844.
[4] E. C. to Duke of Buccleuch, 17 and 19 December 1845.
[5] E. C. to Lord Normanby, 17 August 1844.
[6] E. C. to Dr. Southwood Smith, 22 July 1844.
[7] E. C. to Woollett Wilmot, 7 October 1844.

impression, and where repetition, reinforcement, and a closer discussion were most required. If the main strands of Chadwick's argument are disentangled from the mass of the evidence, it becomes clear that the foundations for reform had been laid more deeply and firmly, and that some of his propositions had advanced from the stage of suggestion to that of demonstration.

The first step had been to sweep away the complaints and denials of the ruffled Sewers Commissioners. They were answered out of their own mouths. In Richard Kelsey, surveyor to the City Commission, for example, Chadwick found a perfect spokesman for their ignorance and complacency.[1]

Asked if he possessed a plan of his district, he replied triumphantly that he had; he admitted, however, that it did not show the levels, though he kept a private memorandum of this essential information. "Can you tell, on inspecting the map, which way the water falls in all the drains represented?" Chadwick asked him. "I could tell, because I know," was the reply, "but no stranger could tell."[2] He confessed indeed that the district might contain some sewers of which he possessed no record. "The maxim of the Commissioners," he declared, "is never to make any sewer so small as that a man cannot get into it easily";[3] so that even for courts and alleys a sewer 3 ft. x 2 ft. 2 in., sometimes 4 ft. x 2 ft. 4 in., with brickwork 14 in. thick, was laid down. Sewers of this size, he admitted, presupposed accumulations, which were removed at a contract price of 6s. per yard, the brickwork of the sewer being torn open where no manholes existed. These brickwork caverns, rarely inspected and irregularly cleansed, had sometimes been put to strange uses. In one parish, Kelsey revealed, the beadle had been buried in a sewer. In another a sewer had been surreptitiously used as a burial-ground, exploration revealing two flat tombstones and six or seven coffins.[4]

[1] *First Report of Health of Towns Commission*, vol. ii, pp. 203–31.
[2] Ibid., vol. ii, p. 208.   [3] Ibid., vol. ii, p. 211.
[4] But these immense sewers might have better uses, as Chadwick pointed out to Colonel Rowan of Scotland Yard in April 1848, when the loyal middle class were preparing to deal with a Chartist attempt to seize the metropolis. The Chartists might throw up barricades in the streets, from which it would be difficult to dislodge them. But, suggested Chadwick, a band of two or three hundred sewer men might be sworn in as special constables, to creep unsuspected along the sewers and emerge at manholes in the rear of the startled revolutionaries. (E. C. to Col. Rowan, 8 April 1848.) Three months later one

House drains, he considered, should not be less than 15 in. in diameter; for a small house they should be even bigger, as they were more likely to be blocked. Asked his opinion about the possibility of replacing the existing brick drains with pipes four or five inches in diameter, he replied scornfully, "half a brick would stop it"; "in poor houses you can never keep them free from coals, cinders, bottles, broken pots, and all kinds of old rubbish"—and if a grating were inserted to prevent the entry of such dejecta, it would of course be wrenched away by the feckless tenants.[1] Main streets in the City were cleansed every day, all others two or three times a week; courts and alleys "ought to be cleansed" twice a week, but Kelsey was not certain that this was done. He could only account for the filthy places in his district, he said, by the filthiness of the people.[2]

It was against this background of ignorance and crude empiricism that Chadwick brought forward his technical experts, Dr. Dyce Guthrie, S. O. Foden the architect, and John Roe, the surveyor of the Holborn and Finsbury Commission,[3] to show that brick sewers costing £2 10s. a yard might be replaced by terra cotta tubes at one-third the cost or by pipes of common clay which were manufactured in Glasgow for no more than 2s. a yard. To put in a cesspool cost about £5, and to clean it £1 a year; yet for £4 a house could be fitted with water-closet, sink, water-pipe and improved house-drains. For an addition of 2½d. a week to their rent the working classes could enjoy the combined benefits of a water-closet and a constant supply of water.

Without a constant supply of water to every house, however, it was useless to think of water-closets and self-cleansing sewers. Could such a constant supply be provided? To Chadwick at Gwydyr House came the engineers of the London water companies to explode this fantastic hypothesis. Thomas Wicksteed, engineer of the East London Waterworks Company,[4] was con-

---

of the men engaged on the subterranean survey then being conducted by the Metropolitan Sewers Commission was found to be a confederate in a plot to blow up Parliament and the Government offices, the explosive to be laid in the sewers, which were five feet high and offered easy means of access to the conspirators. (E. C. to Sir Henry de la Beche, 29 July 1848.)

[1] *First Report of Health of Towns Commission*, vol. ii, p. 223.   [2] Ibid., p. 220.

[3] Ibid., vol. ii, pp. 241–63 (Dyce Guthrie); pp. 315–24 (Foden); pp. 154–180 (Roe).   [4] Ibid., vol. ii, pp. 11–27.

vinced that it was theoretically impossible to keep water at
pressure in all the mains and service pipes at the same time, and
that the Company's method of intermittent supplies on alternate
days was therefore the only practicable one. Moreover, "if he
[the landlord] was to put a separate supply to those houses by a
lead pipe, the lead pipe would be there in the evening, but it
would be gone in the morning."[1] He advised therefore that the
poor should continue to draw their supplies from cast-iron stand-
cocks, which offered less temptation—and of which, in his district, there was one to every hundred houses. Wicksteed's company obtained its water from the River Lea; the supplies were not
filtered, but the more obvious impurities were removed by passing
the water through settling reservoirs; and in fourteen years, he
claimed, there had not been six complaints of bad water from the
company's 50,000 tenants. The Southwark Water Company,
according to its engineer, Joseph Quick,[2] supplied 18,000 houses,
2,000 of the lower-class tenements being served by 250 stand-cocks.
In this district 5,000 houses had no supply at all, and their 30,000
inhabitants depended on pumps and such rain-water as they
could catch. Water-carriers were still to be seen in Clapham and
Rotherhithe, charging a halfpenny for two pails, though the
company's pipes ran close to the houses; two objections were
raised by the landlords to laying on a supply for their tenants: the
lack of drains to carry away the waste, and the immediate outlay
required for the service pipes.

To controvert the evidence of the London engineers Chadwick
brought forward Thomas Hawksley of Nottingham, who had
designed and constructed the Trent Water Works fourteen years
before.[3] This company supplied 8,000 houses in Nottingham,
with 35,000 inhabitants, and charged no more than a penny a
week for an unlimited supply to working-class tenements. Hawksley was as firm as Chadwick that such a service should be com-
mercially remunerative, not a form of charity, and he revealed
that, despite its low charges, his company paid five per cent on
its capital-outlay, and its £50 shares sold at £70 to £73. He
rejected with scorn the London engineers' thesis that larger mains

---

[1] First Report of Health of Towns Commission, vol. ii, p. 23.
[2] Ibid., vol. ii, pp. 114–36.
[3] Ibid., vol. ii, pp. 27–97.

would be required for a constant supply, pointing out that in practice he had been using smaller mains and service pipes than was customary. Lead service pipes in his experience were rarely stolen, the task of cutting them being highly inconvenient when they were filled with water at high pressure. Tenants, who had previously been obliged to pay water-carriers a farthing a bucket, cheerfully paid the extra penny a week on their rent for an unlimited and constant supply. Hawksley foresaw a Utopian future—streets cleansed by jets; constant water supply, water-closets, and glazed earthenware house-drains in each house at a total cost of less than £5; warm baths in public bath-houses at 3d. a head; even "baths introduced into the houses of labouring men for the use of themselves and families."[1]

Chadwick had an instinct for selecting the right experience and the right advisers, and for combining the partial solutions of the practical men into a working whole which was at once logical in its theoretical foundations and technically sound in its practical application. He perceived at once that Hawksley's evidence was complementary to that of the Holborn surveyor, John Roe. Hawksley showed the way to cheap domestic supplies of water, as Roe had revealed the possibility of cheap and efficient removal of domestic waste and excreta. If the two were combined in a unified system, the solution of the main problems of urban sanitation was in sight.

There remained the question of the town refuse. The position as described by William Thorn, a member of the oldest firm of scavenging contractors in London, was far from encouraging.[2] Two years before a contractor had given the parish authorities in Marylebone £1,850 for the refuse, but the bottom had since dropped out of the market, and in 1844 the parish had been obliged to pay the contractor for his services. Some portions of the refuse paid for the cost of removal; ashes and breeze were in demand for brick-making, "hard core" was used on the roads, rags were wanted for paper-making, horse-dung and cow-dung were sent out by barge as far as eighty or ninety miles from the capital. But night-soil was almost a complete loss. Some was baked and exported to the West Indies; the remainder accumu-

---

[1] *First Report of Health of Towns Commission*, vol. ii, p. 31.
[2] Ibid., vol. ii, pp. 369–82.

lated in laystalls, for which there was increasing difficulty in finding suitable sites.

Now it was precisely in the night-soil, which in London was the least valued portion of the refuse, that Chadwick saw the possibilities of the greatest profits. Captain Vetch[1], when consulted about the improvement of Leeds, had assured the Town Council that, if his plans were carried out, in ten years the sale of the sewage to local farmers would bring in £10,000 a year. Examples were numerous of the profitable utilisation of sewage as manure. At Ashburton liquid sewage had been applied to the land for the last forty years. Three hundred acres near Holyrood Castle were irrigated by the Foul Burn, into which one-third of the sinks, drains, and privies of Edinburgh emptied, and the annual value of the land, which produced four or five crops a year, was estimated to be £15,000 or £20,000. Abroad, irrigation by liquid sewage was employed by the farmers of New Spain, Barbary, Andalusia, and Milan. Reflecting on these examples, Chadwick asked himself, if a water company, giving the excellent service Hawksley described at so moderate a cost, could return a profit of five per cent, what might be expected of an enterprise which undertook not only the water supply but also the removal of the town refuse, and drew additional profit from the sale of sewage manure to the neighbouring agriculturists? In that calculation was born the delusive project of his Towns Improvement Company.[2]

In the minutes of evidence of the First Report Chadwick, selecting his witnesses and pointing his questions with a barrister's skill, thus confronted the defenders of the old order with the authoritative denials of men who had themselves originated improvements or had observed them in action. Ready to hand, he proved, in the successful experience of Hawksley, Roe, Foden, Vetch, Dean, were the makings of a scientific system of municipal engineering, in which the three aspects of urban sanitation, drainage, water supply, and sewage disposal, might be integrated into an organic whole.

It was intended that the Second Report should outline the Commissioners' proposals for future legislation. On 13 December 1844 Chadwick laid before the Duke of Buccleuch the draft

[1] *First Report of Health of Towns Commission*, vol. ii, pp. 432–43.
[2] See below, pp. 118–22.

of a Public Health Bill, together with a lengthy memorandum
in which he explained and defended his main recommendations.[1] It is in these papers, and not in the reports of the
Commission nor in the Act of 1848, that Chadwick's views on
public health policy are most truly reflected; and they call,
therefore, for consideration in some detail.

Was not the best solution, as Lord Normanby urged, to confer
enabling powers upon the existing local authorities? There was
one short and conclusive answer to this proposal: the existing
local authorities had in general mismanaged all such powers as
they did possess. Of the fifty towns examined, the Commissioners
were unanimously of the opinion "that in scarcely one place can
the drainage or sewerage be pronounced to be complete and good,
while in 7 it is indifferent, and in 42 decidedly bad as
regards the districts inhabited by the poorer classes";[2] as for the
supply of water, "only in six instances could the arrangements and
the supplies be deemed in any comprehensive sense good; while in
13 they appear to be indifferent, and in 31 so deficient as
to be pronounced bad, and, so far as yet examined, frequently
inferior in purity."[3] There were four good reasons, in Chadwick's
view, why municipalities were unfitted for the task of administering public health measures. In the first place, their boundaries
usually did not take in the suburbs, erected subsequent to the
granting of their charters; yet it was in the suburbs that the best
outfalls for the town drainage were commonly to be found.
Secondly, the structure of municipal government was permeated
with influences opposed to sanitary reform, the interest-begotten
hostility of small property owners, the jealousies and suspicions
generated by party feuds, the enveloping atmosphere of patronage
and jobbery. Thirdly, the municipalities were too ignorant to
understand the engineering problems involved, as was proved by
the defective provisions of all the Improvement Acts promoted by

---

[1] "Health of Towns Improvements. Proposed outline clauses of a Bill for
the issue of amended Commissions of Sewers, Drainage, Water Supply, Paving,
and Health of Towns Improvements," MS., 13 December 1844.
"Health of Towns Improvements. Draft Report of Observations and
Recommendations on a Bill for the Drainage, Better Supply of Water, and
Improvement by other means of Health of Towns," MS., 13 December 1844.
[2] A quotation from the *First Report*, v.l. i p. xv.
[3] Ibid., vol. i, p. xviii.

them in recent years.[1] Finally, there was scarcely a town of any size where the main public health functions were not shared out between clashing and uncoordinated authorities, a trading company supplying the water, the Corporation draining the borough, a body of Commissioners under a Local Act performing the same service for the suburbs, a road trust doing the cleansing and paving.[2]

The lesson was clear. For geological and engineering reasons, special districts for drainage and towns improvement must be established. For economic, political, and social reasons, those special districts must have a special administrative authority, comprehending in its scope the whole of the public works in the area. Chadwick proposed in fact to refurbish the ancient machinery of Crown-appointed Commissions of Sewers, as he had earlier suggested in the *Sanitary Report*, giving them wider powers and a new direction, and putting them under the tutelage of a department of the central Government, which would guard against improper appointments and ensure the efficient execution of their duties.

The composition and functions of the central department Chadwick described as he explained his arrangements for financing the vast new schemes of local works. He proposed to lay the charge for improvements upon the parties immediately benefited, the occupiers, in proportion to their terms of enjoyment; and to ensure that they would pay no more than their fair share for the benefit they received, he suggested that the charge, principal and interest, should be spread over a period of thirty years. This recommendation involved two further proposals—

[1] The Birkenhead Act (6 & 7 Vict., c. 13 Local), for example, "from the habit of not looking beyond the immediate local experience," recognised all the old evils of working class housing, blind alleys, cellar dwellings, cesspools, etc. Chadwick had written severely to one of its promoters: "I shall feel it my duty to ask the attention of the Commissioners . . . to the regulations set forth in the sanitary report on Birkenhead—in proof of the necessity of some extraneous security other than the builders' own interests, for the protection (it might be said of those very interests) of the health of the population: in other words to ensure that the experience already obtained, as to the causes of disease and the practical means of prevention, shall be properly consulted and applied." (E. C. to John Laird, 22 October 1844.)

[2] See, for example, Chadwick's analysis of the Liverpool Local Acts, *Second Report*, vol. i, p. 42, footnote: "Table showing want of consolidation and inconsistent powers of various authorities under Local Acts in Liverpool."

that local authorities should be empowered, with the consent of
the central Government, to raise loans on the security of the rates,
and to execute the domestic works under contract, with all the
consequent economies of large-scale business; and, secondly, that
there should be a compulsory rate for drainage purposes, its
collection being consolidated with that of the water rates and
other local charges.

In this financial machinery of public loans and compulsory
rates Chadwick saw yet another argument against the grant of
self-acting powers to local authorities. For it was not only the
interests of the present tenants which must be considered, but also
the interests of those who would be occupying the premises in
thirty years' time; and there must be some security that the works
were of a quality to last so long and be of benefit to those
reversioners and absent parties in proportion to the share of the
cost which would fall upon them. Now this was a responsibility
which the local authorities could not be trusted to shoulder alone.
It was only too likely that they would fall under the influence of
building speculators, who would push them into extravagant jobs,
the cost being passed on to future occupiers.

Here then was the main ground upon which Chadwick based
the supervisory powers of the central department. Before granting
to the local authority the privilege of distributing charges, the
central department must satisfy itself, on behalf of the reversioners, that the works had been efficiently planned and executed.
The procedure should be—first, a survey of the district conducted
by the Board of Ordnance; then an examination by a competent
engineer, who would produce plans, together with estimates of
the outlay involved; and finally the preparation of a report, to be
distributed in the locality. After this preliminary inquiry, which
would condition local opinion for the reception of the coming
changes, the case would come for consideration by the central
department. What should be the character of that department?
It should be, thought Chadwick, a judicial committee of the Privy
Council; for essentially the functions it was called upon to perform
were judicial in their nature—"the legal distribution of the
charges, and the protection of reversioners and the pockets of the
absent, the determination of the principles, and the settlement of
the amounts of compensation." But the judicial committee should

act upon the advice of "one responsible properly qualified legal officer." It was this man who would occupy the key position at the centre. He would direct the local inquiries and prepare a report upon their findings. The commissions, which the Privy Council would issue to constitute the new public health authorities, would be addressed to persons nominated on his recommendation.

Such a procedure offered many advantages. It would present a small target to the anti-centralisation party. There would be the minimum of new machinery at the centre. Moreover, no wholesale powers of initiation were to be conferred on the central Government. The Privy Council might direct an inquiry to be made on receipt of a petition from the locality; but failing such an appeal, they should take action only if the death rate from zymotic diseases exceeded a certain fixed proportion. Many towns would thus be able to maintain their freedom from interference by Whitehall on the ground that their bad drains and contaminated water did not kill sufficient numbers to justify the intervention of the Privy Council. A further advantage was its great cheapness. Liverpool had spent £2,600 not long before in obtaining Local Acts for water supply and towns improvement. Under the arrangement Chadwick proposed, the cost would have probably not been more than £200 or £300, to cover the expenses of a competent engineer while he examined the town and prepared a plan of works; and such a plan would have saved the Corporation from wasting £50,000 on an erroneous and inefficient scheme. Finally, it was a flexible procedure, by which "the plaister may (to use a homely illustration) be cut and fitted to the sore place to which it is applied." The preliminary inquiry would enable the public health machinery to be adapted to the needs and resources of each individual locality, whether it were a village or a city, a town in Scotland or in Ireland, or for that matter a town in the colonies.

Though Town Councils found no place in Chadwick's administrative scheme, he was less severe on water companies. Reproved for the restrictive practices and wasteful competition of their unregenerate past, they might yet be integrated into the framework of local government. In the past proprietary rights in town water supplies had been inadvertently conceded by Parlia-

H

ment to private and irresponsible water companies; those rights should now be resumed, and converted into an express public trust. The motive of private profit and the energy of private enterprise, thought Chadwick, could be harnessed to the public interest by contracts between the local Commission and the local water company, which would protect consumers against commercial rapacity and guarantee universal supplies at constant pressure, while giving the public at the same time the benefit of the superior efficiency of capitalist management. Companies would be prepared to construct and maintain waterworks, he believed, for a guaranteed profit of 6 per cent—that is, $1\frac{1}{2}$ to 2 per cent above the common rate of interest on money borrowed. "Not 6 per cent additional interest, not even 10 per cent additional interest, would fairly insure the ratepayers for the risks of an additional expenditure by any probable local body, even with the proposed securities of a previous examination of their plans of works."

It has been necessary to consider at some length this memorandum by Chadwick, since it reveals strikingly the strength and weakness of his views on public health policy, and indicates the main points around which the sanitary debate was to revolve for the next few years. What was to be the nature of the executive body in the locality and of the controlling body at the centre? These were the two main administrative questions to be settled; and to both questions, in his advice to Buccleuch, Chadwick gave the wrong answers. His suspicion of local representative bodies issued in the recommendation that public health measures should not be entrusted to the inefficient and party-ridden municipalities, but should devolve upon a body of *ad hoc* commissioners, appointed by the Crown on the basis of their fitness for the work. But who is "the Crown" in this context? A committee of the Privy Council—who are to act on the advice of a single responsible legal officer. There is no doubt whom Chadwick had in mind for the post, for who but Edwin Chadwick possessed the necessary knowledge, experience, and energy to grapple with the problems presented by this vast new field of administration? The whole broad province of sanitary engineering and sanitary legislation Chadwick had now taken for his own, and, surveying Whitehall and Downing Street, he could see no one else—certainly no

Minister of the Crown—to whom he was prepared to lease his proprietary rights. It should be noted that at no time did Chadwick press for a Government Board on the lines of the Poor Law Commission. A few days before he presented his memorandum he had told Buccleuth, "Colonel Colby [of the Board of Ordnance] who has had much plague with Boards, ventures as an axiom that for doing business almost the worst individual appointment is better than the best possible Board. I do not go so far but having been the scapegoat of proceedings against which I have remonstrated shall have one day some large revelations on Board management."[1] His model was not the "Three Kings," with their unhappy associations of divided authority and frustrated effort, but Kay-Shuttleworth's position of quiet power as secretary to a Privy Council Committee.

It appears strange that a man who had helped Bentham to write the *Constitutional Code* should not have seen that only by the establishment of a separate State department under a Minister of Health could sanitary measures claim the attention and attain the prestige as objects of government that they deserved. Chadwick had not learned—and never would learn—the lesson of the Poor Law Commission, and he continued to deplore the system which entrusted the direction of administration to the temporary masters of a shifting Parliamentary majority. It must be recognised, however, that in 1845, in the existing state of Government opinion on the subject, the case was strong for any arrangement which would afford Chadwick the chance to guide and shape public health policy. At the Privy Council office he would be under the protecting wing of Lord Lansdowne, a good friend to himself and to the sanitary cause. There was the further advantage that the arrangement was "small, simple, tentative, and easily altered and extended, as circumstances might require, and ... comparatively inexpensive." The department would be small at first, but could be made as big as the task it had to handle; the single appointment of counsel to the Privy Council could be made as big as the man who filled it. There was much to be said for it as an interim solution for the experimental period when what was primarily needed was a ready adaptability, a capacity for the rapid assimilation of new ideas and new functions; when the new

---

[1] E. C. to Duke of Buccleuch, 2–5 December 1844.

department must win its ground against the vigilant hostility of the interested minorities who hated its intervention, and the larger body of critics who opposed on principle any extension of Government activity.

The Royal Commission on the Health of Towns was a continuation of the inquest on municipal government opened in 1835; and Chadwick's team of engineers and doctors probed more deeply than the bright young lawyers who had drawn up the indictment of the closed corporation. In Chadwick's view the transference of municipal authority from a Tory oligarchy to a ratepaying democracy of shopkeepers and Dissenters had not made the Town Council in any respect a more fit instrument for local government. The investigation had presented him with only too many examples of Town Councils sitting contentedly amidst their filth, exhibiting neither the desire nor the ability to introduce improvements. The municipalities were cramped in their areas, destitute of the most important functions of government or sharing them with intrusive bodies of *ad hoc* commissioners, torn by party strife and dominated by the petty interests of landlords and shopkeepers; so handicapped they faced the problems of a society passing through an industrial revolution with the inhibitions of the ratepayer and the confident ignorance of the "practical" man of business. That was the picture as Chadwick saw it. And, indeed, there was little in the eighteen-forties to suggest how far the municipalities were destined to become the chosen instrument of the modern State for realising the good life for its citizens.

On one question, therefore, the memorandum reveals that Chadwick had changed his mind since 1842. In the *Sanitary Report* he had spoken with approval of public management, and had urged that the example of the Manchester Gas Works might be profitably followed in the supply of water. Now, however, though he insisted vigorously that the unchecked individualism of early buccaneering capitalism must cease, he was convinced that only the motive of private gain could ensure efficient and economic service, and that, indeed, "the evidence almost goes so far as to establish this that the worst company would almost be better than the best corporate municipality."[1] This was a very crude overstatement of his position, less an induction from the evidence

[1] E. C. to J. Hodson, 10 April 1845.

taken before the Commission than an expression of Chadwick's roseate hopes for his Towns Improvement Company. The testimony of his witnesses was, in fact, more balanced on this point than the conclusions he had drawn from them. Thomas Wroe, manager of the Manchester Gas Works, had shown that they supplied 1,000 cubic feet for less than 6s., the charge in other towns, where the supply was in the hands of companies, being usually 8s.; and the Gas Works had already returned to the town a profit of £370,000, which had been spent on the erection of a Town Hall and other improvements.[1] On the other hand, however, Thomas Hawksley, on whose evidence Chadwick leaned so heavily, threw his influence on the side of private enterprise; and the brilliant success of Hawksley's company in Nottingham outshone the few examples of publicly managed water supplies which Chadwick discovered in operation at Huddersfield, Brecon, Halifax, Hull, and Bath.[2] He was quite convinced, he told Buccleuch, of the "general utter incompetency of the municipal corporations in England to carry out such works." Hull Corporation, for example, had spent £55,000 in giving an intermittent supply to 8,000 houses; fourteen years before, when the price of iron was higher, it had cost the Nottingham Company only £32,000 to lay on a constant supply to the same number of houses; and while the Nottingham Company made a satisfactory profit by charging the lower class of tenements a penny a week, the Hull Corporation was obliged to charge double this sum. The difference was not due to jobbery on the part of the Corporation: "it is only such a result as must always be expected where people have not an interest in comparing pecuniary results with pecuniary expenditure in the erection and management of works."[3]

There is much to criticise in the form in which Chadwick cast his local and central machinery; but in his conception of the proper relationship between the centre and the localities there is much besides that is admirable. In the preliminary inquiry— the prototype of the modern procedure of local inquiry by

[1] *First Report*, vol. ii, p. 343.
[2] At Bath, for example, which Chadwick had previously looked upon as a favourable instance of public management, he found that the Corporation charged 10s. per annum for 40 gallons a day, as compared with the Nottingham charge of 4s. 4d. (*Second Report*, vol. i, p. 88.)
[3] E. C. to Duke of Buccleuch, 23 May 1845.

inspectors of the Ministry of Health and the Ministry of Town and Country Planning—he had devised an adaptable instrument of infinite flexibility, which, while paying due respect to local idiosyncrasies, would bring the local authority firmly into line with the policy of the central department. It was to prove its value a few years later at the General Board of Health.

The proposal to distribute the cost of new works over a period coincident with the benefit derived from them wears so simple and commonsense an air that its importance may easily be overlooked. In Chadwick's hands it becomes an argument for the most powerful weapon wielded by the General Board of Health: the scrutiny by the central department of all local improvement schemes, and the loans by which they were to be financed. It has, however, a further significance, which was presently to be exploited to the full by the propaganda of the Health of Towns Association. The bitterest objections to sanitary reform were raised by property owners who feared that drains and water meant heavy additional burdens upon themselves. Thomas Cubitt, the building contractor, spoke for this class when he declared that "the public" were not prepared to go to the extent of putting a water-closet in every house: "I think that if people were obliged to put them, it would be considered a very severe tax upon them."[1] Chadwick's reply was to demonstrate that, if the charge were spread over thirty years, the cost of fitting new house-drains, closets, and water pipes would dwindle to a weekly payment of $1\frac{1}{2}$d., which was within the means of even the poorest tenants, and was considerably cheaper than the cost of the existing privies, cesspools and stand-cocks. It was good arithmetic and good economics; but it fought a slow battle with the "landlord fallacy" that stinks and damp formed part of the tenant's risk, and the equally powerful ratepayers' fallacy that fever nests were cheaper than public works.

How the Duke of Buccleuch received Chadwick's draft Bill and the accompanying memorandum there is no evidence, but Chadwick records that throughout December and January he was kept busy "endeavouring to stop mischief."[2] It is clear, however, that the Commissioners were not willing to act up to the

[1] *First Report of Health of Towns Commission*, vol. ii, p. 265.
[2] E. C. to T. Bamfield, 26 January 1845.

strength of the arguments he directed at them, and the thirty recommendations into which they expanded the general conclusions of the First Report departed in several important respects from the advice contained in the papers he had laid before Buccleuch. Nevertheless, "the main propositions are I expect secured," he told a friend, "but very slenderly supported by reasons."[1]

"We therefore recommend," ran the first proposal, "that in all cases the local administrative body appointed for the purpose have the special charge and direction of all the works required for sanatory purposes, but that the Crown possess a general power of supervision."[2] Whether the "local administrative body appointed for the purpose" should be the Town Council or an *ad hoc* body established under royal commission, whether it should be elective or nominated by the Crown, were questions left open for further debate, and Chadwick's suggestion that the Privy Council should be indicated as the supervisory authority was equally rejected. For the next three years the nature of the local authority and of the controlling department at the centre was to be discussed in Parliament, with Chadwick working continually, in letters and memoranda and personal interviews, for his local Commission of Crown nominees, acting under the guidance of a judicial committee of Council. There was another significant omission. The Report recommended that, on appeal from the local authority or a certain number of the inhabitants, the Crown should direct an inquiry into the sanitary condition of any district, and should be empowered to enforce the execution of the law;[3] but Chadwick's proposal that the inquiry should be conducted automatically on the evidence of the excessive mortality as shown in the Registrar-General's returns, contemplated the gift of more aggressive powers to the central Government than the Commission were prepared to advise. Similarly they found no place for the flexible, powerful instrument of the local inquiry. A plan and survey must precede any scheme for works of town drainage; the Crown should have power to define and enlarge from time to time the area for drainage included within the jurisdiction of the local authority—these principles were recognised, as they must be in the face of the overwhelming technical evidence. But the local

---

[1] E. C. to T. Bamfield, 26 January 1845.
[2] *Second Report*, vol. i, p. 25.　　　[3] Ibid., vol. i, p. 39.

inquiry by a Government inspector, with the scope and intention that Chadwick would have given it, reached beyond this, fumbling towards a conscious perception of social purpose which a Royal Commission of 1845 could not but regard as unsafe. Even more disappointing to Chadwick's hopes was the casual mention of the Officer of Health. Almost as an afterthought the twenty-ninth recommendation proposed that the local administrative body should have the power to appoint, subject to the approval of the Crown, a properly qualified medical officer to inspect and report upon the sanitary condition of the district.[1] A few lines dealt with the functions of an official to whose importance Chadwick had devoted eighteen months of agitation and thousands of words of argument.

On the other main points he carried the Commission with him. The local authority should have wider powers in sanitary matters than had hitherto been granted either under Local Acts or by the Statute of Sewers. It should be responsible for the paving of all streets, courts, and alleys, and for the construction of house drains as well as the sewers. It should be invested with the rights to all the dust, ashes, and street refuse. It should have powers, subject to approval, to buy out mill-owners and others whose property rights were an obstruction to proper drainage, and to purchase property for the purpose of opening thoroughfares, improving ventilation, and increasing the general convenience of traffic.[2]

But of the greatest importance were the resolutions on water supply. The Commission recommended that it be obligatory on the local administrative body to procure a supply of water in sufficient quantity not only for the domestic needs of the inhabitants, but for cleansing the streets, scouring the sewers and drains, and extinguishing fires. Where a company controlled the supply it should be required to comply with the demands of the local authority on equitable terms; and the latter should be empowered to purchase the waterworks, with the approval of the Crown, if the proprietors were willing to dispose of them. Competition between water companies should be discouraged as far as practicable. The three recommendations which followed made it clear that the service should be extended to all dwelling-houses, and that the supply in all cases should be constant, and at as high a

[1] *Second Report*, vol. i, p. 122.   [2] Ibid., pp. 52, 65; 72; 44, 107.

pressure as circumstances permitted. Unqualified approval was given to Chadwick's proposal that the waterworks should be executed, maintained, and kept in good repair by public companies, as lessees or contractors for terms of years, with liberty of redemption by the public upon conditions previously settled. In phrases which echoed his memorandum to Buccleuch the Report declared that companies would consider a return of six per cent an adequate inducement, this being 1 to 1½ per cent above the usual market rate for such investments. This would be cheap "as compared with the risk of mismanagement by local boards, composed of persons having no professional skill, and liable to be misled as to the materials and magnitude of the proposed works, as well as to the numbers of officers requisite to maintain them. It might be difficult to ensure that a local body should be so constituted as to give the same constant attention to economy in the expenditure of other people's money that contractors would do in the expenditure and management of their own."[1]

The financial machinery outlined by the Commission was also substantially that proposed by Chadwick. Loans for constructing public works might be raised by the local administrative body on the security of the rates, the approval of the Crown being first obtained. The expense of the works would then be charged upon the properties benefited, in the form of a special rate upon the occupiers, the whole sum with interest being recovered by annual instalments within a certain number of years.[2]

With the publication of the Reports of the Health of Towns Commission, the second phase of the public health movement was concluded. The first phase, to expose the evil, had been the primary task of the *Sanitary Report*. That report had also contained a sketch of Chadwick's ideas on the course legislation should take. But it was the revelations, not the recommendations, of the *Sanitary Report*, which had attracted attention. Now the technical and administrative possibilities had been explored by an authoritative body of Commissioners, whose advice came with more weight that that of a single civil servant of equivocal reputation. The third phase, to translate those recommendations into legislation, was now opened.

[1] *Second Report*, vol. i, pp. 95, 99–104.　　　[2] Ibid., pp. 60–1.

CHAPTER V

SANITARY PROFITS AND PROPAGANDA

THROUGHOUT these busy months of 1843 and 1844, while Chadwick had borne at Gwydyr House the main burden of the Health of Towns investigation, two further anxieties had weighed upon him. The first was the behaviour of the Marquis of Normanby. As Lord Lieutenant in Ireland Normanby had antagonised the Anglo-Irish community by his friendship with Catholics and his clemency in political cases, thus revealing that beneath a somewhat flippant and flamboyant exterior he concealed an unexpected strength of principle. As Home Secretary he had been converted to the cause of sanitary reform in the backstreets of Whitechapel; with the best of intentions he had sponsored a set of remedial measures which Chadwick, from a fuller knowledge, could only judge to be incomplete and ill-designed and now from the opposition benches he directed a jealous eye upon Sir James Graham's leisurely handling of public health questions. At the beginning of the 1844 session Lord Normanby rose to inquire what the Tories had done with his three sanitary Bills. When the Whig Government fell, Graham had promised to take the Drainage Bill under his own special care; nothing more had been heard of it. After an unaccountable delay of twelve months, Graham had appointed a Commission of Inquiry, though Chadwick's Report of 1842 proved the necessity for immediate legislation, and "the result of its perusal must be to convince any one that more information was not what was required upon the subject." The remedies were simple enough. "Centralisation" was not necessary; it would have been sufficient, as in his own Bills, to confer more powers upon existing local authorities.[1] In May, Normanby resumed his attack, presenting a petition from a public meeting of 3,000 Edinburgh

[1] *Hansard*, vol. lxxii, pp. 220–8, 5 February 1844.

working-men, the first petition on such a subject that had ever
been received from the lower classes. Four years had passed since
the need for a general measure had been considered, said
Normanby, two years since the *Sanitary Report* had appeared, and
another year was now elapsing without anything being done.[1]

Chadwick resented the imputation that the months devoted to
maturing his engineering and administrative plans for the Health
of Towns Commission constituted a quite unjustified delay. To
avoid superficial legislation, time was well spent in designing
measures, and, what was equally important, in cultivating opinion
for their reception. As he told R. A. Slaney, who shared Normanby's impatience, "the cause is progressing, the evidence is telling,
and in due time a fullness of opinion will be manifested to carry the
measures which can only be carried with the strength of a strong
opinion. What I am most afraid of is separate and ineffectual
measures."[2] In the virtuous indignation of a Minister out of
office at the tardiness of his rivals in power, Chadwick saw a
further danger—that sanitary measures might be dragged into the
arena of party politics, where they would lose the cool detachment of a scientific investigation in the heated atmosphere of a
faction fight; and where, moreover, they were likely to escape
from his control. Thus he wrote to James Simpson, who at his
suggestion had drawn up the petition from the Edinburgh
workers which Normanby presented to the Lords: "I should have
deprecated the giving the proposed petition to Lord Normanby or
doing anything which would give the proceeding a party complexion as I fear that will do. The fact is Lord Normanby's
measures against which Dr. Southwood Smith and others were
strongly remonstrant would, if they could have been carried out,
have spread bad drains throughout the country at an enormous
expense, and not have mitigated and in all probability have
aggravated the evils intended to be remedied. He stopped all
proceedings in the getting up of local sanatory reports and under
his influence the sanatory report itself was stopped and never
probably would have appeared but for his removal from power.
Now that it has appeared he is very complimentary. Still, however, the objection to such a presentation is its party complexion.

[1] *Hansard*, vol. lxxiv, pp. 541–5, 2 May 1844.
[2] E. C. to R. A. Slaney, 23 November 1844.

Why could not Lord Dunfermline who may be said to be the natural representative of Edinburgh attend and present the petition?"[1]

In a long and effective speech Normanby closed his 1844 campaign on 26 July with an address to the Crown, hoping that in the coming session the specific attention of Parliament would be called to the sanitary question. In the past few days he had revisited the eastern districts of London, and had come away with the impression that no such misery existed in any other civilised country. He warned the House that there was danger in further delay; "the sick bed is the place in which there is most time to brood over neglect, or to feel gratitude for sympathy."[2] The Duke of Buccleuch, armed with a memorandum from Chadwick,[3] had no difficulty in demonstrating that when they were in office the Whigs had been as dilatory as the Tories, and he suggested that a large part of Normanby's enthusiasm for sanitary reform sprang from a desire to score off the Government.

Chadwick's second great anxiety at this period was the apathy of the public at large. "I am crying out Pestilence! and for the relief of the masses," he wrote to Thomas Carlyle, "but can get no one to hear of means which will affect the pockets of small owners in small corporations who have votes for the election of members of parliament and who set up the cry of self-government, as against any regulations which may lead to immediate expenditure for putting in better condition the houses for which they exact exorbitant rents."[4] In particular he was keenly disappointed with the reception of his Report on Interments. While he was writing it, feeling had risen to a pitch of healthy indignation; the Officer of Health, the central proposition, had been welcomed by all the clergy he had met; "and yet soon after the appearance of the report that which had previously been a storm, almost, of agitation subsided."[5] In a stream of letters in December 1843 and January 1844 Chadwick had urged his friends—Dr. Holland in Manchester, Dr. Laycock in York, James Simpson in Edinburgh,

---

[1] E. C. to James Simpson, 25 April 1844.
[2] *Hansard*, vol. lxxvi, pp. 1460–80, 26 July 1844.
[3] "Memoranda of answers to the imputations of blame in respect to alleged delay to adopt sanitary measures," MS., 13 July 1844.
[4] E. C. to Thomas Carlyle, 20 June 1844.
[5] E. C. to Dr. P. H. Holland, 3 August 1844.

Southwood Smith in London—to get petitions signed by the
working-men in all large factories. If Scotland did not agitate, he
warned his Scottish friends, Scotland would go without the
Officer of Health, as it had gone without the Vaccination Acts;[1]
while Dr. Laycock was exhorted to sound the alarm in the *Lancet*
against the danger of leaving the cause of death to be verified by
the present registrars instead of by a qualified medical practitioner.[2] "I can get petitions pretty smartly poured in from
Lancashire," Lyon Playfair had promised, adding that Bury was
about to send a memorial calling for Officers of Health, and he
would see that Preston and Ashton did the same.[3] But six months
later Chadwick had to confess to Dr. Holland, "I have *heard*
of two or three petitions, your own is the only one I have
seen."[4]

"I must own my disgust at the carelessness and selfishness of our
public men," he confided to a German economist. "An excess of
selfishness or of what Bentham calls the 'self-regarding virtues'
without any compensating power of the 'extra-regarding
virtues' is perhaps characteristic of our people. It is, however,
to this excess, to strong stomachs and appetites that our manufacturing and commercial energy is to be ascribed."[5] The problem
was that before the Government could be brought to act, hard-
headed business men in the Commons—fully endowed with the
"self-regarding virtues" and the self-satisfied possessors of those
"strong stomachs and appetites"—had first to be convinced that
they were not being stampeded into rash and expensive action by
the exaggerations of cranks and sentimentalists. Gentlemen,
walking round their mills or their estates, had spoken to sturdy
workmen, who had lived half a century and raised a numerous
progeny in districts which were now (surely extravagantly)
described as "fever nests." They felt it was being overdone, this
danger from stinks and the propinquity of filth. After all, many
themselves lived in houses of fashionable but insanitary design,
with cesspool odours rising dankly from the servants' basements,
and crawling nameless things in the water. At the Westminster

[1] E. C. to J. H. Burton, 7 December 1843.
[2] E. C. to Dr. T. Laycock, 13 January 1844.
[3] Lyon Playfair to E.C., 15 January 1844.
[4] E. C. to Dr. P. H. Holland, 3 August 1844.
[5] E. C. to T. Garnier, 19 September 1844.

School, where some educated their sons, cesspools were strategi-
cally sited on either side of the entrance to the dormitory. The
drains beneath the very building in which they sat, deliberating
the welfare of their humbler countrymen, were so bad that a
daring surveyor, who had once ventured into them, had declared
that it was a relief to get back into the public sewer. So, only too
often, Chadwick's political friends listened to him and seemed
impressed; they went away vowing that something must and
should be done; but once they were beyond the range of that
earnest and importunate eye, the warning lost its urgency, and
the firm outlines of their resolve softened into polite generalities of
goodwill. His keenest arguments were turned by the tough inter-
twined fibre of the opposition—the inertia of the localities, "the
laissez faire of evil people,"[1] the indifference of Ministers, the
ignorance and complacency of powerful men about the un-
cleanliness of the towns.

Hence, in May 1844, Chadwick wrote to Lord Ashley:

"There is certainly a very large class of questions affecting the
condition of the labouring classes on which external aid will be of
much service if it be powerful and not merely a small buzz that
goes on unheeded. There are many small interests adverse to the
condition of the labouring classes that might by such aid be use-
fully kept in check by the representations of a body that would be
properly attended to if well directed. . . .

"Your Lordship has seen how frequently interested parties are
seated at Boards of Guardians, who are ready to stop anything
which may lead to expenditure for the proper repair of the
dwellings of the labouring classes.

"Where measures of drainage are proposed, and the works
carried out by Commissioners of Sewers are found to be defective a
cry is raised nothing must be done for fear of offending the
Commissioners, and the active Commissioners in several instances
are found to be precisely the same sort of persons as those of whom
you have heard as Guardians.

"When additional supplies of water are called for, for the salu-
brity and cleanliness of the dwellings of the working-class population one cry raised is 'Oh the interests of the companies is too
powerful to be touched.'

[1] E. C. to the Rev. Theobald Mathew, 26 April 1845.

"An associated voice should surely be raised on the other side."[1]

What was needed was some hearty and persistent campaigning, with lectures and pamphlets and letters to *The Times*, public meetings to pass resolutions, and deputations to the Home Secretary headed by noble well-wishers, to convince Ministers that, if only for their own peace of mind, something must be done. But a civil servant could hardly appear as the leader of a movement to bring the pressure of external opinion to bear upon Her Majesty's Government; and, even if he had not been disqualified by reason of his office, this was work for which he was constitutionally unfitted. When James Simpson, in an address to a meeting of Edinburgh workmen, told them that Edwin Chadwick had counselled the labouring classes to join in petitions to the authorities, he was annoyed at this indiscreet mention of his name in connection with a public agitation.[2] He preferred to exert his influence from the official anonymity of Somerset House. Chadwick, indeed, was no platform agitator. In private conversation he could use with effect his inexhaustible stores of information, his close argument, his intimacy with detail, the authority of his personal knowledge which caused men to listen to him with respect. But a public speaker required other qualities, qualities which, as his unsuccessful Parliamentary candidatures in later life showed conclusively, Chadwick conspicuously lacked. His public utterances were lame and dull, tied down to notes, bristling with statistical minutiæ, and sounding like extracts from one of his own blue-books.

So the formation of a Health of Towns Association was left to other men, to Ashley, Normanby, Ebrington, and above all to Dr. Southwood Smith, who had revealed a flair for propaganda in the illustrations he had caused to be drawn for the Report of the Children's Employment Commission. When, in December 1844, Chadwick heard that Southwood Smith was organising a meeting at Exeter Hall, he expressed his hearty approval; but he wrote warningly to the Doctor, "I must beg of you to be careful not to mix me up with the meeting. It will do no good and may hinder much my power of being useful."[3]

[1] E. C. to Lord Ashley, 11 May 1844.
[2] E. C. to James Simpson, 3 February 1844.
[3] E. C. to Southwood Smith, 9 December 1844.

The meeting, which took place on 11 December 1844, was presided over by Lord Normanby; and it may be supposed that not the least of the benefits Chadwick expected from the campaign was that it diverted his Lordship's energies into the safer channels of a non-political agitation. He had visited the huts of hundreds of negro slaves in the West Indies and the cabins of Irish cottiers, he told his audience, but "he would rather pass his life in any one of the first, or in most of the last, than he would inhabit one of those dens or cellars too often used as dwellings of the industrious poor of this country." Dismissing the Health of Towns Commission as "but a bad substitute for action," he hoped that "they would separate this day with a firm determination to do all that in them lay to prevent the seasons again revolving still to find so dreadful a contrast existing between an increasing national prosperity and a deepening misery of the masses."[1] As a result of the meeting a Health of Towns Association was founded, with Southwood Smith and Professor W. A. Guy as secretaries; and in the following months branches were established in Edinburgh, Liverpool, Manchester, York, Halifax, Derby, Bath, Rugby, Marlborough, Walsall, Plymouth, and Worcester.[2]

In the next few years the Association, in lectures and pamphlets and petitions, hammered away at Southwood Smith's proposition that "the heaviest municipal tax is the fever tax." Its lecturers, Lord Ebrington, the lawyer James Simpson, the clergyman the Rev. C. Girdlestone, the doctors W. A. Guy, R. D. Grainger, J. Toynbee, instructed audiences of both the working and middle classes in the elementary principles of ventilation, drainage, and civic and domestic cleanliness. In Liverpool a *Health of Towns Advocate* was started by Dr. John Sutherland, fifteen hundred copies of the first number being distributed gratuitously. In January 1847, on the eve of the introduction of Lord Morpeth's first Health of Towns Bill, the Metropolitan Association began the publication of a *Weekly Sheet of Facts and Figures*.[3] Joseph Toynbee organised in London an ancillary Metropolitan Working Classes' Association for Improving the Public Health, which adopted

---

[1] *Abstract of Proceedings of Public Meeting at Exeter Hall, December 11, 1844* (pamphlet), pp. 5, 12, 13.
[2] *Health of Town Association: Report February 24, 1847* (pamphlet), pp. 7, 9.
[3] Ibid., p. 10.

the motto, "We can be useful no longer than we are well"; the example was followed at Newcastle and Gateshead where a Working Men's Association, which included thirty "foremen and other influential workers," was formed in friendly alliance with the local Sanitary Association.[1] In many other towns the working classes, under middle-class guidance, set up associations, which were prolific in advice to their fellow workers and in memorials to the Government. But not everywhere was there this docile acceptance of middle-class tutorship; and Chadwick heard that at Glasgow "some noisy, brawling, turbulent Chartists had got mixed up with the agitation," and that "their way of doing business had disgusted the more discreet."[2]

It was all a bit vulgar and demagogic, thought some of Chadwick's friends. He was rather apologetic himself. "Needs must," he told the Bishop of London, "where the opposing interests are so strong as they are . . . and so influential with Members of Parliament."[3] But though he refused to have his name connected openly with the Association, he took full advantage of this powerful instrument of propaganda which lay so ready to his hand, and, by a kind of ventriloquism, its publications incorporated the memoranda he supplied to them, and its deputations spoke arguments he had suggested. Thus, on 3 November 1846, he sent Ashley a review of progress since 1837, together with the mortality bill for the quarter, which showed some 15,000 deaths above the average, proving that "if we are idle death is not." It was a "singularly important" paper, thought Ashley. "I made use of it today at a meeting of the Health of Towns Association, which I hope may at last produce some movement on the part of the Government. It is almost the boldest document ever published by a subordinate department."[4]

It was, taking the country as a whole, a sprawling, loosely knit campaign, much less a pitched battle fought to a general's plan than an affair of local skirmishes under guerrilla leaders. In the years of the cholera especially, little agitations, auxiliary to the

[1] *First Annual Report of the Newcastle and Gateshead Sanitary Association*, 1848, pp. 14–15.
[2] Thomas Beggs to E. C., 11 April 1846.
[3] E. C. to Bishop Blomfield, 18 November 1847.
[4] E. C. to Lord Ashley, 3 November 1846; Lord Ashley to E. C., 6 November 1846.

I

national movement though often quite independent in their origin and development, were ignited in many places by the energy of some public-spirited individual or group, to blaze fiercely for a few months or a year or two, perhaps, and then to flicker out as the enthusiasm or the wholesome fear departed. In 1849, for instance, the Christian Socialists were busy in the slums of Bermondsey, and had a wild scheme for waylaying the Prince Consort with a memorial against the sanitary condition of the district.[1] Chadwick seems to have known nothing of their activity—or, it may be, he studiously ignored "Parson Lot" and his Chartist friends. There must have been many enlightened clergymen like Charles Kingsley who asked their parishioners, "Who Causes Pestilence?" and whose sermons attacked the *Deus ex machina* theory of judgments and visitations."[2] There must have been even more sturdy doctors like Kingsley's Tom Thurnall, pitting their science and blunt commonsense against the dirt and prejudice which surrounded them, devoted allies of Chadwick and the General Board of Health against "that 'local government,' which signifies, in plain English, the leaving the few to destroy themselves and the many, by the unchecked exercise of the virtues of pride and ignorance, stupidity and stinginess."[3] As a propagandist movement, however, the public health agitation did not approach the power of the Anti-Corn-Law League. Middle-class opinion never organised itself so formidably behind Ashley and Normanby and Southwood Smith as it organised itself behind Cobden and Bright, and the *Weekly Sheet of Facts and Figures* never exerted anything like the influence of the *Anti-Bread-Tax Circular*. The Anti-Corn-Law League put before the public a single, easily comprehended aim, the repeal of a set of laws which possessed the ideal quality for the propagandist's purposes that they could be shown to be taxes on the people's food. The Health of Towns Association faced a complex of problems, often of a technical nature, about whose solution there was frequently a division of opinion even in their own ranks. Both professed to be dealing with the same disease, the "Condition of England

[1] G. Kendall, *Charles Kingsley and his Ideas* (1947), p. 76.
[2] Ibid., pp. 75, 77. "Who Causes Pestilence?" was the title of a series of sermons delivered by Kingsley at the end of 1848.
[3] C. Kingsley, *Two Years Ago* (3rd ed., 1860), p. 213.

Question"; but the Leaguers prescribed a specific, while the sanitarians could recommend only a prolonged and exacting course of therapeutics. The extraordinary success of Cobden and Bright was won because they combined the appeal *ad misericordiam* of the farm labourer's "I be protected and I be starving" with a cogent economic exposition that Repeal would bring increased trade, higher wages, and even a better market for the farmer. The weapons of the Anti-Corn-Law League, though they were sharpened and given their cutting edge by the misery of the lower classes, were forged out of the solid core of middle-class interests. But was there any profit in sanitation? Maybe there was, if you cared to go into the figures of Chadwick's Towns Improvement Company, or if you accepted his thesis that the labourer, as much as any productive machinery, repaid care and money spent. But how could sewers compete with railways as fields for investment? Projects for bringing drains and water into the homes of the people were looked upon as too "philanthropic," "humanitarian," and "patriotic" to be good business. The capitalist contributed to schemes for improving the condition of the labouring classes in much the same spirit as he put money on the plate at church, expecting to draw his return not in hard cash but in the transcendental currency of Butler's "Musical Banks."

It was this feeling which Chadwick had set himself to combat since the earliest of his social investigations. Nothing disgusted him more than the attitude of those who looked complacently on the poor as objects of charity, and who found an easy discharge from the labour and responsibility of seeking a solution to the problems of human misery by means which sapped the independence of the workers. He believed that charities created much of the misery they were intended to relieve and could not relieve all that they created. It might even be said, he thought, that if the trustee of a fund for the distribution of alms ate and drank the money himself, or if the man appointed to administer a charity for the sustenance of foundlings kept a mistress instead with the proceeds, they would have performed a work of public benefit; the corruption being confined to one rather than being diffused amongst a multitude. Moreover, charity of this kind was directed only towards the visible and pitiful effects, and failed to come to grips with the physical causes which produced them.

Lady Bountiful was well-meaning but muddle-headed. She was touched by the sight of the sick labourer, lying untended in his damp, cold room, surrounded by the circle of his pale, ill-fed children; but she sent him medicines, blankets, and fuel, instead of removing by drainage the dampness and pestilential miasma which caused the disease; she sent him money and food, instead of eliminating the depressing factors in his environment which led him to spend at the beershop the wages which would have sufficed to feed and clothe his family. She would have done better to have followed the example of the benevolent lady of St. Margaret's parish, who, instead of distributing alms amongst her tenants, spent a hundred pounds on the drainage of their houses.

Chadwick regarded mistrustfully, therefore, the activity of those whom the world called "philanthropists"—Dr. Southwood Smith, for example, "who is a man of benevolence merely and who has mismanaged the Sanatorium."[1] Not benevolence but self-interest was the motive which should be invoked by the social reformer. The logic of Chadwick's argument runs simply enough. More and more he looked to the great capitalists, whose crude creative energy was equipping Britain with an expensive, ill-planned, but modern system of communications, to furnish the brains and the money to rebuild the towns. Such men would move only if they were guaranteed a safe six or seven per cent on their outlay. Now all Chadwick's inquiries and experiments tended to prove that profits as high as this could be made on the construction of sanitary works; and that the capitalists were overlooking an immense untapped market right under their noses— the millions of the working class, dirty, ill-clad and miserably housed, the supply of whose needs would form the basis of a score of new industries. It followed, if this were a true picture of the situation, that it was a grave error in tactics to let it be put about that model houses and reconstructed sewers could return no more than four per cent. Thus, when Southwood Smith outlined to him in July 1844 the plans of the Society for Improving the Dwellings of the Industrious Classes, he was quick to offer his advice and

---

[1] E. C. to Lord Lansdowne, 31 July 1844. A forerunner of the modern nursing home, the "Sanatorium" was opened in 1842 at Devonshire House, Regent's Park, as a "home in sickness" for members of the middle classes. (C. L. Lewes, op. cit., pp. 80–4.)

sympathy, but he firmly declined to allow his name to appear as one of the Committee. He was confident, he explained, that if large capital were engaged a profit of six or seven per cent could be obtained from a superior dwelling let at the same rents now charged for wretched hovels; but the Doctor based the institution on charity and benevolence and proposed to restrict the profits to four per cent, so discarding the powerful stimulus of commercial success. He urged on Southwood Smith, therefore, that the Board of Trade should be asked to reconsider the limitation of interest which had been inserted in the Society's charter, and "to place the proceedings on a commercial principle simply, as being really the most benevolent in its ultimate operation to the working classes."[1]

By the end of 1844 Chadwick was telling his friends that there was little chance of introducing comprehensive measures of sanitary improvement with the speed and vigour he desired, unless they were carried out by commercial bodies. Water supply, he assured one, would everywhere be best entrusted to "a private Company on *proper conditions and with new securities for the public*: making the Company *lessees* instead of proprietors."[2] Administrators, he informed another, could not have the same vital interest in success, or the same motives to vigilance and economy in the expenditure of the public money as capitalists had in spending their own.[3] This excessive enthusiasm for private enterprise (but, be it noted, under strong securities for the public interest) was out of character, and was soon to wilt. It had its origins in a complex of considerations: his scorn for local administrative ability, his anxiety to get sanitary reform under way without waiting on the slow pace of a reluctant Government, the influence of the engineer, Thomas Hawksley, whose Nottingham Water Company seemed a model of efficiency and economy. Possibly his marriage in 1839 to Rachel Dawson Kennedy, fifth daughter of John Kennedy, the cotton manufacturer, had left him more open to the arguments of Manchester. Certainly he had lately made the personal acquaintance of some of the great railway capitalists, and had imbibed from them something of the

[1] E. C. to Southwood Smith, 1 July 1844.
[2] E. C. to J. Hodson, 10 April 1845.
[3] E. C. to Raikes Currie, 26 October 1844.

romantic theory of capitalism, the hero of which was the self-made man, who, by energy, thrift, and a strict attention to "sound economic principles of trade," forged upwards from the bottom of the social pyramid to become the chairman of a company. Such a man, for example, was James Morrison, the railway director, who had come up to London with all his worldly goods in a cotton pocket handkerchief, had prospered, married a partner's daughter, and was now worth three millions. There seemed no reason why Edwin Chadwick also, if he turned his abilities to commerce, should not in due time become a millionaire.

On these twin postulates, therefore—that municipalities were incompetent to manage such services as gas and water supply; and that, of all motives to appeal to, self-interest was the steadiest and most powerful—was based Chadwick's grand scheme for a Towns Improvement Company. His interrogation of witnesses before the Health of Towns Commission had left him, as we have seen, with the conviction that there was money to be made not only out of the supply of water but also out of the disposal of sewage. The figures of practical engineers and farmers could be shown to prove it. For a penny a week supplies of water, constant and at high pressure, could be extended to lower-class houses; for another penny those houses could be drained; for another pavements and roadways could be washed and swept. A company could safely contract to perform these services at a fair rate of profit, and in addition it could count on an immense return from the sale of rich town manure to progressive farmers. Three points were essential to the scheme. The company must have a monopoly of the field of supply. It must contract for all three of the interdependent services of water supply, drainage, and sewage disposal. And, finally, the service must be universal, to all classes of the community, and paid for by a compulsory rate. For, as he explained to Thomas Hawksley, "the best securities for a fair and liberal and permanent profit will be in the close consultation of the wants conveniences comforts and means of the greatest number of the poorest classes of the consumers and in moderate profits on extended supplies, rather than very high profits on narrow supplies."[1]

[1] E. C. to T. Hawksley, 25 November 1844.

The field of operations open to such a company seemed bound-less. In Britain, in the colonies, in every country in Europe, there were scores of towns which needed water and sewers. Carlisle, Durham, Frome, Kidderminster, Salisbury, Merthyr Tydfil, Stourbridge, Walsall, Wednesbury, West Bromwich, Wrexham, Wolverhampton—these were only a few of the places without an adequate water supply. Berlin had already asked Chadwick's advice, and he had heard that he was a greater prophet in Germany than in England. Paris, again, would make the best enterprise in Europe; if only Guizot would take his mind off Algiers and draw his head for a moment out of the clouds of high politics, Chadwick could show him how the highest rooms in Paris could be supplied with filtered water for three sous a ton, as compared with the nine francs at present paid to the *porteurs d'eau*.[1] Turning over these possibilities, Chadwick was flushed with the vision of himself as managing director of a vast public utility company with ramifications in every country, which would be the instrument for carrying out his sanitary schemes and would serve at the same time as a "golden bridge for escape" from the insults to which he felt himself exposed at Somerset House.[2]

The scheme began promisingly. Sir John Easthope, the first chairman of the London and Southampton Railway, gave his "very hearty concurrence," and declared his willingness to invest £50,000 or more.[3] Other capitalists of European reputation, among them Raikes Currie, Sir George de Larpent, James Matheson, James Morrison, John Moss, Edward and Anthony Strutt, J. L. Ricardo, Rowland Hill, Nassau Senior, fell under the spell of Chadwick's tale of gold from sewage. "Such a conjunction, such an Assembly of Eagles on the same perch had perhaps never before been seen," he exclaimed in delight.[4] The company was registered on 7 August 1845, with Lord Francis Egerton as its chairman, three millionaires amongst its backers, and a team of technical consultants chosen by Chadwick for their known sympathy with the most advanced ideas in sanitary engineering—Thomas Hawksley and Chadwell Mylne for water

[1] E. C. to T. Hawksley, 11 August 1844; to Sir John Easthope, 28 November, 31 October 1844.
[2] E. C. to T. Hawksley, 8 August 1845.   [3] E. C. to T. Hawksley, 22 October 1844.
[4] E. C. to Sir John Easthope, 2 October 1845.

supply, John Roe and Butler Williams for drainage, Smith of Deanston and Captain Vetch for sewage disposal. It was proposed to raise £1,000,000, on which a return of at least six per cent, and perhaps nine or ten per cent, was promised. In a tour of the provinces Chadwick expounded to local capitalists the advantages of investing in a venture which offered double the return of the average railway speculation, and combated everywhere the heresy of a water supply divorced from drainage and sewage disposal. At Bristol the Merchant Venturers showed a disposition to co-operate; at Leicester, Lancaster, and Exeter, he secured influential converts; at Manchester he addressed members of the Corporation for an hour, and made an impression on Cobden. He returned in high hopes to London with engagements to the extent of £700,000. From Lyons, too, came an attractive offer; the Paris negotiations seemed hopeful; and inquiries were received from Athens, Berlin, Frankfort, and Munich.

But good will and promises and five competent engineering reports remained the extent of the company's achievement. Chadwick's prospectus was swamped in a sea of railway advertisements; his engineers were lured away by offers of seven and a half guineas a day as railway surveyors; and his millionaires succumbed one by one to the madness of the great railway boom. At Leicester, after six months of negotiation with local capitalists, who were reluctant to see the control of the town's water supply pass to a London company, only £7,000 of the £70,000 required could be raised. At Manchester and Bristol Chadwick's company found itself opposed by separate water schemes, which drew away support because their offers seemed less speculative. The optimistic prospectus was founded largely on the experience of Thomas Hawksley, and it was a severe blow to Chadwick when this expert of his own choice began to exhibit heretical tendencies. He was bewildered when Hawksley accepted a retainer from the Lancashire Water Company in September 1845. How could Hawkesley square advocacy of a new company with his published views which condemned the intrusion of second capitals into the same field? Such a scene would rejoice the old-style water engineers, the Simpsons and the Wicksteeds exceedingly![1] When Hawksley began to cast doubts on the accuracy of

[1] E. C. to T. Hawksley, 31 August 1845.

Chadwick's figures for the returns from sewage irrigation, the break became complete. It was certainly strange, if Hawksley was so dubious of the soundness of the scheme, that he waited eighteen months, and until Chadwick was having difficulty in raising capital, to reveal it.

But the most fundamental weakness of all was the impression which had spread in business circles that the company had philanthropic objects. "One of our Capitalists had objected to *me*! as tending to taint the list with benevolence and philanthropy," Chadwick told the chairman with uneasy heartiness.[1] "So good a commercial man as Mr. Bates," he wrote urgently to Nassau Senior, "should not be allowed to labour under the delusion that there is any more patriotism in the objects of the proposed Company than there is in the every day operations of his own counting house in supplying the wants of the needy in all parts of the world with goods, or money, and receiving in tale, and measure, in a solid and tangible shape the expression of their sense of gratitude for the amount of service rendered to them. . . . He owes some apology to the gentlemen whose names are on the prospectus for so injurious a supposition."[2] But it was in vain that Chadwick pointed to the adhesion of John Moss, the chairman of the Grand Junction Company, "a firm minded man who would not let his feelings get the better of his pecuniary judgment";[3] in vain that he declared that for the sake of humanity the percentage should be looked to with the eye of a Shylock.[4] It was whispered that a company to furnish the houses of the poor with water and drains must be humanitarian and patriotic, and as such offensive to the business conscience.

Some £600 had been spent on the prospectuses, advertisements, and reports of the Towns Improvement Company, of which nearly £500 had come out of Chadwick's pocket. The money had not been entirely wasted. For a moderate outlay the company had examined seven towns, Manchester, Salford, Bolton, Leicester, Bristol, Exeter, and Derby, and had produced exploratory reports on the first five of these, indicating how between two and

[1] E. C. to Lord Francis Egerton, 1 November 1845.
[2] E. C. to Nassau Senior, 11 April 1845.
[3] E. C. to Lord Francis Egerton, 1 November 1845.
[4] E. C. to the Earl of Lovelace, 8 March 1845.

three million pounds might be profitably spent on their improvement. A surgeon of Manchester, Dr. P. H. Holland, had produced a report on that city which was adjudged by Chadwick
to be the best of its kind that had yet appeared.[1] Altogether this
field-work in the service of the company undoubtedly stood
Chadwick in good stead when he came to direct the activities of
his Inspectors at the Board of Health.

After 1846 the Towns Improvement Company fell into a state
of suspended animation from which Chadwick never succeeded in
awakening it. But to its curious history there was a still more
curious appendix. By a flash of characteristic ingenuity, Chadwick
had conceived the idea of distributing sewer manure by pumps
mounted on canal boats, and now, with three other sanguine
spirits, Dr. P. H. Holland, Robert Rawlinson the engineer, and
Joseph Whitworth the inventor, he formed an association to conduct an experiment on the Bridgewater canal. His hopes—as
usual—were high. Farmers were shaking their heads over the
shortage of manure, yet the sewers of the towns were veritable
guano mines. The rich refuse of the towns might be ferried down
in boats to the barren and starving farm land, and the produce
would float back to feed the workers in the factories. "Chadwick's
Elixir" would make the banks of every canal green and fertile.

The idea found little favour, however, with the rugged farmers
of South Lancashire, and they listened with a canny scepticism to
these plausible strangers, with their pumps and jets and hundreds
of yards of canvas hose, who promised them agricultural miracles,
and offered to manure their fields in return for half the extra crop
obtained. Where Dr. Holland, who had been put in charge of the
experiment, did find employment for his floating pump, few of his
hopeful clients noticed that remarkable transformation of their
produce which he had led them to expect. Part of the misfortune
Chadwick attributed to the unhappy Dr. Holland, who was not
the man to cope with "this plaguy irrigation." But the failure was
due chiefly, he felt, to the farmers of the old "round frock" school,
who could not be convinced that they might pay an additional
rent by saving the manure which they now wasted. It was a
psychological phenomenon, this bucolic resistance to new ideas.
As an example of "agricultural logic," Chadwick would tell how

[1] E. C. to Dr. P. H. Holland, 28 December 1845.

the Duke of Bedford attempted to prove to one of his tenants that a certain piece of ploughing could be done as well by two horses as by the four at present used by the farmer. Words failing to carry conviction, the Duke gave an actual demonstration. "The only response which his Grace obtained was that way might be all very well to be worked by a Duke *but he as a farmer could not afford it.*"[1]

Chadwick continued the experiment till the end of 1849, paying expenses out of his own pocket, despite Holland's continually more depressing reports and the prudent secession of his allies. It was a courageous act of faith, and when defeat could no longer be hidden, he was keenly disappointed. The successful application of sewer manure to agriculture, he believed, would do more than anything else to encourage the adoption of a better system of drainage and water supply and the universal introduction of the water-closet. And to the end of his life the productive powers of liquid sewage remained his "King Charles' Head," the fascination of a fortune from town guano drawing him back time and again to the idea of a Towns Improvement Company.

[1] "Notes on Agricultural Logic," MS., n.d.

CHAPTER VI

STRUGGLE WITH THE SPECULATORS

THE Queen's Speech at the opening of the 1845 session referred to the Health of Towns Report, and voiced the hope that it would form the basis of a measure for "promoting the Health and Comfort of the poorer Classes of My Subjects."[1] So, for the first time in history, a British Government announced that its legislative programme included a Public Health Bill. The period of inquiry, begun in 1838, was ended; and Chadwick's seven years of ceaseless investigation and argument had brought the Government to the point of action. The question remained whether that action would be as bold and as comprehensive as he had planned. He had wished—as the memoranda he had laid before Buccleuch show clearly—that the Commissioners would embody their recommendations in the actual clauses of a Bill, dictated by himself, and so strongly buttressed by the evidence and the authority of a Royal Commission that it must pass without substantial alteration by the legislature. The Government had other intentions, however, and a couple of months before the Health of Towns Commission presented their Second Report the preparation of a Public Health Bill was entrusted to the Earl of Lincoln, First Commissioner of Woods and Forests. The decision made two things plain: that the Government looked upon the Bill as the minor measure of a minor department, and that they felt themselves in no way bound by the conclusions of an inquiry dominated by Edwin Chadwick.

Lord Lincoln immediately turned his back on the Health of Towns Commission, and sought his authorities among the builders and architects of the Woods and Forests—whose "working men are entirely of the old school."[2] The success or failure of the

[1] *Hansard*, vol. lxxvii, p. 4, 4 February 1845.
[2] E. C. to Lyon Playfair, 14 December 1844.

Towns Improvement Company depended very largely upon the provisions of Lincoln's Bill; and it was the future of this, his "golden bridge for escape," which was Chadwick's chief anxiety throughout 1845. If the recommendations of the Commission were adopted, companies of the old style, with their separate water schemes and restrictive policies, would be handicapped, and facilities would be granted to a company prepared to carry out combined works by a contract under public regulation. As the 1845 session advanced his hopes rose that Lincoln might be persuaded to ignore the "prejudices of various pestilential interests,"[1] and give his backing to a well-drawn Bill; in which event the Towns Improvement Company might at once take the field, examining places and recruiting local capitalists, in readiness for a sweeping campaign on the collapse of the railway boom. Lincoln's Bill made a momentary appearance in July 1845, and was then withdrawn for consideration and amendment during the recess.[2] Another year's delay! And there was nothing to attract Chadwick's capitalists in Lincoln's proposal to establish elective boards in the localities, "which would hold out inducements only to the petty tradesmen of a country town, who alone will serve under the orders or humour the caprices of the other petty tradesmen of country towns."[3]

While Chadwick thus watched anxiously the delaying and possible crippling of his main measure, on the interments question he faced complete deadlock. Throughout 1845 Sir James Graham maintained an imperturbable front. When a newspaper report was brought to his attention, describing the practice in the Clerkenwell churchyard of disinterring bodies after a few days, chopping them with a spade, and burning the pieces in a bonehouse, he consented to make inquiries—but thought there would be some difficulty in removing the cause of the evil.[4] A week later he observed that he feared that to prohibit burial within the walls of a city "would not be in harmony with the feelings of a great body of the people."[5] Chadwick exploded into protest. Who were these people who were so attached to the practice?

[1] E. C. to Lord Ebrington, 25 June 1845.
[2] *Hansard*, vol. lxxxii, p. 1077, 25 July 1845.
[3] E. C. to R. A. Slaney, 8 July 1845.
[4] *Hansard*, vol. lxxvii, p. 1234, 26 February 1845.
[5] Ibid., vol. lxxviii, p. 325, 5 March 1845.

Was it the working classes, the poor, the uneasy, the heavily laden, who dwelt with complacency upon burial in the over-gorged charnels of the metropolis, where newly buried corpses were hacked and hewn by the sexton's shovel to make way for others? Was it the middle and higher classes, who were abandoning family vaults in the graveyards, preferring to pay heavily for interment in Kensal Green cemetery? Since it was clearly none of these, then who constituted this "great body?" A portion of the clergy! "Are we to endure to have it held up before this country and before all Europe that respect for the dead and the health of the living are to be prostrated for the maintenance of clerical domination, or rapacity for fees or for the lowest traders' pelf? . . . Is it to be allowed to go forth that the moral courage of our leading public men is so low, or their perceptions so obtuse, or their capacity so feeble that administrative measures which have been carried out in Austria, Prussia, Russia, Weimar, nay even in Spain, and are seen to elevate the feelings of the population are beyond the capacity of our parliament or our Government!"[1]

On 8 April 1845 W. A. Mackinnon challenged the Government with a resolution condemning intramural interment. Faced with an inescapable decision, Graham came out openly in support of the existing system. Waving aside the "exaggerated views entertained on the subject," he declared that it would not be easy to stop people being buried in the places where their kindred lay; if they adopted Chadwick's suggestion, and prohibited absolutely interments in towns, public feeling would be greatly excited, if not grossly violated. He refused to admit that the public health was endangered; there was no metropolis in the world where health was so well preserved. Were the Government to undertake the arrangements for burial, it would be intruding in a field where private companies were beginning to enter; so they should take care "lest, by a compulsory enactment, they interrupted that course of feeling, which, if left to itself, would remedy the evil." Graham was decisively beaten in the debate, and Mackinnon's resolution was carried by 66 votes to 49.[2] Chadwick, who judged that the vested interests in burial fees had prevailed with the Home Secretary, was delighted, but the victory brought no change in the attitude of the Government, now clearly resolved

[1] E. C., MS. fragment, n.d. [2] *Hansard*, vol. lxxix, pp. 330–59, 8 April 1845.

to belittle the nuisance because of the trouble they would be put to in applying a remedy.

The Corn Laws dominated the Parliamentary scene in 1846, and it was soon evident that until the manufacturer and the landlord had played out their parts in the drama of the session, the public health reformers must possess themselves in patience. But the year showed some notable advances, and the fact that not all of them originated directly with Chadwick proved that the "Sanitary Idea" was pushing out roots into many influential quarters. An Act was passed to authorise Town Councils to establish public baths and washhouses, defraying the cost out of the rates (9 & 10 Vict. c. 74). A Nuisances Removal Act (9 & 10 Vict. c. 96) empowered Boards of Guardians in the rural areas to indict nuisances before the Justices of the Peace, and, where the order for removal was met by recalcitrance or continued neglect, to take steps to execute it at the expense of the person responsible. Sanitary legislation thus made its first tentative step into the country districts; and for the narrow purposes of the Act the parish was replaced as the responsible authority by the Poor Law Union, with its superior efficiency, its paid medical staff, and its responsiveness to control and instruction from the centre. Another clause of the same Act authorised the Privy Council to issue emergency Orders if any place should be threatened by "formidable contagious or epidemic disease." This measure was, in fact, the first payment made by fear on an insurance policy against the cholera, which even then was advancing on the south-eastern frontiers of Europe.

To balance these small gains there was another check on the interments question, and a further delay in the introduction of a Public Health Bill. In April, W. A. Mackinnon brought in a Bill drafted by Chadwick on the conclusions of the Interments Report.[1] "Sir James Graham has become so unpopular," Chadwick wrote hopefully to the Bishop of London, "that it is more than probable that his opposition would contribute to the successs of Mr. Mackinnon, who will receive support from both sides of the house."[2] Graham unbent so far as to allow him to circulate privately amongst the Bishops the provisions of the Bill; but with the collapse of the Tory Government, it disappeared once

[1] *P.P.*, 1846, vol. i, p. 255.   [2] E. C. to Bishop Blomfield, 9 March 1846.

more from view. Not until the General Board of Health was installed at Gwydyr House did Chadwick get the opportunity to carry out his interments scheme.

Lord Lincoln's Bill reappeared, unchanged, at the beginning of the session,[1] and Chadwick promptly joined with Southwood Smith to draw up a detailed report on its provisions for publication by the London branch of the Health of Towns Association. This interesting pamphlet illuminates not only the defects of the Government measure, but also certain peculiar limitations in the view-point of the sanitary reformers themselves.[2] On the whole, the report conceded, the Bill was a great improvement on earlier attempts. It recognised the principle that the whole of the natural drainage area, and the public works therein, should be under a single authority. It protected the interests of the community by the supervision of an impartial Government Inspector; it provided for local surveys by competent engineers; it permitted local authorities to enter into contracts for the maintenance and execution of combined works, under the supervision of a paid surveyor; it stipulated that an inspector of nuisances and a medical officer of health should be appointed. All these things were new, and all were steps in the right direction. The tone changed sharply from satisfaction to criticism, however, when the report went on to consider the administrative machinery. This novel and complicated subject was to be entrusted to a man whose every moment of time was already in incessant demand from the vast and undifferentiated functions of an unwieldy department: the Home Secretary—Cabinet Minister and party leader, occupied with Irish affairs, the regulation of factories and prisons, the supervision of Poor Law Unions, the control of the magistracy and the Metropolitan Police. Even Sir James Graham, with his "athletic strength and powerful intellect," exhibited plain signs of overwork, and—Southwood Smith charitably suggested—the failure of measure after measure in his hands was due in large part to the inadequate attention he could afford to give them. The practical result must be to abandon public health to the chance zeal of a clerk or some other unknown and irresponsible sub-

---

[1] *P.P.*, 1845, vol. v, p. 363.

[2] *Report of the Committee to the Members of the Association, on Lord Lincoln's Bill*, 1846; written by Southwood Smith, in consultation with Chadwick.

ordinate. It would be far better to charge the duties on the Privy Council, who might delegate one or more of their number to give constant attention to sanitary questions; and where, the report omitted to add, Edwin Chadwick might secure in public health the key position that Kay-Shuttleworth now occupied in education. The reformers were no better pleased with the proposal to establish local Boards, which committed the cardinal error, illustrated time after time in the shady history of the Sewers Commissions, of making a numerous local authority an executive instead of a supervisory body. Responsibility for planning the public works should be concentrated on the local surveyor, a qualified civil engineer; the local Board, while empowered to determine the expediency and efficiency of the works, should not be allowed to interfere in technical matters on which they were incompetent to form a sound judgment. Moreover, they should be completely barred from executing the works by themselves. The merely permissive authority to enter into contracts should be made peremptory—and it was therefore regrettable that the Bill offered no facilities to induce joint stock companies to tender for contracts. Nor was this the only departure from the recommendations of the Health of Towns Commission. The Bill was limited to England and Wales, and London was omitted. The essential point had been missed that the loan for defraying the cost of local works should be spread over a period coincident with the benefit derived from them. There was no stipulation that water companies should furnish a constant supply of filtered water at high pressure; and phrases in the Bill clearly envisaged the continuance of the cesspool and the privy.

Great advance though the Bill was on Lord Normanby's measures of four years earlier, therefore, its provisions showed that the reformers had a long way yet to travel. It was soon clear, however, that there was no chance of the Bill passing into law in the 1846 session. Chadwick resigned himself to another twelve months' delay, until the new Whig Government should recast the measure bequeathed to them by Lord Lincoln. Perhaps, he consoled himself, the change of Government might justify a year's postponement. Lord Morpeth, who succeeded at the Woods and Forests, was certainly more amenable than Lord Lincoln, and no Home Secretary could be less sympathetic than Sir James

K

Graham. When Lord John Russell made an address to his constituents in July 1846, he announced his intention of taking up this grievously neglected field of legislation.[1] Chadwick was cheered; public opinion was advancing on sanitary questions, he felt, and they were being officially thought of at last.[2] Meanwhile the London and provincial branches of the Health of Towns Association passed their resolutions and circulated their leaflets; Southwood Smith and Dr. Holland wrote their articles; and Chadwick still dreamed and planned for the conquests of his joint stock company.

1846 is the year of the Andover Committee, and of Chadwick's final break with the Poor Law Commissioners, which will be described in the next chapter. The defence of his reputation against his official superiors was not the only heavy burden which the events of the session threw upon him. During the lull in the main battle for a Public Health Bill, he engaged in two brisk campaigns against the over-mighty capitalists of water and railways. For to Chadwick the self-government of capitalists was no better than the self-government of local authorities. He had great faith in self-interest. He commended it as the spring of individual vigour and efficiency; and it figured prominently in his thought as the most persistent and calculable element in human character. But he saw no evidence at all that social benefits resulted of necessity from its pursuit, and much which persuaded him that without the barriers erected by the law its undirected energies might disrupt society. He put his trust, therefore, not in the rule of some "invisible hand," blending the interests of the individual and society in a mystic reconciliation, but in the secular authority of the State which, abandoning the superstitions of *laissez faire*, should intervene to guide the activities of individuals towards the desirable goals of communal welfare. In this spirit he made a notable attempt to bridle the irresponsible power of the railway companies, which in this intoxicating boom year he saw thrusting recklessly forward with their plans at the cost of the moral and physical health of the great body of workers in their employment. He aired the scandals of railway gang-labour indicating how they could be removed by Government inspection

[1] E. C. to Dr. P. H. Holland, 4 July 1846.
[2] E. C. to J. Whitworth, 28 September 1846.

and the recognition of employers' liability for accidents, and forced a reluctant Government to set up a Committee of Inquiry. This is not the place to tell that now almost forgotten story,[1] but his contest with the water companies was fought on similar issues and illustrates the same point.

The publication in the previous year of the Second Report of the Health of Towns Commission, foreshadowing public control of water supplies in the not too distant future, had been followed by a sudden rush of water companies to seize the most eligible sources for the supply of towns. In this Chadwick saw a double danger. At the very moment when legislation was under consideration for combining water and drainage in every town, and for extending to all classes constant supplies of pure water, separate water companies on the old model, with their intermittent service and restrictive policies, were establishing themselves in positions of vantage; in some places, indeed, rival companies were being formed, threatening to develop a type of competition condemned by the Royal Commission only a few weeks before. Once established, such companies would be obstacles to the introduction of the new principles; they would be able to demand large compensation if they were disturbed; and Chadwick had no doubt that their promoters were, in fact, speculating on forcing the inhabitants to pay heavily when a Public Health Act had been adopted.[2] In the second place, these separate schemes endangered the Towns Improvement Company, his chosen instrument for the execution of sanitary works. Investors knew there were dividends in water, but they were not so easily persuaded of the profit to be derived from drainage; if, therefore, Chadwick's company were denied control of the water supply, it would lose the "commercial force, which is so salutary in overcoming the *vis inertiæ* of the towns themselves."[3]

Hence Chadwick condemned "this hurrying and grabbing of water sources,"[4] and instructed his friends that the Press should

---

[1] *Papers read before the Statistical Society of Manchester on . . . labourers engaged in the construction and working of railways*, 1846; *Report of the Select Committee on Railway Labourers, P.P.*, 1846, vol. xiii, p. 411; and my paper on "Edwin Chadwick and the Railway Labourers" in the *Economic History Review*, Second Series, vol. iii, No. 1, pp. 107–18, 1950.

[2] E. C. to R. Monckton Milnes, 23 February 1846.

[3] E. C. to Lord Francis Egerton, 2 April 1846.

[4] E. C. to Thomas Hawksley, 3 November 1845.

open fire at once on all separate water schemes, for "all those which gain ground will take it from us, from better measures."[1] Early in 1845 he had drawn up a set of conditions, and had urged on the Government that the promoters of Private Bills for water supply should be informed that they must insert them or lose their Bills.[2] These proposals, however, in which benefits to the consumer were nicely balanced against privileges to the company, had proved too strong for the Government to accept. The only result of his representations was the insertion into some Bills of a clause subjecting the promoters to any general regulations that might later be approved; and this, as he complained, was too feeble a safeguard to deter the speculators. Failing to secure allies among the Tory Ministers, he declared a private war against the water companies in the summer of 1845, employing Thomas Hawksley, the Nottingham engineer, as his champion before the Select Committees. A few incidents of this obscure struggle may be pieced together from the fugitive notes and memoranda he directed to his friends on the Committees, and to supporters who were conducting parallel campaigns in the localities. There was a keen contest over the Manchester Waterworks Bill, which proposed to raise £600,000 for extension of plant which Hawksley calculated could be laid down de novo for £250,000. The company put forward James Simpson, a London engineer of the old school, as their expert to testify that a constant and universal supply would cost them another £100,000. Hawksley in rebuttal stated that if the Manchester company was not prepared to give a constant supply of filtered water at a penny a week to labouring-class tenements, the Towns Improvement Company would; and he went on to combat the company's assertion that filtration was unnecessary, and their demand that they should be paid extra for the supply to water-closets.[3] Chadwick appeared in person to protest against a Bill promoted by the Sheffield Waterworks Company for leave to raise fresh capital, twice as much as he estimated the company should require to give a superior supply— and he had the unusual humiliation of being routed by James

[1] E. C. to Dr. P. H. Holland, 1 November 1845.

[2] "Health of Towns. Points for consideration in respect to Contracts for the execution and maintenance of Works of Water Supply, Drainage and Cleansing by Companies, under Private, Local, or General Acts," MS., n.d.

[3] E. C. to Dr. P. H. Holland, 29 May 1845.

Simpson.[1] But he and Hawksley scored one notable success. The enlightened provisions of the Nottingham Inclosure Act[2] owed much to their strenuous intervention, in the teeth of bitter opposition from the Corporation. The truth was, Chadwick heard from Hawksley, the Corporation was in fear of the "Cowocracy," the Freeman's Rights Committee, "an interest I am sorry to say of the most ignorant corrupt and degraded kind— an interest which has been the curse of Nottingham as respects its Social Sanatory and Commercial prosperity for many years past."[3] The contention of the Nottingham Councillors, despite the statistics, that Nottingham was the healthiest of all the large towns, their corruption (Hawksley told him that since 1800 a quarter of a million had been spent in direct bribery in the city),[4] and their resistance to the proposal to replace cesspools by water-closets— all confirmed Chadwick in his view that the defence of the public health could not safely be entrusted to municipal authorities.

In 1846 forty-five drainage and waterworks Bills were introduced, twice the number for a normal year. Two rival companies were racing to secure water sources for Bristol, both of which the engineers of the Towns Improvement Company had examined and rejected as too hard. For Manchester, Liverpool, and Edinburgh also there were two competing water Bills.[5] While the Health of Towns Association debated with Lord Lincoln, and the Government moved slow-footed in the direction of control, the speculators were strengthening their grip on the necessities of the public. At this critical moment Chadwick lost his champion. Hawksley was seduced from the cause by an offer from the Lancashire Waterworks Company, one of the companies whose principles he had been engaged in attacking. Chadwick regarded his defection as an act of treachery, personal communication between the two men broke off completely, and Hawksley was to be reckoned a few years later amongst the bitterest enemies of the General Board of Health. To fill his place Chadwick chose Joseph Hume, the leading Radical advocate of retrenchment,

[1] E. C. to Thomas Hawksley, 18 July 1845; to J. Parker, 1 June 1845.
[2] 8 & 9 Vict. c. 7 (Private).
[3] Thomas Hawksley to E. C., 9 February 1845.
[4] Thomas Hawksley to E.C., 22 September 1844.
[5] "Memoranda on the mode of passing local acts," MS. fragment, n.d., c. April 1846.

whose voice had recently been raised against the exorbitant fees
charged by Parliamentary agents for the drafting of Private Bills.
On 7 April Hume moved, in the terms of a resolution which
Chadwick had put into his hands,[1] for a Select Committee to
examine how far the principles of the Health of Towns Commission could be carried out in the Bills now before the House for
the erection of new waterworks and the execution of drainage,
paving, and other improvements.

Against this background of Chadwick's attempts to check the
speculators in water supplies, the full significance of the Private
Bill Committee of 1846 can now be seen. Chadwick had changed
the direction of his attack. To fight the speculators in detail, to
contest each separate Bill in turn, was too wasteful of energy and
too uncertain in result. He determined, therefore, to cut at the
root of the evil—the method by which Parliament conferred
privileges on sectional interests in matters which affected the
community as a whole. The witnesses before Hume's Committee
were marshalled by Chadwick, and some were briefed by him; he
cast himself for the chief part, however, and in his evidence replied
to questions which he had earlier suggested to Hume. Before the
Committee, and even more forcibly in a series of private memoranda intended, it would appear, for Hume's information, he
subjected the whole system of Private Bill legislation to a searching
criticism. Under the forms of a legal conflict between private
interests, questions of vital public concern, affecting the health and
cleanliness of the community, its law and police, trade and communications, were now debated and decided. A glance over a
Private Bill would soon reveal by whom it was drawn, and for
whose benefit. A Waterworks Bill, for example, would contain
summary and stringent remedies for the company against the
consumer, but no similar remedies for the consumer against the
company; a tenant whose supply was defective in quantity or
quality must pay nevertheless or have his supply cut off altogether.
A local improvement Bill, vesting the property in the dust or night-
soil in the scavenger, would provide penalties against any person
who should remove it, but no corresponding penalties against the

[1] "Memoranda on the modes of passing local acts," MS., n.d. The paper
ends in the actual words of Hume's motion, and was probably drawn up for his
instruction.

scavenger who neglected his duty, though much suffering and offensiveness might result from that neglect.[1] This exaltation of sectional interests above those of the general public was the natural consequence of the procedure by which the Private Bill Committees collected their evidence. Interested parties, wealthy enough to fee professional advocates and send witnesses to London, were powerfully represented before the Committees; but the inhabitants at large, and especially the labouring classes, were usually unable to obtain a hearing, and in any event they lacked funds to make the investigations on which an informed opposition could be based. As Chadwick was arguing in the parallel campaign on which he was then engaged, Hudson and his lawyers were heard, but not the railway labourers. The truth was that the Committees lacked both the time to give a full examination of the facts, and the technical knowledge to reach a sound judgment; and they grounded their conclusions upon the opinions of the professional experts who came before them. In consequence, Chadwick alleged, "a most pernicious system of trading in professional evidence" had developed. "Men of science receive retainers: and the past experience will shew give evidence according to the retainers on one side or the other as may serve with the interests of the party retaining them. . . . The imputation on lawyers of the indiscriminate defence of right or wrong by the indiscriminate use of truth and falsehood, admits of palliation, if not of defence. All the world knows upon what conditions the lawyer speaks: that what he gives as facts are the facts of his client: the advocate's cited cases and not his assertions are relied upon. But the science of the scientific man is taken to be his own science and not the science of his client, made up for the cause."[2] Committees on water Bills, for instance, could not be expected to be conversant with hydraulics; hence while one Committee listened to Chadwick's experts and declared in favour of constant supply, another leaned to the engineers of the London companies and pronounced it to be impracticable.

The object then must be to remove these important decisions from the atmosphere of partiality and ignorance which now surrounded them. The method Chadwick had already indicated in

[1] "Local Acts. How and for whom composed," MS., n.d.
[2] MS., n.d., on Private Bills.

the reports of the Health of Towns Commission. A preliminary inquiry must be made on the spot by a competent officer, unconnected with the locality and deputed by a department of State—a known and responsible informant, instead of the unknown and irresponsible persons who were at present professionally retained to give "opinion evidence" before Committees. He would hear parties who were not now heard; and those who were now heard would be heard more conveniently, and at greatly reduced expense.[1] "The facts and information are paramount: and those can only be obtained quickly, completely, economically, and satisfactorily *in situ*."[2] For sanitary reform the factor of expense was of the first importance. The town of St. Helens, when it planned waterworks costing £3,000, had to spend another £1,000 in obtaining Parliamentary permission to erect them. In many villages and small towns the legal and Parliamentary costs of a drainage scheme would equal the expense of laying down the house drains; and the costs for a water Bill would equal the outlay for the tenants' water pipes.[3]

Though Chadwick's criticisms of the water Bills were toned down, and he failed in his attempt to halt them completely, his hand is evident throughout the Committee's report.[4] The great mass of the so-called Private Bills, they declared, were essentially public in character, yet the public were not represented before the Committees by any competent or qualified person. They recommended, therefore, that in future, where only ordinary powers were sought, means should be made available for executing projects under the authority and supervision of a Government department, without the necessity of applying to Parliament. With this object, Public General Acts should be passed for all classes of Private Bills, except those which, like Divorce and Estate Bills, were personal in their nature. The procedure under such Public General Acts should be on the lines indicated by Chadwick:

---

[1] "Mr. Chadwick's Suggestions relative to Private Bills. Previous Examination," MS., 18 May 1846.

[2] "Local Acts. How and for whom composed," MS., n.d.

[3] *Report of Select Committee on Local Acts*, *P.P.*, 1846, vol. xii, p. 1; Q. 337.

[4] One of Chadwick's memoranda, "Local Acts. Considerations in respect of expenses and means of reducing them," is drafted in the form of a Report from the Committee. The Report actually presented contains many of the same points, put more succinctly, and phrased less strongly.

a memorial from the promoters to the department concerned, a local inquiry conducted by an inspector sent down by the department, a written report from the inspector to the department, which would then decide whether or not to grant the required authority. If it appeared likely, however, that private property would be seriously interfered with, the parties should be left to the ordinary mode of proceeding by application to Parliament; with this important difference—there should be a preliminary investigation on the spot by a Government inspector, so diminishing the great expense for the attendance of agents and witnesses in London, saving the time of Members now consumed in Committees on Private Bills, and furnishing those Committees with the local and trustworthy information which was now wanting. Finally, the report advised, to obviate the evils resulting from lack of uniformity in the construction of Private Bills, a series of Clauses Consolidation Acts should be passed, covering police, waterworks and sewage, towns improvements, and the other main subjects for which powers were usually sought.

Three weeks after its appearance the Report bore its first fruit in a Preliminary Inquiries Act (9 & 10 Vict., c. 106). This provided that the promoters of certain classes of Local Acts— for establishing waterworks, for draining, paving, lighting, cleansing, or otherwise improving any town, district, or place, or for making, maintaining, or altering a burial ground—should notify the Commissioners of Woods and Forests, who would then send a surveying officer to make a local survey, examine the promoters and their plans, and hear the evidence of local officials and other witnesses. In this way, mainly through Chadwick's efforts, another wide province of administration was brought under the jurisdiction of the Government Inspector. The experiment, as it happened, was disappointing, and the Preliminary Inquiries Act was repealed in 1850 as an acknowledged failure[1]—not, Chadwick believed, because of any defect in its basic conception, but because of the manner in which it was carried out by the Woods and Forests.

In the following year a further recommendation of the Com-

---

[1] See F. Clifford, *History of Private Bill Legislation* (1885–7), vol ii, pp. 890–7; O. C. Williams, *Historical Development of Private Bill Procedure and Standing Orders in the House of Commons* (1948), vol. i, pp. 115–17.

mittee was acted upon, and a batch of eight Clauses Consolidation Acts passed into law.[1] In Chadwick's eyes these were of far less importance than the local inquiry. "It appears to me that you have laid too much stress on model Bills," he told Hume. "We must carefully distinguish between mere legislative style and form, which there is no great difficulty in improving, and the matter which can only be improved by laborious investigations of particular subjects in different localities, to which mere lawyers accustomed to deal with evidence brought before them are most unapt."[2] But there was, in fact, something more than "mere legislative style and form" in the Clauses Acts of 1847, and in their choice of models they bear witness to the influence of the public health reformers. Thus, the Towns Improvement Clauses Act obliged the Commissioners to appoint a qualified surveyor and an inspector of nuisances; it prohibited the building of any house without adequate drainage; it permitted the Commissioners to appoint an officer of health; it permitted them to contract for a supply of water, and to construct house drains, charging the cost on the owner. The Waterworks Clauses Act limited the profits of the company to ten per cent; it imposed penalties on the company which neglected to comply with a legitimate demand for a supply to be laid on; it obliged the company to furnish water for such public services as cleansing the sewers, watering the streets, and supplying baths and wash-houses; and it required the undertakers to provide a constant supply of wholesome water under pressure, sufficient for the domestic use of all the inhabitants. By the Model Acts, therefore, a little was done to clip the independence of the water capitalists, to raise the technical standard of local works, to widen the obligatory functions of local authorities, and to put still wider powers within their reach if they should choose to take advantage of the offer.

[1] Markets and Fairs Clauses Act, Gasworks Clauses Act, Commissioners Clauses Act, Waterworks Clauses Act, Harbours, Docks, and Piers Clauses Act, Towns Improvement Clauses Act, Cemeteries Clauses Act, Town Police Clauses Act; 10 & 11 Vict., cc. 14, 15, 16, 17, 27, 34, 65, and 89.

[2] E. C. to J. Hume, 12 April 1846.

CHAPTER VII

RETREAT FROM SOMERSET HOUSE

In 1845 the "disgustingly voracious habits"[1] of two paupers in the Andover Workhouse, who attempted to supplement the meagre bread ration by scrapings from the green bones they were employed in crushing, led to a violent outcry in the Press. The Poor Law Commissioners ordered an investigation by Parker, one of the Assistant Commissioners, and seized an early opportunity to dismiss him and make him a scapegoat for public dissatisfaction. This action brought to the surface all the submerged antipathies in that unhappy office. Rallying to his standard all the Poor Law malcontents—Parker, Day, Coode, Tufnell—Chadwick led an attack on the opinions and business methods of his chiefs; and the Select Committee appointed in July 1846 to investigate the Andover scandals found that an inquiry into bone-crushing and the morals of workhouse masters had widened into a discussion of the whole constitution and working of the Poor Law Commission.

In the course of his nine examinations before the Committee, Chadwick skilfully planted one barb after another in the flanks of the Commissioners. The scepticism they had openly avowed for the fundamental principles of the Act it was their duty to execute; their displeasure when abuses were brought to their attention which would require action on their part; their conduct of business by conversations at casual meetings, by private letters from single Commissioners, by unrecorded transactions in their separate offices; their toleration of the allowance system; their attempt to revive the labour rate; their suppression of the Bolton and Macclesfield report—all the accusations which had been fermenting in his mind for the past twelve years boiled over before the Committee. The Commissioners, backed by the Poor Law critics on the Committee, retorted in kind. An attempt was made to

[1] G. Nicholls, op. cit., vol. ii, p. 394.

fix on Chadwick the full responsibility for the inadequate dietary scale in use at Andover and for other rigorous and unpopular measures, such as the order which disallowed fees for tolling church bells at a pauper funeral. "Well, then, if you will have it you must," cried Frankland Lewis, "Mr. Chadwick was an able man, but I thought him as unscrupulous and as dangerous an officer as I ever saw within the walls of an office."[1] It was the petulant rage of a little man; but it served to add one more touch to the picture of Chadwick as a kind of Poor Law Inquisitor, Disraeli's "monster in human shape," brooding in the recesses of Somerset House over fresh plans for separating old men from their wives, spaying the daughters of the poor, and slowly starving paupers to death on a diet of bread and gruel. Chadwick, it would appear, immediately challenged Frankland Lewis after this wild outburst, and received sufficient amends for the two to part with a friendly handshake. The Commissioners could not really have it both ways: if they kept the business firmly in their hands, as Frankland Lewis claimed, allowing their officers to make no suggestions, then Chadwick could hardly be held responsible for the harshness of Poor Law administration. Indeed, as Chadwick pointed out, of all the papers attacked in the House of Commons only one was by him; he had therefore complained to George Lewis how unjust it was that all the unpopularity fell upon himself—to which Lewis had replied that he would get no redress if he applied for it.[2]

[1] Report of Select Committee on the Andover Union; *P.P.*, 1846, vol. v, p. 1118. He made it clear later that he did not intend "unscrupulous" as a general stricture on Chadwick's conduct, but only as a description of his actions with reference to two documents, one being the Instructions to overseers and churchwardens in March 1836, which contained the disallowance of fees for tolling at pauper funerals. Of this document the Hammonds write: "Chadwick trod on this universal sentiment as if all life had gone from it." (*Age of the Chartists*, p. 75). There seems no reason to doubt Chadwick's statement, however, that the regulation was inserted by Coode into his draft; and that he had urged the Commissioners to obtain statutory authorisation for this and other charges (p. 1281). On plain issues of fact, such as dates and the report of evidence, he was as punctilious as his legal training could make him—and this remains true, even if it be admitted that at times he also showed the lawyer's skill of advocacy in his manipulation of those same facts.

[2] Ibid., pp. 935–6. Echoing the Parliamentary critics, historians have in general much exaggerated his power to influence the course of Poor Law administration. Thus, it has been asserted that "the history of the Poor Law between 1834 and 1847 is the history of an experiment in centralised adminis-

The report of the Committee was a severe condemnation of the Commissioners' part in the Andover affair. Chadwick read it with a triumph he made no attempt to conceal. He had been the principal actor before the Committee, he reflected, and had repulsed all his assailants in turn; and yet he had brought up none of his reserves, "which are heavier than my adversaries or the public suppose."[1] His momentary elation soon gave way, however, to dark conjecture about the future of the Poor Law Act —and the future of its author—when the Bill for the continuance of the Commission came under discussion in the following session. *The Times*, he noted, was taking the line that the fault lay not with the Commissioners but with the law, which it was impossible for anybody to execute.[2] Nor, looking more closely at the printed evidence of the Andover inquiry, was he satisfied that it conveyed the right impression. If it blackened the reputation of the Lewises, the character and opinions of Edwin Chadwick did not shine forth in contrast so brightly as he had hoped. But Sir George Grey, the Whig Home Secretary, remained deaf to his pleas that he should be permitted to make a full public statement in self-vindication.[3] His fears increased. Was not George Lewis married to Lady Teresa Lister, one of the Villierses, sister of Lord Clarendon and sister-in-law of Lord John Russell, "a lady who invites Senior to the most fashionable parties"?[4] "In such a country as this, with a position to maintain amongst public men of aristocratical connexions, it is not easy to contend without pecuniary resources to fall back upon," he confided to an American cousin. "And my family drains and various pecuniary losses other than the American have given me more anxiety than the conflict itself. The Government have to decide upon the case, but my chief opponent is the brother-in-law of Lord John Russell, and

---

tration, and of what that experiment produced in the hard and energetic hands of Chadwick, checked from time to time by wiser colleagues" (J. L. and B. Hammond, *Age of the Chartists*, p. 60). It seems sufficient to comment that this gives a totally unfounded impression that the "experiment" was under his control; that the "colleagues" were, in fact, his superiors; and that they may be acclaimed as "wiser" than he only if their sceptical attitude to his preventive policies is discounted.

[1] E. C. to Sir Charles Shaw, 4 September 1846.
[2] E. C. to the Earl of Liverpool, 24 August 1846.
[3] E. C. to Sir George Grey, 17 January 1847.
[4] E. C. to W. E. Hickson, n.d.

Lord Clarendon, two Cabinet Ministers and two others. Lord John Russell I have cause most to distrust because he has dealt unjustly towards me, and to condemn the Commissioners will be to condemn the arrangements to which he was a principal party. The public however are I believe with me."[1]

Relations at Somerset House were now extremely strained, with Chadwick muttering in his office and the Commissioners caballing against him with the Whigs. A chance encounter in the street with Frankland Lewis led to a scene as violent as that before the Andover Committee; and one, moreover, which did not end in a handshake.[2] Russell and Clarendon, he was told, had a majority with them in the Cabinet determined to uphold the Commissioners against the report of the Andover Committee;[3] and "Lady Teresa was in good spirits."[4] "If I am not put down," he reflected bitterly, "three carriages must be put down which have been kept up on my labours whilst I have walked."[5] It was, he felt, quite another Rowland Hill case— but Edwin Chadwick had had three Colonel Maberlys to deal with.[6] His fears seemed justified when, in the debates on the Poor Law Amendment Bill in June 1847, Lord John Russell came out strongly in support of "the Lewis interest," piling all the discredit which attached to that unpopular measure upon the shoulders of their intriguing Secretary. Vainly Chadwick tried to awaken in his Parliamentary friends a sense of their responsibility towards himself and the reformed Poor Law. They retained an adamant and cheerful confidence that right views would prevail and justice would be done to him without any necessity for putting themselves out to assist that desirable end. "This Government is renowned for its facility in abandoning all measures and all men," Brougham agreed heartily.[7] "You may see that D'Israeli bantered Lord John about you, but it was all done in a good-humoured jocose tone, and can do you no harm," Poulett Scrope reassured him.[8] Pleydell Bouverie would have pointed out to Russell the absurdity of blaming Chadwick for irregularities over which as Secretary he had no control—if only he had thought of it at the

[1] E. C. to Andrew Boardman, 3 October 1846.
[2] E. C. to W. D. Christie, n.d.   [3] E. C. to E. Gulson, n.d.
[4] E. C. to W. D. Christie, 7 February 1847.
[5] E.C. to W. E. Hickson, n.d.   [6] E. C. to W. E. Hickson, n.d.
[7] Lord Brougham to E. C., n.d.   [8] J. Poulett Scrope to E. C., n.d.

time.[1] George Nicholls wrote a testimonial to his exemplary conduct during the fourteen years they had worked together, and when it was read in the Commons several other gentlemen were moved to add a word or two of approbation.[2]

All this was highly gratifying, but the Lewis interest remained firmly entrenched, and the Government seemed in no haste to make a public profession of error. In a truculent mood Chadwick began to draw up his Grand Remonstrance. The "Letter of Edwin Chadwick Esq. in vindication of his conduct to the Right Honourable Sir George Grey" (21 June 1847) was a wordy, argumentative, and execrably written paper, with seven appendices, and a mass of facts carefully verified by the evidence of the Assistant Commissioners. It recited the history of his protests against the Commissioners, and outlined the course of preventive administration which he had designed and they had done their best to frustrate. He backed up his own case with a long and lively letter from a former Assistant Commissioner, E. C. Tufnell, who confirmed the correctness of the impression Chadwick had given to the Andover Committee. Chadwick's friends—among them the Bishop of London, the Duke of Richmond, Lord Liverpool, Lord Fortescue, Lord Lansdowne, Lord Ellenborough, Lord Radnor—read the draft of his paper; they read Tufnell's corroborative evidence; they assured him that he had an excellent case—but no two of them were agreed as to the steps he should take to obtain redress. "Such a letter ought to satisfy any *statesman* of his good fortune in having the writer of it at his disposal," said J. S. Mill, "—but whether any of these men have sufficient brains to appreciate brains in another, remains questionable."[3] It was now quite clear, in fact, that the jury had pronounced its verdict, though it was in cool defiance of the judge's summing-up. The Government had made up its mind, and decided on its course, and no representations, however authentic, could change its attitude. The debates on the Poor Law Bill had closed without any retraction of the slurs on Chadwick's motives and conduct, and that "mass of error and delusion," Frankland Lewis, was still disseminating the statements which he thought he had

[1] E. Pleydell Bouverie to E.C., 23 May 1847.
[2] G. Nicholls to E. C., 27 May 1847.
[3] J. S. Mill to E. C., n.d.

refuted once and for all before the Andover Committee.[1] Whoever was to form the reconstructed Poor Law Board, it seemed that Edwin Chadwick was not to be of their number, though a friendly Peer might wonder "who upon earth is to rule at Somerset House to be St. Sebastian (who was martyred by being shot at with Pagan arrows) in each house of Parliament?"[2] To Lord Ellenborough he wrote bitterly, "As the bill at present stands it might be intituled 'An Act to enable the Government to dismiss without reasons assigned, those who otherwise cannot be removed without justification or compensation.' "[3] A few days before the Health of Towns Bill, his lifeboat, had foundered in the Commons, as will be described below. The future looked black that July.

It was time, he felt, to unmask his batteries. Hitherto his "Vindication" had circulated only amongst his personal friends, but now he began to prepare it for publication. He even contemplated legal action against his former chiefs, and drew up "Heads of Representations or Articles of Charge against George Cornewall Lewis Esquire and Sir Edmund Head Baronet for acts of Malfeasance of Nonfeasance and Misfeasance in the performance of the duties of their office as Commissioners under the 4th and 5th Will. IV. c. 76 and other Acts for the relief of the poor." But now he ran into difficulties. E. C. Tufnell declined the honour of appearing as a leading witness in any public scandal, and imposed a ban on the publication of his letter. He was too late, however, to prevent Lord Brougham reading extracts from it in the House of Lords. There was an immediate outcry that this was a breach of official confidence. "Can any one help deep disgust," wrote Chadwick to Brougham, "that there should be no feeling of concern, for immense maladministration affecting large masses, positive breaches of law and disastrous misconduct, which ought to have been the subject of judicial inquiry and impeachment, and no feeling for the sacrifice of an able officer like Mr. Parker, but affected horror at an accidental revelation of one part of the misconduct, by the removal of a barrier of privacy or confidentiality which is a misprision and public offence ever to have imposed. The official confidentiality and honour I have only found to come

---

[1] E. C. to Lord ?, n.d.   [2] Lord Lovelace to E. C., 2 October 1847.
[3] E. C. to Lord Ellenborough, 12 July 1847.

within Dean Swift's simile of conscience as being like a pair of breeches, a garment made to conceal lewdness and nastiness and readily let down for the convenience of either."[1]

A truculent civil servant, with a grievance, the makings of a case, and a following in Parliament and the country, could not have been too pleasant a thought for the Whig Government. He would be a nuisance and a bore, if he were not a danger. So it was timely in more than one sense when the Prime Minister decided that Chadwick might profitably occupy himself with an inquiry into the sanitary condition of London. To the reasons for that inquiry, and to Chadwick's other activities in 1847, we must now turn.

Chadwick's great hope at the beginning of the 1847 session was that his ten years of inquiry and recommendation would at last bear legislative fruit. But the Public Health Bill which Lord Morpeth introduced on 30 March[2] was not Chadwick's Bill, though it displayed extensive evidence of the influence of his reports and memoranda and of the criticism which the sanitary reformers had directed at Lord Lincoln's abortive measure. It was understood—though by no means was it promised by the Government—that he would be offered a place in the new administrative arrangements; and it was mainly with an eye to his own freedom and power of action that he looked over the clauses of Morpeth's Bill. The central authority was to be a "Board of Health and Public Works," composed of five members, three of whom would be paid, with the First Commissioner of Woods and Forests as president. Thus, Lord Lincoln's proposal to bring the public health under the ægis of the Home Secretary was abandoned in favour of machinery modelled on the recently established Railway Board. The lesson of the discredited Poor Law Commission had not yet been digested; the new Board would have a Parliamentary spokesman (even two, as the other unpaid member might well be a Member of Parliament), but the First Commissioner of Woods and Forests, though sitting as president, was in no sense a ministerial head, since he shouldered no more reponsibility for policy than any other member of the Board. The weakness and inadequacy of this arrangement were to be sharply revealed when the General Board of Health came later under the

[1] E. C. to Lord Brougham, 13 July 1847. [2] *Hansard*, vol. xci, p. 617.

L

presidency of Lord Seymour. It meant, moreover, the end of Chadwick's visions of himself working the Public Health Act as standing counsel or secretary to a committee of the Privy Council, and with considerable misgivings he looked forward to a Board on which he might find himself in the company of uncongenial fellows. In the local machinery, too, the Bill turned its back on Chadwick's recommendations. In corporate towns the town council would exercise sanitary powers; in non-corporate towns the members of the local authority would be elected by the rate-payers, with the exception of a certain proportion, not to exceed one-third, who would be nominated by the central Board. On the financial arrangements, however, his arguments had had more effect. "There is something in the very sound of 'rates,'" Morpeth declared, "which weighs fearfully in the balance against health, industry, content, and all the virtues." As Chadwick had urged, the burden would be eased and the ratepayers' alarm allayed by granting powers to local authorities to raise loans on the security of the rates, the principal to be recovered from occupiers by instalments spread over thirty years.

The measure was pushed through its Second Reading and the motion for Committee by comfortable Government majorities; and then the critics took command of the field. It was a very vulnerable Bill. Opponents could bang away with the cheering certainty of doing damage to one or other of its rambling outworks. Presently Morpeth found himself engaged in a brisk contest over every clause, occasionally rising to a more extended struggle on the broader ground of general principles, such as the inalienable rights of every middle-class Englishman and the tendency of all Governments to job. From the first the Bill was "the object of singular Protectionist aversion,"[1] and in Committee spokesmen of the landowners strongly opposed a measure which might burden them with taxation for municipal improvements.[2] "The country was sick of centralisation, of commissions, of preliminary inquiries —of all sorts of jobs," cried Hudson, the Railway King. "The people wanted to be left to manage their own affairs; they did not want Parliament to be so paternal as it wished to be—interfering in everybody's business, and, like all who so interfered, not doing

---

[1] *Times*, 3 July 1847.
[2] *Hansard*, vol. xciii, p. 716 (Divett), p. 717 (Buck), p. 728 (Newdegate).

its own well."[1] It was the crude "Hands off!" of the self-sufficient capitalist; and it was strengthened by an older argument from the eighteenth century when Colonel Sibthorp exclaimed against the appointment of Commissioners under Government patronage. "He objected also to their being salaried, entertaining a strong feeling that if they had not patriotism enough to give their services for the good of their country, they were utterly unworthy of so important a trust. He objected also to the appointment of three inspectors. These things led to a great deal of bribery of a peculiar kind; and he had served long enough in that House to be extremely jealous of all Governments, whether Whig or Tory. They all could, and did, do a great deal behind the scenes; and there was a great deal of secret service money spent."[2]

In the country at large the Bill caused little noise. Thirty-two thousand signed petitions in its support, and 287 sent resolutions against it; but apart from this minority the public did not seem greatly concerned about the defence of its own health. Chadwick sent some notes on the Bill by Southwood Smith to a friendly editor, with the tart comment "Admitting the justice of the Rajah of Suttara's claim and of the Portuguese and of delinquents, I must say that the condition of the population would seem to have a right of precedence."[3] In the hope of getting the measure through before the end of the session, the Metropolitan Sanitary Association urged Morpeth to make concessions. London was dropped from the Bill; the element of nomination in the local Commissions also disappeared; it was agreed, to pacify the water interests, that local authorities should contract for their supplies with existing companies. The number of Commissioners on the central Board was cut to four, of whom one only was to be paid. But by 8 July it was clear that Morpeth's concessions had not gained their object of securing an easy passage for the Bill. Whatever had been gained in postponing the clash with metropolitan interests was lost in the feeling which the exception aroused in the Press and the provincial representatives, who saw in it one more instance of the influence of the City Corporation and the phalanx of sixteen metropolitan M.P.s. Nobody was greatly surprised when Lord John Russell announced that the measure could

---

[1] *Hansard*, vol. xciii, p. 748, 18 June 1847.   [2] Ibid., p. 727, 18 June 1847.
[3] E. C. to ? (probably *The Times*), 7 July 1847.

not be proceeded with during the present session; and nobody could disagree with his verdict that this was partly due to the importance of the subject, partly to the defective framing of the Bill—but "another cause may be, that unnecessary opposition has been made for the purpose of delay."[1]

One point above all had impressed Chadwick as he read the Bill after it had passed the Committee stage. Only one paid Commissioner, and that one at £1,000 a year! Was this the value the Government set upon the execution of the new measure? Even the extreme Radical papers, such as the *Weekly Dispatch*, scoffed at the cry of patronage in this connection.[2] It would have been worth several salaries to have secured the services of South-wood Smith, with his literary skill, his special knowledge of the medical aspects of the subject, and his popularity with the Press and the medical profession.[3] If he himself accepted the post, he must sacrifice £200 a year of his present salary—though three members of the Government, to induce him to withhold his remonstrances about the Poor Law, had assured him that his future position would be a change for the better. "Look at my present position!" he wrote heatedly to Nassau Senior. "After every appeal of mine has been affirmed: every remonstrance made sustained against adverse inclinations: I who have had no charges preferred against me, no hearing and no public condemnation by impartial members, *I* am proposed to be in effect removed arbitrarily to a lower place in emolument which all who believe myself to be contemplated regard as a public and intentional slight." And he could draw no comfort from the hope that the position offered would improve in time. Had he not been told, on the word of a Prime Minister and a gentleman, as the condition on which he accepted the office of secretary to the Poor Law Commission, that he would have the status of a fourth Commissioner? He would decline the paid Commissionership with its derogatory salary, he told Senior, but he would put in a claim for an unpaid seat at the new Board, where he would continue to give such gratuitous service as he had all along given to sanitary measures. At the same time he would claim to be retained at the

---

[1] *Hansard*, vol. xciv, p. 25, 8 July 1847.
[2] E. C. to Joseph Hume, 5 July 1847.
[3] E. C. to Nassau Senior, 7 July 1847.

Poor Law Board, on the grounds that his remonstrances had been upheld by the Government and the Law Officers, and that his were the best experience and information available.[1] Chadwick liked to think that the way he had managed the two Bills, the Poor Law and the Health of Towns, did Russell some damage in his constituency, the City of London, in the 1847 election. Even Richard Lambert Jones, an old adversary on the City Commission of Sewers, stopped him in the street one day to tell him that the Corporation considered he was being sacrificed for having performed his duty to the public.[2]

On 8 July the Public Health Bill was thrown out, and Chadwick with it. Somerset House had closed its doors behind him. He faced a period of twelve lean months before Morpeth's revised Bill could become law. Already he had warned his American dependants that they could expect no help in the coming year, when he was summoned to an interview with the Prime Minister. He was to be put in charge of a Commission of Inquiry, Russell told him, not into the sanitary ills of the capital, which had been sufficiently demonstrated, but into the specific remedies which might be applied to correct them. Possibly the thought of Chadwick, with his indiscreet pen, at a loose end for twelve months was too much for a Cabinet whose part in the Andover affair could not be too kindly scrutinised. But in any event the problem of metropolitan government, at the sight of which Morpeth had "struck his flag and cut his stick,"[3] loomed blackly on the legislative horizon of the coming session; and Chadwick, with his zest for investigation and his unrivalled grasp of sanitary and administrative principles, was the only man who, in the space of a few months, could draw up the indictment of the present régime and indicate the lines of future reform.

But there was a more powerful reason. In the last few months the knowledge of the sanitary reformer had taken on a heightened value. In the hot season of 1845 cholera had broken out in Kabul. Sweeping through Afghanistan and the north-west provinces of India, it advanced into Persia and Asiatic Turkey, where it was halted by the winter of 1846–7. In the spring it was again on the

[1] E. C. to Nassau Senior, 7 July 1847.
[2] E. C. to Lord Ebrington, 20 July 1847.
[3] Roebuck; *Hansard*, vol. xciii, p. 732, 18 June 1847.

march, striking south into Arabia and Egypt, north into the lands round the Caspian. The northern invasion divided, one wing thrusting through European Russia into Finland and Sweden, the other along the lower Danube into Austria and Germany. In September 1848 the cholera was at Hamburg, whence it took ship to Edinburgh, appearing unmistakably in the Scottish capital at the beginning of October 1848. More than twelve months before that date cases of indigenous fever were being scrutinised anxiously in England for the characteristic symptoms of this exotic disease. What put a wholesome fear of filth into the governing classes was the spectacle of the unhastening, unchecked advance of this epidemic, traversing thousands of miles at the heels of the overland caravans and spreading westwards along the great interior waterways of Russia. For this was the second time in one generation that cholera had swept through Europe; and not since the English Sweat landed with Henry Tudor at Milford Haven in August 1485 and, as Polydore Vergil describes, journeyed to London as his camp follower, had Britain experienced so novel and so terrifying an epidemic as the Asiatic Cholera which struck down its first victim in Sunderland in October 1831. A few months of cholera in 1831–2 caused more alarm than centuries of home-bred typhus, which killed its thousands yearly in the slums of the industrial towns. It was the dramatic suddenness of the cholera attack which spread terror. In the space of a few hours the sufferer might be lying pulseless and blue, his body shaken by repeated vomiting and purging, his limbs twisted with cramp; and in the existing state of medical knowledge one half of those who passed into the blue, or collapse, stage of the disease were doomed. "Bleeding, brandy, opium, calomel, ammonia, quinine, croton-oil, cold water, the warm bath, the cold effusion, all varieties and contrarieties of treatment possible, have been employed alike in vain."[1] For this reason, though the influenza epidemic of 1847 killed more of the middle and upper classes than the cholera of 1848–9, it aroused nothing like the same amount of apprehension. Nor was this all. Typhus was a poor man's disease, the louse being no longer seen in polite society. At the end of the eighteenth century a respectable

[1] *Second Report of the Metropolitan Sanitary Commission*, p. 22; *P.P.*, 1847–8, vol. xxxii, p. 253.

middle-class physician was noting complacently that fever was rare in Liverpool; though, to be sure, Dr. Currie was treating a steady average of three thousand typhus cases a year at his dispensary. But the comma bacillus was a social climber; excreted by some lowly sufferer in Fore Street, Lambeth, or Hairbrain Court, it might penetrate the half-hearted filter defences of the water companies to poison his betters in the broad squares of the West End.

Assured of the backing of an apprehensive Government, therefore, Chadwick cast an imperial eye over the vast, disorderly province of the metropolis. Outside the walls of the City, London in 1847 was a tangle of overlapping jurisdictions and conflicting authorities. Some three hundred local bodies—including seven Commissions of Sewers, 172 vestries, and nearly a hundred paving, lighting, and cleansing boards—jostled and frustrated each other, each clinging with determination to its minute segment of power and dignity, with the object, it would seem, rather of keeping out other authorities than of conferring benefit on the population beneath its care. In the parish of St. Pancras alone there were sixteen separate Paving Boards, acting under twenty-nine Acts of Parliament. While the drainage and surface cleansing of London was thus minutely subdivided between a host of public authorities, other vital sanitary services were shared by eight joint stock cemeteries and nine water companies. The Royal Commission on Municipal Corporations, which dealt with the capital in its second report in 1837, had concluded that London must have a unified government, but it had not ventured to decide whether it should take the form of a Government Commission or of a newly created municipality. If the Government ever really intended to take action on this report, the edge of their resolve was turned by the hard core of vested interests in the City. The chaos remained, and grew worse year by year, a challenge to all Chadwick's principles of administrative consolidation. For the remaining years of his official career the problems of London's drainage, water supply, and burial services were to occupy a major part of his energies.

There was little attempt by the Government to conceal the real purpose of the investigation on which he was now engaged. It was to convict the works and administration of the Sewers Commissioners, and to furnish arguments which might be used to justify to the public the resumption by the Crown of the powers they had so ineffectively wielded. Lord Lincoln and Sir James Graham had earlier taken tentative steps towards superseding the Commissions, but had drawn back—apparently, Chadwick observed, for fear of offending the Commissioners. "Something must be said publicly," he wrote sharply to Morpeth, "of the state of mind which inflicts disease and death extensively on thousands out of deference to conventional feelings of individuals, which feelings are most improper for those individuals to entertain."[1] For the Sewers Commissions stood plainly condemned by Chadwick's Sanitary Report of 1842 and by the Health of Towns Commission of 1844–5; and Chadwick fretted at the needless delay which the Government's caution imposed upon him. Within a fortnight of the interview with Russell, he submitted to Morpeth some "Memoranda of results in relation to the Metropolis, promised by E. Chadwick," a paper which, in its reckoning of sanitary profits and economies, struck the confident note of the commercial prospectus. Three districts might in future be drained for the cost of two, two courts and two houses at the cost of one hitherto drained by private builders—provided that sound administrative arrangements were adopted. The secret lay in the consolidation of the whole of the natural drainage area of London under a single Commission of Sewers. Over £60,000 a year might thereby be saved on establishment charges, on the expense of rate collecting, and on the outlay for Commissioners' dinners. Consolidate at once, without waiting for the results of the new inquiry, Chadwick urged on Russell and Morpeth. If the Sewers Commissions remained in their present hands, the doomed Commissioners would resist to the utmost of their power. The more enlightened of the surveyors had already come into conflict with their reactionary masters; John Roe, for example, whose flushing machine had been coldly received by the Holborn and Finsbury Commissioners, and that "extraordinary man," John Phillips, the self-educated journeyman bricklayer who had risen to the surveyorship of the Westminster division and had shown up the defects of a system of sewerage pronounced perfect by the President of the Association of Civil Engineers. These experienced officers

[1] E. C. to Lord Morpeth, 5 August 1847.

were agreed that it would be well worth suspending all the
drainage works now under construction for the sake of a complete
survey, and they assured Chadwick that if they were emancipated
and secured against dismissal they would willingly co-operate
with the Commission of Inquiry in the preparation of remedial
measures.[1]

Morpeth approved highly of Chadwick's papers, but Russell
was lukewarm; and a strong letter from the Lord Chancellor,
which Morpeth would show to Chadwick only in abstract, put an
end to his hopes of a *coup d'état*.[2] Consolidation must be postponed until the investigation was completed; and Chadwick
foresaw that whilst the Sewers Commissioners would not obstruct
the inquiry so openly as to expose themselves to a supersedeas,
there would be "no work with a will."[3]

Besides Chadwick and Southwood Smith, the Commission of
Inquiry included Lord Robert Grosvenor, who was Russell's
choice, and Richard Lambert Jones, representing the interests of
the City of London; while Chadwick had made sure of a majority
in favour of progressive measures by insisting on the nomination
of Professor Owen, "the Cuvier of our day."[4] Russell had
wanted to appoint the son of Sir John Bowring as assistant secretary to the Commission. Chadwick retorted bluntly that it would
look like a political job, and instead secured the post for Henry
Austin, a young engineer who had carried out some pioneer
sanitary work of considerable promise.[5] Early in September 1847
the Commission moved into the rooms in Gwydyr House where
the Health of Towns inquiry had met two years before. "I have
seen enough and supped enough of horrors not to avoid more
except where it may be absolutely necessary," Chadwick told
Morpeth at the outset of his third sanitary expedition. "A man
who has had two fevers in the sanitary cause, may be placed on
the footing of an officer in the Army who has led two forlorn
hopes and is excused a third. I certainly shall put forward younger
men for the enterprise."[6] Within a few days, however, he was

[1] E. C. to Russell, 8 August 1847.
[2] Morpeth to E. C., 9 August 1847; E. C. to Morpeth, 11 August 1847;
Morpeth to E. C., 19 August 1847.
[3] E. C. to Morpeth, 19 August 1847.   [4] E. C. to Russell, 4 August 1847.
[5] E. C. to Morpeth, 24 July 1847; to Sir George Grey, 25 August 1847.
[6] E. C. to Morpeth, 11 September 1847.

revisiting the lower districts of Bermondsey in Professor Owen's company.[1]

As early as possible Chadwick withdrew, with his two allies, Owen and Southwood Smith, into the seclusion of a sub-committee on the cholera, and the main propositions of the reports were hammered out in this congenial atmosphere, removed from the "Parliamentary influences, fidgets, and groundless alarms" of Lord Robert Grosvenor,[2] and Jones's continual insistence on the rights and dignity of the Sewers Commissions. To save time and avert opposition from the City, they confined their attention to the seven districts for which the Crown was responsible, and the attack on the City sewers, which were no better than those under the other Commissions, was postponed. The first report of the Commission of Inquiry was signed on 20 November.[3] At their opening meeting Professor Owen had informed them that in the medical schools it was strongly believed that a cholera epidemic was impending.[4] On that grim note of warning the report opened. If the cholera came, were the defences of London any stronger now than in 1831? A few of the old open sewers had been arched over, some additional lines of common sewer laid down; but most of the new sewers were not supplied with a sufficient sweep of water to carry off their contents. The improvements made in the past sixteen years were, in fact, negligible. As Chadwick had already written to Russell: "We have compared the state of all the districts most severely visited by the Cholera, and shewn that there has been no material improvement in their sanitary condition. It is as I think, proved, that in the majority of the districts the Commissions are positively not to be entrusted with the cleansing of a ditch, and moreover that the districts, even for that purpose, interfere with each other."[5] London was wide open to the cholera in 1847 as in 1831. But, thought the Commissioners, the London of 1847 had one great advantage over that of 1831. It was now known how the cholera was generated, and how it might be prevented. Medical observers who had watched the last epidemic had shown that generally it followed the track of rivers and water-courses; but the most deadly explosions had

---

[1] E. C. to John Forster, 1847.   [2] E. C. to Morpeth, 18 November 1847.
[3] *P.P.*, 1847-8, vol. xxxii, pp. 1, 57.   [4] E. C. to Russell, 6 October 1847.
[5] E. C. to Russell, 10 November 1847.

taken place near some extraordinary accumulation of filth, the mouth of a sewer, a "bone vessel" laden with manure, a fever nest like Three Tuns Court. It was the lower districts of the towns which usually harboured such accumulations; but impure air could not be fenced in, and the deaths of great numbers of respectable artisans and shopkeepers proved that a contaminated atmosphere was an "incomparably more powerful predisponent" to the disease than extreme poverty and the lack of adequate food. The conclusion was inescapable. There was only one safeguard: "that safeguard consists in sanitary arrangements."[1]

Could the cleansing of London be safely left, however, in the hands of the existing Commissions of Sewers? The chief preventive measure must be the flushing of the sewers; only one district, Holborn and Finsbury, had flushing machinery in systematic use, though its advantages had been demonstrated years before. It would be necessary to divert upper streams under one Commission to cleanse the sewers of lower levels lying under a different jurisdiction; such collective action the present Commissioners had shown themselves incapable of understanding or executing. The works they had built were a standing memorial to their ignorance and incompetence. Private Acts to confer increased powers had been obtained by two Commissions; Bills were now in agitation by two more—and not one of them contained provisions for the supplies of water without which the sewers could not act properly. The clerk to the Surrey and Kent Commission, after confessing that few house drains were joined to their new main sewers because of the offensive effluvia which were thrown back through the privies and water-closets, went on to reveal that his Commission now proposed to spend £100,000 on extending the same system. As Chadwick commented in a confidential report to Lord Robert Grosvenor, "No sane person would go on, so expending their own money as these same commissioners are now going on spending the money of others."[2]

---

[1] *First Report of the Metropolitan Sanitary Commission*, p. 33.

[2] "Metropolitan Special Commission. Notes on the Evidence examined," MS., 7 October 1847.

"The sewers establishments were mere 'Castles of Indolence,'" he wrote later (to Frederick Byng, 11 September 1848). "I scarcely know of any old Government offices which were worse or so bad. Now and then a Court with about the degree of business to give the excitement of Sessions work for the relief

The cholera and Chadwick's revelations were together too much for the Law Officers, and within a few days of the signing of the report they concurred in his proposal to recall the Commissions and re-issue them to the same individuals for each district. Chadwick asked for a small Commission, fitted by special knowledge and experience to supervise the paid officers in the execution of a comprehensive drainage scheme. All that was really wanted, he thought, was a sufficient number of Commissioners to supply a working quorum of six; and the public should see from the character of the appointments that scientific and medical skill was being brought to bear on the problems of metropolitan drainage. The central Government had long been accustomed to intervene in the administration of London, stepping into the breach left by the absence of organs of municipal government. The police, roads, cemeteries, and markets of the capital had all in turn received special attention from Parliament, while plans for metropolitan improvement had been considered by a Select Committee in 1838 and a Commission in 1844. Chadwick's plans for London were in the direct line of this tradition. The model of government he advised was the one he had recommended consistently for local sanitary administration since 1842: government by commission, efficient because it was composed of selected brains, responsible because its powers were defined by Act of Parliament and its conduct came under the jealous scrutiny of the legislature.

Over a thousand Commissioners were superseded by the writs of November and December 1847,[1] and their powers transferred

---

of a Country Squire; now and then a new sewer to be considered, on the report of the Surveyor; Chief Clerks with good Salaries, going there in the middle of the day, hearing a complaint or two, reading a newspaper for an hour or two, and then going home to his Country house, or to some other place of emolument; Clerks of the works seeing to the performance of half labour by labourers with extra pay; the Surveyor now and then seeing to the work, and hearing the reports of the Clerk of the Works; but leaving early to amuse himself with a farm or to attend to any private professional engagement which might offer itself."

[1] The numbers were as follows: Westminster and part of Middlesex, 240; Holborn and Finsbury, 150; Tower Hamlets, 179; Poplar and Blackwell, 67; Surrey and Kent, 280; Greenwich, 116; St. Katherine's-by-the-Tower, 33. The first six of these were superseded on 30 November 1847, the last on 4 December.

to a select body of twenty-three, including seven Members of Parliament, three doctors, two clergymen, two lawyers, the proprietor of *The Times*, a geologist, a physiologist—and, despite all Chadwick had written, four of the discredited Sewers Commissioners.[1] A dozen or more of these were personal friends of Chadwick; but the new Commission, small as it was in comparison with its predecessors, was larger than he would have wished. And he soon made it plain that he considered it was too large by just the number of those who opposed his views. Moreover, the jurisdiction of this consolidated Commission halted at the walls of the City. It was indeed no more than an interim solution, into which the Government had been driven more by the transient threat of the cholera than by any consideration of the enduring problems of London's sanitary administration. Chadwick was presently manœuvring to replace this temporary body by a permanent executive modelled closer to his liking. Unsatisfactory though he thought it, however, he had good reason to congratulate himself; in the Metropolitan Commission of Sewers London, for the first time in its history, had an administrative body charged with the responsibility of planning and constructing public works for the whole metropolitan area outside the City.

[1] The Commissioners were: Lord Morpeth, Lord Ashley, Lord Ebrington, the Hon. Frederick Byng, the Dean of Westminster, Sir James Clark, Sir Edward Buxton, Sir Henry de la Beche, Joseph Hume, John Walter, R. A. Slaney, William Broderip, John Bullar, Professor Owen, Dr. Arnott, Dr. Southwood Smith, the Rev. William Stone, John Bidwell, Robert Hutton, Thomas Puckle, R. L. Jones, John Leslie, and Edwin Chadwick.

CHAPTER VIII

PUBLIC HEALTH ACT, 1848

LORD MORPETH introduced his revised Bill on 10 February 1848. Once again Chadwick's hopes were at the mercy of the "winds and waves of speech in the house."[1] Would their lumbering measure, with its 150 clauses, go to pieces again, as in the previous year, and be given up, an abandoned wreck, when the session came to an end? The Bill was, he knew, in the hands of a man who wished it well. As a Howard, the heir to the sixth Earl of Carlisle, Lord Morpeth was a power among the Whigs. He had shown himself a sincere and courageous friend to progressive movements—as Chief Secretary in Ireland encouraging agrarian reform, as a visitor to the United States startling Bostonians by attending an Anti-slavery Fair, as a Whig grandee in England giving a lead to men of rank by supporting mechanics' institutes and the Health of Towns Association. To the Public Health movement Morpeth brought the prestige of his family name, and the personal popularity won by his characteristic charm and transparent goodness of heart. He was, says Harriet Martineau, "the best and most beloved man in the company of statesmen of his day and generation."[2] All this was to the good; but in his private thoughts Chadwick wondered whether Lord Morpeth's resolution was firm enough, whether his temper was not too equable. Was it sufficient in the Parliamentary leader of the sanitary agitation to possess moral idealism, a gracious sympathy of manner, an exquisite politeness? One could be too polite to the vested interests which cast their shadows over the health of millions; one could be too accommodating to slum landlords, and listen too patiently to the defenders of local self-government. Perhaps Morpeth earned at too great a price Disraeli's commendation that he was one of the most popular men in the House and

[1] E. C. to ? , n.d.   [2] *Biographical Sketches*, 4th ed., 1876, p. 142.

158

in the country. For his part Morpeth, the politician, found Chadwick, the administrative theorist, too punctilious and unbending in his views. "You must not suspect me of any disposition to undervalue your advice or to slight your counsels," he assured Chadwick, "but as I have to make things *go down* with Senates, Boards, and Bodies of men, there must be often a want of the identity of proceedings which otherwise I might be glad to exhibit. . . . I hope we shall keep all things smooth, which is not only pleasanter, but at the present constitutes our highest prudence."[1]

As in 1847, the Bill provided for a central Board of Health with five members, two of whom were to be paid, under the presidency of a responsible member of the Government. On the petition of one-fiftieth of the rated inhabitants the General Board would have powers to introduce the machinery of local sanitary administration into a district, and to influence its working by the advice and surveillance of a number of Superintending Inspectors. The amount of central interference, Morpeth explained reassuringly, "was really at present confined to a very few items";[2] the General Board would be authorised to advise the original formation of the district, to arbitrate on questions referred to them by the Local Boards, to enforce a uniform procedure in certain matters where such uniformity was desirable, to audit the accounts of the local authorities, to give or withhold their sanction to the execution of local sanitary schemes. A Local Board would be established by an Order in Council or a Provisional Order, which would prescribe the number of members the Board should have. In a corporate town the municipal council would select the Board from amongst its own members; in non-corporate towns the Board of Health would be elected by a system of plural voting similar to that in use for the election of a Poor Law Guardians. The powers of Local Boards fell into two classes: it was imperative upon them to compel owners or occupiers to provide house drains, to ensure a constant water supply (by the compulsory purchase of existing waterworks if necessary), and to appoint a surveyor and an inspector of nuisances; they could also exercise permissive powers to appoint an officer of health, to reconstruct the sewers, to pave

---

[1] Morpeth to E. C., 7 June 1848.
[2] *Hansard*, vol. xcviii, p. 737, 5 May 1848.

streets, to make regulations for the disposal of filth and refuse, to provide places for public recreation. Neither Scotland nor Ireland was covered by the Bill; and the problem of London and its hundred Local Acts was reserved for a separate measure.

It was by no means the best Bill that could be devised, thought Chadwick as he looked over its provisions—but it was the best they were likely to get.[1] The machinery of central control was certainly not of Chadwick's planning. "I must do the best I can and how I can," he told his friends resignedly, "—the Board is an exceedingly hazardous affair but there seems to be no other chance."[2] Presently, however, Morpeth was wavering before the critics who condemned the Bill as a Government job, to create new Commissioners and a numberless host of Inspectors in the face of a Budget deficiency of two or three millions, and there was talk of entrusting the measure to a Board of unpaid Commissioners. "That of course excludes those who cannot live on air, or who like myself have no private fortune."[3] Obviously the proposal was aimed at himself, probably out of jealousy at the C.B. with which the Prince Consort had recently honoured him.[4] It reflected the ignorance of men like that talkative eccentric, Colonel Sibthorp, who had once declared that the whole sanitary service was unnecessary, and that half a crown a day would be sufficient remuneration for an Inspector, who would be expected to superintend a novel type of engineering works—three to ten guineas a day being the usual payment to engineers in private employment.[5] Once again Chadwick began to fear that his proposals would be accepted but their author rejected. He would be glad to be paid piece work to execute the Act on the principle of "no cure, no pay," he told Joseph Hume, urging him to raise his voice against such cant and humbug.[6] The following day Hume obtained the consent of the House to the appointment of a single paid Commissioner, but Chadwick still retained a forbid-

---

[1] E. C. to Dr. P. H. Holland, 29 February 1848. He told Lord Campbell, 26 June 1848, "I have never been able to take any part in the framework or details of the Bill since the first meeting at Lord Morpeth's: I do not feel myself responsible for it, and do not feel confident as to its working other than as a commencement."

[2] E. C. to W. E. Hickson, 4 March 1848.

[3] E. C. to ? , n.d.   [4] E. C. to W. E. Hickson, 9 May 1848.

[5] E. C. to Morpeth, 17 May 1848.   [6] E. C. to Joseph Hume, 17 May 1848.

ding picture of himself sitting as a resented and unhonoured
figure at the bottom of a Board of titled amateurs. He must be
assured a position where he could initiate measures and defend
them, he told R. A. Slaney; a Cabinet Minister or a recognised
official chief he would not mind, but he had strong objections to
acting under any honorary Commissioners whatsoever.[1] What
honorary Commissioners could be found whose special qualifications would give public confidence? Apart from Viscount
Ebrington, who was there in Parliament who could assist the
measure? Did not all experience show that unpaid service was
always the most extravagant? To cut the Bill free of the dead
wood of patronage appointments, he urged Russell and Morpeth
to consider whether even at this stage the measure might not be
reshaped, and the dangerous expedient of a Board dropped in
favour of the machinery he had outlined in 1844, with Edwin
Chadwick acting as paid secretary to the President of the Council.
Such an arrangement "would follow in a beaten course," since
the Privy Council were already invested with functions relating
to the public health; and "if the measure succeed, as it will
succeed, if fair play be given to it, the expansion of powers and
extension to other parts of the country might, I apprehend, be
most readily given to it under such auspices."[2]

In Committee Morpeth's original proposal was eventually
whittled down to a Commission of three, one only to be paid,
under the presidency of the First Commissioner of Woods and
Forests. Though he regretted that "the principle of single seated-
ness"[3] had not been adopted, Chadwick found some satisfaction
in the small size of the Board; unless there were very special
qualifications of knowledge and zeal, he had told Morpeth, every
additional member of a Board was an additional trouble to
inform and keep right.[4] It is noteworthy that once again, as in
the debates of 1847, the principle of ministerial responsibility for
the policy of the new department was not clearly envisaged by the
Government, nor by any of the critics, friendly or hostile, in the
House, with the exception of Lord Lincoln, who continued to
urge that public health measures should be put under the jurisdiction of the Home Secretary. This solution Chadwick rejected,

[1] E. C. to R. A. Slaney, 16 May 1848. [2] E. C. to Russell, 14 May 1848.
[3] E. C. to W. E. Hickson, 4 March 1848.   [4] E. C. to Morpeth, n.d.

M

partly because in his view sanitary administration should be kept free from the party influences introduced by a changing political head, partly because public health measures were too important to receive merely the fractional attention of an already over-burdened Minister—but chiefly, it would appear, because he judged the question by one sovereign test, the amount of authority it would ensure to himself.

In its arrangements for local administration, also, the Government Bill departed from Chadwick's original recommendations. "I have already remonstrated on the new powers to be given to the town councils which I entirely distrust," he told the Bishop of London. ". . . What I apprehend is, that they will go into all kinds of waste, and then it will be said, how much has been spent for Sanitary measures, and how ineffective they have been."[1] The main bulwark in the Bill against a flood of local jobbery was the provision that any proposal by the local authorities to spread sanitary charges over a period of time must receive the sanction of the General Board. This safeguard, "so important a key point for the central control,"[2] was struck out, without discussion, by the Commons, so permitting the Local Boards, freed from the restraining hand of the central department, to embark upon all manner of extravagant schemes, to be paid for by such instalments and within such period as they themselves should appoint. The local officers, the surveyor and officer of health, were guaranteed some security of tenure by the provision that the approval of the General Board must be given for their dismissal; but since their remuneration and conditions of service were left to the local authority, their independence of view and action were far from assured. Central control over the officers and finances of the Local Boards was in fact clipped so close by the Commons that at one stage Colonel Sibthorp was under the gratified illusion that the Government had very nearly abandoned its plan of "centralisation."[3] Chadwick now pinned his hopes on the Lords to save the Bill from complete futility.

The debates in the Commons had revealed how much the public health reformers had yet to do to enlighten the ruling

---

[1] E. C. to Bishop of London, 16 June 1848.
[2] E. C. to Morpeth, 3 June 1848.
[3] *Hansard*, vol. xcviii, p. 872, 11 May 1848.

classes and shake them out of their obstinate self-satisfaction. Many Members refused to recognise in Chadwick's sombre picture the visage of their own towns. They deplored the "anonymous slanders" on one place after another, put out by the Health of Towns Association, and rejected indignantly the unsavoury descriptions of the home life of the poor as "an unfounded calumny upon the meritorious classes to which those statements referred."[1] Urquhart could not believe that Stafford was unhealthy.[2] Divett declared that the Commissioners in Exeter had laid out £100,000 in improving the city, and the place had never had less sickness.[3] Hudson, who had lived thirty-three years in York, had canvassed the electors' houses six times, and had gone among the lower classes as a Methodist exhorter, had seen nothing approaching the scenes described in the report put out by the York Sanitary Committee.[4] Yet—Morpeth cited a petition from Stafford, referring to the high mortality in the town, and signed by all but one of the medical men, all the clergy and ministers of the different denominations, the late mayor, a majority of the aldermen, and a large proportion of the town council;[5] Lord Ebrington, recently returned from Exeter, had attended a meeting under the chairmanship of the mayor where citizens had complained warmly about the lack of drains and pure water;[6] and not a medical man in York impugned the report which Hudson so contemptuously rejected.[7] So, in the Commons, Members asserted and denied as their limited observation and emotional prepossessions taught them. Sanitary science lacked as yet the well-knit logic of established knowledge, and in that unfenced country of the half-known and the merely surmised, opinion could canter on a free rein. Nothing caused so much confusion, for example, as the reformers' well-meant attempt to demonstrate a firm correlation between disease and the offensive exhalations of organic decay; for, as the bacteriologists were later to show, the nexus of cause and effect did not lie here. The connection between noxious emanations and the itch was much more pronounced, as Snow observed, but because men knew

---

[1] *Hansard*, vol. xcviii, p. 773, 8 March 1848 (Charles Pearson).
[2] Ibid., p. 716, 5 May 1848.   [3] Ibid., p. 1174, 18 May 1848.
[4] Ibid., vol. xciii, p. 1284, 6 July 1847.
[5] Ibid., vol. xcviii, p. 734, 5 May 1848.
[6] Ibid., p. 727, 5 May 1848.   [7] Ibid., vol. xciii, p. 1283, 6 July 1847.

what caused the itch, they did not fall into the error of laying it to the account of every unpleasant smell. While some Members, therefore, could point to the warning of undrained districts where the inhabitants had been decimated by an explosion of fever, others could show cheerfully insanitary populations which for generations had been drinking unfiltered water and piling ordure round their doors without any catastrophic retribution.[1] Chadwick, who had been twice attacked, and Southwood Smith, who had had three bouts of typhus, were convinced of the danger; and when he heard remarks that the danger was exaggerated, Chadwick would recall the honourable list of casualties in the service —the Roman Catholic priests who had visited the Liverpool Irish; the doctors, Lynch and Mitchell and Dyce Guthrie; and the Health of Towns Commissioners who had retched on the corners of dark back streets, Playfair, Smith of Deanston, and Sir Henry de la Beche.[2] Here, he felt, in the deaths and physical discomfort of healthy, well-fed members of the middle classes was evidence to satisfy all who were not blinded by self-interest.

Openly or under cover of such arguments, the voices of threatened interests were raised against the Bill. A smoke-suppression clause roused the manufacturers; the proposal to extend municipal boundaries to take in country districts stirred up the representatives of the agricultural areas. Divett objected to the transfer to the local Boards of private undertakings for the supply of gas and water; if Parliament fixed the charges, these matters were best left in the hands of private bodies. He detected in the Bill the hand of Chadwick, who would gain under it a position of power and importance, such as he had already secured for himself at the Commission of Sewers.[3] This was not the only personal attack endured by Chadwick in the course of the debates.[4] Some speakers, he believed, were paying off old Poor

[1] See, for example, a letter on sanitary statistics in the *Morning Chronicle*, 3 April 1848. In 1832 Shoreditch, "a district sacred to Cloacina," was most exempt from cholera, having one case per 1,203 inhabitants; while the City, the best drained district, had one in 155. If this were a fact, concluded the writer, it was an argument for abolishing sewerage altogether.

[2] E. C. to Morpeth, 30 June 1847.

[3] *Hansard*, vol. xcviii, p. 725, 5 May 1848.

[4] He appealed to Lord Lincoln to use his influence to discountenance this practice of attacking civil servants, "the absent, and really defenceless." "For years Mr. Stephen was attacked for Colonial measures; latterly Mr.

Law scores; Tatton Egerton, for example, whose practice as owner of a close parish of pulling down cottages and drawing labour from other parishes had been condemned in Chadwick's evidence before the Settlement Committee in 1847, and who now declared that the appointment of "a certain individual" would be distasteful to the manufacturing districts. The answer to this, Chadwick told Russell, was that from Leeds, Liverpool, Manchester, Bolton, Lancaster, Warrington, and elsewhere, appeals had come to him for advice and assistance.[1]

Provincial jealousy flared up when it was seen that London was escaping again, as it had escaped the Municipal Reform Act. Why should London be exempt, demanded Colonel Sibthorp, in preference to his own constituency, Lincoln, which was clean enough, and had not a poor man in it?[2] "It was in London, in stinking London, in filthy London, that sanitary measures should begin," cried Wakley, the editor of the *Lancet*, adding his grumble against the "soup influence" of that "nasty turtle-eating corporation."[3] "Help I pray you against Banks!" wrote Chadwick to *The Times* correspondent, the Rev. S. G. Osborne. "He wishes to do nothing in sanitary measures until the Metropolis is included but he is most zealous he says for them. Cannot you now press forward the claims of the Dorsetshire villages, and of his own cottages to his sanitary zeal. Pray give him a sermon on the times from Psalm 74 v. 21 prayer book version: 'All the earth is full of cruel habitations,' but let your voice of exhortation be raised soon."[4]

Most significant, because it was a direct confrontation of the fundamental principle of the Bill, most powerful, because it was backed by many of the municipalities, was the attack on "that mode of foreign government which was known by the name of

---

Trevelyan for Irish measures, and from the commencement of the Poor Law Amendment Act, I, for measures which were the work of another Department." (8 May 1848). Lincoln replied (9 May 1848): "I consider attacks upon any Gentleman employed by a Responsible Minister of the Crown unjustifiable. *If* the Bill *be* yours, it has been adopted by Lord Morpeth—he will reap all the merit if it succeed and upon him must fall the blame if it fails—this in my opinion is the only safe Parliamentary view of any question."

[1] E. C. to Russell, 14 May 1848.
[2] *Hansard*, vol. xcviii, p. 711, 5 May 1848.
[3] Ibid., vol. xcvi, p. 414, 10 February 1848.
[4] E. C. to the Rev. S. G. Osborne, 6 May 1848.

centralisation."[1] It had long been the pride of the country that the Government had little to do in the management of internal affairs, declared Urquhart, the Member for Stafford. If the country was in a sink of filth, it was because the House had passed laws affecting the labour and industry of the population. The Common Law provided ample means for putting down all nuisances; if anything more were required, it should not take the form of this "clumsy, encumbered, and almost unintelligible Bill" which superseded the functions of Parliament by enabling another body to set aside laws and impose taxation; a simple and facile measure might grant to municipal authorities the powers they needed and subject them to penalties if they neglected to put them into operation.[2]

Many of those who kicked at any measure of control of their own activities, however, were ready to take a fair-minded view of regulations directed at somebody else, and were even prepared to suggest how such regulations could be profitably extended. Viscount Duncan wanted to know why Morpeth had avoided the window-tax; Horsman wondered what "mysterious difficulties" prevented the Government from tackling the interments question; Reynolds regretted the exclusion of Scotland and Ireland.[3] These fractions of support added up to a quite considerable total, and in reply to the clamour of energetic interests there went up a counter cry of satisfaction that the Bill did so much and regret that it did not do considerably more.

Outside the House public attention was distracted by the exciting Continental news, by the spectacle of thrones toppling and Metternich packing his bags for London. As in 1847 and earlier years it was a vociferous minority on either side which fought over the principles of sanitary government. The doctors and clergymen of the Health of Towns Association conducted a vigorous campaign of lecturing, letter-writing, and lobbying, and drafted petitions for signature by the working classes; and Chadwick found time to supply ammunition to local leaders in strategic points. From the strongholds of local self-government, the City and the metropolitan parishes, rose an angry hum of disapproval.

[1] *Hansard*, vol. xcvi, p. 1022, 21 February 1848 (Urquhart).
[2] Ibid., vol. xcviii, p. 711, 5 May 1848, and p. 1175, 18 May 1848.
[3] Ibid., vol. xcvi, pp. 404, 406, 420, 10 February 1848.

The Common Council resolved unanimously to condemn the Bill.[1] No place in the world had so complete a system of drainage as London, said the City Remembrancer.[2] "It would turn out to be nothing but mere humbug," a Builder Commissioner forecast of the sanitary movement.[3] "Read 'Morpeth' as 'Metternich,'" cried one Tower Hamlets ratepayer.[4] The *Morning Chronicle* was the chief vehicle for these protests; and the most active pen in the service of local self-government was that of Toulmin Smith, whose writings gave to the opposition such shape and philosophy as it possessed. A legal antiquary of a deeply encrusted Toryism, he saw in the Public Health Act one further episode in that Whig plot by which the Anglo-Saxon institutions of the kingdom were gradually being replaced by the government of Whig Commissioners, and the ancient Common Law defences of person and property were being overthrown by "ink and paper law-making." "If this act, or anything like it, passes into a law, it will have to be recorded in history that the Court of Star Chamber was abolished in 17 Car. I, A.D. 1641, but was re-established, with greatly increased powers, in 11 Victoria, A.D. 1848."[5] His solution to the sanitary problem was admirably simple—a closed cesspool should be provided for every house and the Highway Surveyors stirred to activity in laying down new road drains;[6] and to enforce public health regulations the courts leet, vestry, hundred, and county courts should be restored to their original dignity.[7] Where was the need for a central department "to tell the People of England, from a closet at Whitehall, how each man is to make his drains and water-closets, to build his ash-pit"?[8]

From Leeds, Manchester, Bradford, Birmingham, delegates from the town councils were sent to London to protest against the Bill; but in every place where such opposition manifested itself Chadwick could count upon the support of an influential section of the inhabitants. The Health of Towns Association circulated a

---

[1] *Times*, 22 May 1848.
[2] *Sanitary Condition of the City of London: letter to Lord Ashley from the City Remembrancer* (pamphlet), 1848, p. 4.
[3] Ibid., p. 12.   [4] *Morning Chronicle*, 29 March 1848.
[5] Letter to the *Jurist*, 26 February 1848.
[6] *The Parish. Its obligations and powers: its officers and their duties*, 1854, p. 302.
[7] Letter to the *Daily News*, 30 March 1848.
[8] *Centralisation or Representation?*, 1848, p. ix.

questionnaire to sixty-nine of the principal towns of England and Wales, and summarised the returns in a pamphlet which breathed local suspicion of the existing authorities, and scorn for the idea that, unaided and uncontrolled, they could lift themselves out of their present squalor.[1] It was not true, Chadwick maintained, that the town councils would offer the universal resistance to a central department that was prophesied by Divett and other disciples of Toulmin Smith. The people of Divett's own town, Exeter, had invited Chadwick and Southwood Smith to attend a public meeting. "We found our names placarded as intending to address them. The mayor gave us a dinner. I found it extremely difficult to get away and avoid the applications to see places, and I have since been in correspondence with parties in the town who are anxious that steps should be taken." The evidence—the appeals which reached Chadwick from Liverpool, Lancaster, Warrington, Rugby, Edinburgh, St. Andrews, Belfast, Dublin, and elsewhere; the applications addressed to the Metropolitan Sanitary Commission in the mistaken belief that they possessed executive powers—proved that in many places there existed an anxious desire to benefit from the advice and assistance of well-informed authority. Surely such places should be allowed to exercise the right of self-government, and choose for themselves whether or not to adopt the Public Health Act![2]

There were, as *The Times* wisely remarked, just and prudent limits in the capacity of a Bill as there were in the tonnage of an East Indiaman.[3] The loss of some of the subjects which were omitted from the original draft, or were later jettisoned in Committee, was not regretted by Chadwick. The exemption of London, he considered, would not be serious if the General Board were given full powers of inquiry in preparation for a separate measure.[4] Coke and iron manufacturers had risen in protest against the smoke clause, and its excision was judicious.[5] The limit on the duration of the Poor Law Commission had not

---

[1] *Report of the Sub-Committee on the answers returned to Questions addressed to the Principal Towns of England and Wales, and on the objections from corporate bodies to the Public Health Bill*, 1848.

[2] E. C. to Morpeth, n.d., *c.* 10 May 1848.

[3] *Times*, 11 February 1848.   [4] E. C. to Morpeth, 30 June 1847.

[5] E. C. to Morpeth, 8 August 1848.

worked well (it had encouraged some local authorities to go slow
in the hope that in five years' time the Act would be repealed and
the Commissioners hanged), but Chadwick was willing to accept
a term of five years to the Board's life as one of the least injurious
concessions.[1] But, looking over the Bill as it emerged from the
Commons at the end of June, he sighed that it was a mere wreck
of what had been intended.[2] "As it stands it will only enable the
commencement of legislation to be made," he told his friends.
"Great administrative wisdom and experience in the General
Board and Inspectors might still extract some good from its
practical operation; but that if it be put into other than the most
competent hands, more evil than good may arise from it. I never
could have thought that any Government would have conceded
so extensively the power and authority of a central controlling
Board either to pitiless self-interest or senseless clamour."[3] If the
General Board were to exercise any real powers of initiation and
supervision in the localities, those powers must now be inserted
in the Lords. Here, fortunately, the friends of Chadwick mustered
strongly, and he wrote at once to brief the Bishop of London,
Lord Ellenborough, Lord Campbell, Lord Lansdowne, and the
Duke of Buccleuch.

How was the machinery of public health administration to be
introduced into the localities? This was the provision which
would determine the leverage the General Board could exert
against recalcitrant districts, and much of Chadwick's dissatisfaction arose from the inadequacy of the clause to which the
Commons had assented. The Commons had rejected on sight
the original optimistic suggestion that one householder in fifty,
whether he was a ratepayer or not—he "might really be of the
working classes," Chadwick told Lord Lansdowne[4]—should have
the power to bring all the apparatus of sanitary inquisition to
bear upon the obdurate forty-nine. It was now provided that if
one-tenth of the inhabitant householders rated to the relief of the
poor signed a petition, the General Board could set to work. "It
is well to get the smallest wedge," declared Chadwick, his meta-
phors getting hopelessly mixed in his annoyance, "but we should

[1] E. C. to Morpeth, n.d.   [2] E. C. to Sir George Larpent, 20 June 1848.
[3] E. C. to William Lee, 10 July 1848.
[4] E. C. to Lord Lansdowne, 13 July 1848.

be sure that it is really a wedge, and not a rotten staff. For opening the worst-conditioned districts the provision as it now stands will I fear be a mere rush."[1] At Manchester and Liverpool, for example, the signatures of three or four thousand ratepayers would be required to the petition. The trade unions and Chartists, who had begun to notice this "poor man's measure," would not overlook the fact that its initiation depended upon the goodwill of another class, the ratepayers, who were biased against it by the dread of increased rates. "I do not see how any one could get up in the Commons and contend that where there was a heavy infantile slaughter, or where the labouring classes are grievously ravaged by epidemics, there shall be no intervention except on the initiation of the middle classes."[2]

There must then be some formula for intervention, which, once recited, would bring the Board's Inspector posting down from London, whether the local tradesmen were ready to give him a welcome or not. The possible formulæ were canvassed in turn by Chadwick and the Bishop of London, who had expressed his willingness to introduce the "Poor Man's Clause" in the Lords. The excess of deaths from zymotic diseases above the general average for the towns of the whole kingdom might be taken as the test, suggested Chadwick. In 1841 the deaths from epidemic diseases formed 21 per cent of the total; he would propose intervention in any place where the proportion rose above 20 per cent. But in the past the registration of the causes of death had frequently been tampered with; to check any such ratepayers' trickery, they should have at least one further test. Farr advised that it would be best to take the deaths of children under five, which in 1841 averaged 38 per cent of the whole. "Surely," cried Chadwick, "38 per cent of infantile deaths and 20 per cent of deaths from epidemics to be protected against authoritative intervention ought if not the Commons to satisfy Moloch himself! What a piece of evidence of our barbarism must not this hereafter appear to be." He would like also to have "some direct reference to the poor man as a class," on the basis of the expectation of life given in the Northampton table.[3]

When the question came to be discussed in the Lords, however,

[1] E. C. to Lord Lansdowne, 13 July, 1848.   [2] Ibid,
[3] E. C, to the Bishop of London, 12 July 1848.

the Bishop was not present, and—with the best will in the world, as his friends assured Chadwick—they struck out the "Poor Man's Clause," to which they thought the Commons might object, and inserted a smoke abatement clause, to which the Commons certainly would not consent. Thus, the unsatisfactory method of initiation devised by the Commons remained unaltered, at the same time as the obstacles to its working were increased. The Lords had made bad worse. The smoke clause, Chadwick told Morpeth with justifiable exasperation, would bring all the manufacturers into the field against sanitary measures—and there were places in the north where two or three manufacturers exerted such influence over the ratepayers that they could put a stop to any application whatsoever. Then all the butchers, fishmongers, and poulterers, who were threatened with inspection, all the lodging-house keepers and owners of cellar tenements, all persons carrying on noxious trades—all these were ratepayers; and they would find other allies in the middle classes, frightened by stories of heavier rates. Yet, as the provision for initiation now stood, "unheard of combinations" must be looked for amongst these very ratepayers to secure the introduction of measures which would benefit chiefly the working classes![1] Fortunately the set-back was only temporary. Despite Chadwick's protests the Lords insisted on retaining their smoke prevention clause; but in other respects the Bill was much improved before it returned to the Commons. The Bishop of London appeared in the House to press the importance of his "Poor Man's Clause," and it was re-inserted without opposition. The hands of the General Board were strengthened by providing that the local authority must seek their sanction before mortgaging the rates, and that the local surveyor should be irremovable except with their consent. As a further precaution against jobbery, an individual ratepayer was given the right to appeal to the General Board against any exceptionable expenditure by the Local Board. Altogether, as Chadwick told Joseph Hume, "the Health of Towns Bill as amended by the Lords is to some extent a working measure."[2] But would the Commons accept such large alterations in the original Bill? "I understand from the Speaker,"

---

[1] E. C. to Morpeth, 21 July 1848.
[2] E, C. to Joseph Hume, 5 August 1848.

Morpeth informed Chadwick, "that the entire interference with the Bill is, rigidly considered, so irregular that a general condonation must cover all."[1]

Chadwick's fears in this instance proved groundless, however. John Bright rose immediately to attack the smoke clause, and, as Chadwick expected and hoped, it was dropped without further discussion.[2] There was an anxious moment when Morpeth deleted the Bishop's version of the "Poor Man's Clause," but he replaced it at once with a clause suggested by the Registrar General, empowering the General Board to apply the Act to any place where the deaths from any cause exceeded 23 per thousand on the average of the previous seven years. It was not so good a test as the infantile mortality, Chadwick told him; but, he added with satisfaction, "I have had it tried over, and I believe it will give more places."[3] The sanction of the General Board to the mortgaging of local rates was preserved "as by fire," and also the appeal from aggrieved owners or occupiers.[4] "In other respects, it was lamed; it was very badly supported; many friends were absent, and parties directly interested against the Bill mustered strongly."[5]

The Public Health Act of 1848 (11 & 12 Vict. c. 63) established a Central Commission, terminable in five years, and consisting of three members, with the First Commissioner of Woods and Forests as president (s. 5). Their powers of initiating sanitary measures were strictly defined: their aid must be invoked by a petition signed by one-tenth of the ratepayers; failing a petition, they could take action only where the death rate from all causes had reached the figure of 23 per thousand (s. 8). In either case, a preliminary inquiry would be conducted by a Superintending Inspector, who would submit a report to the General Board (s. 9). The Act would then be applied by Order in Council; or, in districts where a Local Act was already in force or where the boundaries were to be altered, by a Provisional Order, which would not become effective until approved by Parliament (s. 10).

In districts possessing municipal institutions, the Town Council

[1] Morpeth to E. C., 26 July 1848.
[2] *Hansard*, vol c, p. 1178, 7 August 1848.
[3] E. C. to Morpeth, 8 August 1848.   [4] Morpeth to E. C., 8 August 1848.
[5] E. C. to the Bishop of London, 8 August 1848.

was to be the public health authority (s. 12). Non-corporate districts were to be given an entirely new authority, a Local Board of Health, the size of which would be specified in the constituent Order (s. 14). Middle-class influence in these Boards was jealously guarded, members being elected by plural voting, ranging from one vote for persons with property to the annual value of £50, and rising by one vote for every additional £50, to a limit of six votes for those possessing over £250 (s. 20). As officers the Local Board were to appoint a clerk, a treasurer, an inspector of nuisances, and a surveyor; for the dismissal of the last of these the approval of the General Board was necessary (s. 37). If they thought fit, they might also appoint a Medical Officer of Health; the appointment and dismissal of such an officer were subject to the approval of the General Board, but his remuneration was to be determined by the local authority (s. 40). Chadwick had thus failed to make obligatory the appointment of the most valuable of the local officials; and though both surveyor and officer of health were secured from summary dismissal, their independence of view was threatened by the fact that their salaries were fixed by the Local Board.

Over forty clauses (ss. 41–85) dealt with the powers to be exercised by the new local authorities, the effect being, as Chadwick pointed out, that for the reasonable expenses of an inspector's survey, a district would be invested with all the advantages of a costly Local Act. Far from restricting the functions of local authorities, Morpeth had explained in reply to the anti-centralisation party, the measure would in many cases greatly widen them. Of the English municipal corporations only twenty-nine possessed Local Acts which conferred powers of drainage, cleansing and paving on the Mayor and Corporation. In sixty-six corporate towns such powers were exercised jointly with a body of *ad hoc* Commissioners; in thirty by Commissioners independently of the Corporation. Sixty-two corporate towns possessed no Local Act whatsoever, to enable either Corporation or Commissioners to perform these essential services within their boundaries. Of the non-corporate towns in England, with more than 5,000 inhabitants, 175 had Local Acts, but 296 were without. "It was upon these 296 towns which had no Local Acts, and upon the 158 corporate towns which had at present either no powers at all, or divided powers, that his Bill would, for the first time, confer the exclusive power within their boundaries of cleansing, sewering, paving, and providing a supply of water."[1] In their details the provisions showed that six years' campaigning by Chadwick and the Health of Towns Association had left its mark. Thus, it was provided that no new house might be built without drains of the size, materials, level, and fall prescribed by the local surveyor, nor without a sufficient water-closet or privy or ash-pit; a house within a hundred feet of a sewer might be required to communicate with it, and in the default of the owner the Local Board were empowered to construct such communicating drains, and recover the cost so incurred (ss. 49, 50). The Local Board —to take a further example—were given powers to provide a water supply, either under public management or on contract with a private company; the supply to be pure and wholesome, and at high pressure. But it was not lawful for the Local Board to supply water if there were a water company already in the district able and willing to do it adequately, on terms fixed by an inspector or an arbitrator. A householder might be required to obtain a water supply, if it could be furnished for a sum not exceeding 2d. a week (ss. 75, 76).

A General District Rate for the purposes of the Act was to be levied on the occupiers of property rated to the relief of the poor, and Private Improvement Rates imposed for works benefiting individual occupiers (ss. 87, 88, 90). To raise money for works of a permanent nature, the rates might be mortgaged by the Local Board. Such mortgage could be made only with the consent of the General Board (ss. 107, 119).

Tenuous as was the element of "centralisation" in the Act, the Lords, responding to Chadwick's concealed guidance, had left the General Board with more aggressive functions than the Commons had been prepared to grant. That is the answer to those later critics who have dismissed the Act scornfully as a "small scheme."[2] Small as it was, it was as much as the Commons could swallow; and very much bigger, in fact, than the sadly botched measure which had been passed from the lower House to the Lords, where Chadwick's friends managed to repair some

[1] *Hansard*, vol. xcviii, p. 736, 5 May 1848.
[2] J. L. and B. Hammond, *Lord Shaftesbury*, pp. 159–60.

of the damage done by the opposition in the Commons. The original Bill was not shaped to Chadwick's liking, as he pointed out to those who saddled its imperfections upon him; and the Act which eventually emerged represented no more than what his adroitness and tenacity had succeeded in preserving after Morpeth's draft had been shot to pieces in the lower House. It was a continual lament of Chadwick's that the schemes of his conception had to be put into the clumsy hands of politicians, and that, after a Parliamentary mauling, the resultant patchwork of compromise and amendment was passed back to him to make into a practical working measure. He might then with good reason deny the paternity of this mongrel measure; but sufficient remained of a recognisable structure for it to be acknowledged as at any rate a family connection of the Poor Law Act of 1834. Such strength and purpose as the Act exhibited, it owed chiefly to Chadwick. This is evident in the ground plan it lays down for the relationship between the local authorities and the central Government. In the attitude adopted towards this fundamental problem by the Poor Law Act of 1834 and the Municipal Corporations Act of 1835 there was a sharp antithesis, the resolution of which supplies the key to half a century of administrative history. Apart from requiring Treasury sanction for the raising of loans by a Corporation and for the alienation of its property, the Municipal Corporations Act did little to restrict the traditional autonomy of the local authorities. On the other hand, apart from the control of police, it gave them no new powers. It left them, diverse in their customs and powers, unequal in their areas and reserves of skill, to meet the problems of the industrial age as best they could, with no Minister or State department charged to guide and teach, and if necessary to admonish and correct them. Against this conception, Chadwick had opposed the principles of the Poor Law Act, those administrative ideas which in the jargon of the time were known as "centralisation" —the tutelage of a specialised central department, exercised through the media of the departmental circular and an expert inspectorate; areas cut to a pattern drawn by the technical demands of administration; a uniform system of *ad hoc* bodies in the localities to serve as the instrument of central policy, entrusted with a minimum scope of function and expected to attain a minimum standard of performance. Nothing so clear-cut as this can be seen, of course, in the Act of 1848. But it was a great step forward that a central Board should have been established, an embryo Ministry of Health, with aggressive powers, however slight at first, to make head against sanitary evils; and that a beginning should have been made towards imposing a code of public health on the country, defining legal minimum standards for drainage and water supply. It was a great point gained that under the Act considerable powers for the defence of the public health and the construction of public works could be readily and cheaply conferred on authorities which had formerly lacked them. By stretching to the utmost the powers with which Parliament had endowed the central Board, by extending the imponderable authority which superior information and capable officers lent to a Government department, by attempting to persuade where to command was out of the question, Chadwick hoped even yet that the new Board would not fail in its appointed task.

One day in May 1848, in the middle of the struggle for the Public Health Bill, a clerk waited on Chadwick at Gwydyr House with an unexpected request—for information how his name should be entered for the Companionship of the Bath.

"All things and Lord John's previous displeasure considered, I was not a little surprised at the honour . . ." he confided to a friend.

"The Prince had made the recommendation as an observer. He had, I found, taken an interest in Sanitary questions and had read the reports.

"I have had one interview with him on the subject of the improvement of labourers' dwellings. I do not remember that I was ever better questioned. I must be strongly biased towards him, but from all I hear of him he appears to be a person who divested of his rank must take a very high position."[1]

The C.B., of which this was one of the first awards for civil services, was the only official recognition that Chadwick's labours were

---

[1] E. C. to W. D. Christie, 29 May 1848. He told W. E. Hickson (9 May 1848): "It was an unexpected and to me a strange affair not initiated by the Government."

to get until the last few months of his long life. It was well timed. At the end of the 1848 session Chadwick could look back on a decade of continuous agitation and inquiry in the cause of public health. At last, crowning the ten years of drudgery, a Public Health Act was on the Statute Book. The machinery for its execution at the centre and in the localities was in process of construction. In London a single authority was at work under his guidance, planning the drainage and water supply of the whole capital. Slowly, but with gathering momentum, the new values which the "Sanitary Idea" set before society were permeating the minds of law-makers and administrators.

N

PART TWO

THE GENERAL BOARD OF HEALTH

1848 – 1854

CHAPTER IX

CHOLERA, 1848–1849

THE six years Chadwick spent at Gwydyr House were the happiest in his official career. He lost for a time the sense of frustration which at the Poor Law Commission, "where all was going back under the evil influence of the Lewis's,"[1] had weighed down the natural buoyancy of his spirit. Sitting at his desk in Gwydyr House, and feeling an intricate administrative machine respond to the thrust of his will; sending out his Inspectors to put chastened local authorities on the cleanly path of tubular sewerage and constant supply; drafting his Bills and memoranda, advising Ministers, receiving deputations of local magnates; taking up with zest the burdens which fell from the fatigued hands of colleagues and subordinates; working twelve or fourteen hours a day; so occupied Chadwick was more content than at any time since the Government had put the Poor Law inquiry into his hands. It will be convenient here to indicate broadly the main problems which claimed his attention. The first in point of urgency and immediate importance in 1848 was the cholera epidemic, the subject of the present chapter. Secondly, throughout the six years the Engineering Inspectors of the General Board were active in the localities, investigating, advising, educating, bringing some two hundred places and over two million people under the Public Health Act. They made blunders here and there, but on the whole this missionary work in the provinces was done well; and it forms the permanent and most successful achievement of the Board. It will be described in Chapters 13 and 14 below. Thirdly, London was a problem on its own, calling for special treatment both on account of its political importance as the capital city and its administrative complexity as the greatest assemblage of people and buildings in the world.

[1] E. C. to W. D. Christie, 29 May 1848.

In London Chadwick met defeat. He failed at the Metropolitan Commission of Sewers to produce a workable plan for the main drainage of the capital. He failed again to replace the anarchy of the burial trade by a planned service under a public monopoly such as he had been advocating since the Interments Report of 1843. He failed finally to break the hold of the water companies and give Londoners the benefits of a publicly owned water supply. The reasons for these three failures will be examined in Chapters 10, 11, and 12; as a result of them the administrative consolidation of London which Chadwick planned had advanced no further than the first step, the unification of the seven Metropolitan Commissions of Sewers. From the end of 1851 Chadwick and his two allies at the Board were on the defensive. Inside Gwydyr House the harmony which at first prevailed was broken when the well-disposed Carlisle was followed by one President actively malevolent and two others indifferent and uncooperative. Outside, with the passing of the cholera, the popular enthusiasm for sanitary reform rapidly subsided; while a score of threatened interests fought in the Press and Government offices to discredit the Board. The decline and fall of the Board will be described in the last three chapters.

Chadwick's self-esteem which at times degenerated into arrogance, his inflexibility of thought, his irritability in the face of criticism, combined to make him an uncomfortable colleague. At Somerset House he had shown that he expected to be first in authority as he was first in knowledge; and that if he could not rule, he would be leader of the opposition. By good fortune, rather than by conscious intention on the part of the Cabinet, he now found himself associated with two men who were fundamentally in agreement with his views, and who in consequence either could see no objection to his proposals, or curbed their opposition for the sake of a smooth-running unanimity. The reformers had indeed been put in office: Chadwick, the brains of the public health agitation, Southwood Smith, its chief organiser, Lord Ashley, the chairman of the London Health of Towns Association. Chadwick, waiting in trepidation for the name of the colleague whom the unpredictable workings of patronage would thrust upon him, was delighted at Ashley's appointment. "It afforded to the Country a guarantee of earnestness, sympathy for suffering, singleness of purpose in labouring for its relief."[1] They presented a strong contrast, the eupeptic Chadwick, who had his disappointments but never his doubts, who entered on every task with such unclouded confidence; and the self-questioning Ashley, with his "prolonged fits of despondency," "whose views are usually the reverse of sanguine."[2] One characteristic they had in common: they both liked their own way; and it is a remarkable fact that in six years of collaboration these two masterful men never clashed. Partly, perhaps, it was because there was a natural division of function between them. For Chadwick undisputed authority at Gwydyr House, the shaping of measures, the delights of power wielded behind the scenes; for Ashley the Parliamentary limelight, the influencing of audiences, the satisfaction of doing good conspicuously. In this way the clauses that Chadwick had had in mind since the time of the *Sanitary Report* appeared before the public in 1851, and went down to history as "Lord Shaftesbury's Lodging Houses Bill."[3] Their agreement was based, however, on something deeper than complementary capacities and spheres of action. Lord Ashley, the Evangelical of the Evangelicals, and Edwin Chadwick, who probably never felt any religious emotion in his life, had a body of beliefs in common, and the currents of their thought—springing from sources so widely separated—yet ran in parallel channels. They dreaded that the sullen resentment of the neglected workers might organise itself behind the Trade Union leaders and the Six Points men. They maintained that if a Chartist millennium were to be averted, the governing classes must free the governed from the sharp spur of their misery, by improving the physical conditions of their lives, and by bringing them under the influence of that judicious education whose conservative power had been known to the privileged since the days of Plato. They saw the remedy in the intervention of the impartial power of Government to check the more obvious crudities of exploitation, and to raise a bulwark for the unprotected against organised economic interests and local governing cliques.

Far from colliding, therefore, these two strong wills supported

[1] E. C. to Lord Ashley, 28 September 1848.
[2] E. C. to F. O. Ward, 1 June 1855; to ?, n.d., c. 1852.
[3] E. C. to M. Charles Verge, n.d., c. 1890.

and encouraged each other, giving to the activity of the Board a multiplied energy. There was firmness, too, in the unobtrusive Southwood Smith, who at the age of seventeen had thrown up a scholarship for conscientious reasons, and who was fond of saying that "Life is not long enough for us to reconsider our decisions."[1] But he was slow—"deliberate," Chadwick called it, to avoid the less kindly adjectives employed by others—and at times of pressure his more forceful friend fretted to see papers accumulating in the Doctor's unhurrying hands. When Southwood Smith suggested that he might act as Secretary to the new Board, Chadwick was firm in his refusal. The post was inconsistent with the Doctor's business habits.[2] Eventually he entered the Board by a side door—the clause of the Nuisances Act which permitted the appointment of a medical member.[3] It was not a gracious entrance for a man whose name was linked with Chadwick's as a pioneer of sanitary reform, nor was it a propitious introduction of medical science to the counsels of the Board. There was always a hint of supercilious amusement, not untouched with jealousy, in Chadwick's attitude to the Doctor, whose heart was bigger than his head.

The easy-going Lord Morpeth was never quite at home at Gwydyr House, with the ebullient Chadwick and the sombre, moody Shaftesbury, both in their different ways so earnest in their sanitary labours. Chadwick he sincerely respected, but found him, with his strong-minded views about every subject that arose, a constant source of embarrassment. He thought it wise to warn at once this formidable colleague of his, who was entering office with expectations sharpened by a series of disappointments, and who over a decade had been maturing large-scale plans of reform: "Whenever I may be inclined upon any occasion, such as I hope and believe will be rare, not fully to go along with you, it will probably arise from a wish to temper too sudden a strain after perfection by what I may feel to be the most practicable modes of dealing successfully with Parliaments and Bodies of men."[4]

There was no question who was master. The voice of the Board was the voice of Chadwick. The majority of the docu-

---

[1] C. L. Lewes, op. cit., p. 4.   [2] E. C. to Southwood Smith, 11 August 1848.
[3] *London Gazette*, 5 October 1848, p. 3615.
[4] Lord Morpeth to E. C., 4 September 1848.

ments they issued came from his pen; the remainder were revised
by him, frequently to the extent of being almost rewritten. When
Ashley and Morpeth spoke in the House, they were briefed by
Chadwick. The Poor Law mutineer had at last a command of
his own, and he was fortunate to have it manned by men who
were ready to give a proper deference to his massive knowledge,
and who would not dissipate time and energy in untidy dis-
sensions.

The first task was to get a staff together. The Government were
uneasily awaiting an attack on their expenditure which was
threatened from all sides in the coming session. When Chadwick
called at the Treasury, Sir Charles Trevelyan, the Permanent
Secretary, assumed an expression "almost of fright at the idea of
being asked for any money; and before I could enter into any
explanations with him he began to exhort that expense might be
spared." But when Chadwick outlined his modest demands, he
"relaxed and highly approved."[1] A Secretary (Henry Austin) at
£400 a year, an Assistant Secretary (Professor Alexander Bain)
at £300, one copying clerk, the messengers and housekeepers
already on duty in Gwydyr House[2]—not even the most apprehensive of Treasury officials could charge the Board with extravagance in staffing an office which was to have control of a new
and complicated field of administration, and to conduct correspondence with local authorities in all parts of England, Wales,
and Scotland. Chadwick had cut his requirements to the bone to
avert Treasury opposition, and when, a week later, his own salary
was publicly announced at £1,200 instead of the £1,500 he had
expected, he felt that the time for protest had arrived. It was
lower than that of an Enclosure Commissioner, an Usher of the
Black Rod, a Town Clerk of Manchester or Liverpool; not to
mention the Secretaries of railway and trading companies—for,
unlike this niggardly Government, commerce knew the wisdom
of rewarding the enterprise and ability of its servants.[3] He got
his £1,500.

The Treasury objected even to the Board's estimate for the

[1] E. C. to Lord Morpeth, 4 September 1848.
[2] Board of Health to the Treasury, 26 September 1848.
[3] E. C. to Lord Morpeth, 30 September 1848. MS. notes, "Payments for
superior service," 1848.

price of a seal, and Chadwick was obliged to send Austin out to
see what could be bought cheaply second-hand.[1] Such cheese-
paring would be merely comic if it did not reveal that the Government conceived of the scope of the new department as being no
more than a subordinate function of a subordinate Minister. At
Chadwick's suggestion, Morpeth urged that two medical observers
should be sent to the Continent as in 1831 to watch the advance
of the cholera and report on the steps which foreign Governments
were taking to meet it. What was the use, replied Sir Charles
Wood, when no one mode of treatment had been found to answer
in all places?[2] It would take more than an impending epidemic
to stampede the Chancellor of the Exchequer into incurring a bill
for a medical wild-goose chase over half Europe.

In ministerial circles a new Board meant places to be distributed, friends to be obliged, and supporters to be placated.
Chadwick, recruiting his staff, had never known the pressure of
applications so heavy; but he had been given a free hand, and he
dropped no crumbs for the hungry crowd of expectants who waited
at the door of the Patronage Secretary. He warned Lord Morpeth,
who had a kindly man's easiness and a Whig's sensibility to the
claims of family and party:[3] "For myself I was early disposed to
accept and act upon favourable representations of men, until the
contrary was proved, and I have paid most bitterly for it. I have
been convinced against my own will that a reverse rule is the
sound one for ordinary cases; but in our peculiar work, I cannot
but feel that it is a strong necessity. To take for granted, to
presume that all will be well, that error may be easily rectified;
that to use Lord Melbourne's expression, "things will shake
right" and as we wish them is the most easy and pleasurable

----

[1] It was fully in character for Chadwick to turn the tables by conducting an
inquiry into the cost of manufacturing seals. He found that the contract price
for seals was £40; yet equally good seals had been obtained for the Sewers
Commission for £5; and with a little thought he himself devised a method of
making superior seals for £2. He received no thanks for his pains. "The
subsequent conversations with the Treasury on minor subjects had been curt
and disobliging and in a tone open to the inference that the inevitable
explanations referred to had by no means promoted cordiality." (MS. notes,
"Administrative Relations of General Board with Treasury," n.d.).
[2] Lord Morpeth to E. C., 18 September 1848. One Medical Inspector
(R. D. Grainger) was eventually sent to Hamburg for a few weeks.
[3] E. C. to Lord Morpeth, 18 September 1848.

course: to scrutinize, to cross-examine, and to refuse: to watch and remove or reprove for partial failures, is disagreeable to me; but not other people's money, but literally extensive life and death, others' pain and misery depend upon the performance of this duty." It was thus no help to a candidate to bring to Gwydyr House a chit from the Treasury or a powerful friend. In selecting the Board's Superintending Inspectors Chadwick looked for men who were not blinded by indurated professional habits, and whose practical experience fitted them to understand the novel combination of works which was the heart of his sanitary scheme. There was Robert Rawlinson, for example, the young Manchester engineer, who had startled the Liverpool Council by his brilliant plan for bringing water to the city from the Bala Lake in Wales, seventy-two miles away; William Ranger, a former lecturer at the College of Civil Engineering at Putney, whose experience had been gained in the Fens and on Pevensey level; George Thomas Clark, railway engineer and archæologist, who had written on public health for the *Westminster Review*, and was later to make a name as the master of the Dowlais ironworks; Edward Cresy, the author of a standard *Encyclopædia of Civil Engineering*, and an expert on hydraulics as applied to house and main drainage; James Smith, "Smith of Deanston," the authority on agricultural drainage, an old ally from the Health of Towns Commission. As Secretary he had named another young engineer, Henry Austin, brother-in-law of Charles Dickens, who had earned Chadwick's special esteem by his plan for draining the low districts of towns by steam power, and who was fighting Chadwick's battles before the Metropolitan Sewers Commission. The selection of such men as these did not make for easier relations with the Treasury subalterns, but it put under Chadwick's command a small corps of competent investigators, most of them young and flexible in outlook, all of them possessed of enthusiasm for the new principles of sanitary engineering, and of practical capacity to carry them out on the spot.

By September 1848 Chadwick already had news of applications in agitation at York, Plymouth, Rotherham, Llanelly, and Barnstaple; while "a Candidate for employment is getting up a movement from Newcastle."[1] In December he was able to report

[1] E. C. to Lord Morpeth, 20 September 1848.

to Lord John Russell that seventy-five places had applied, including Derby, Wolverhampton, Dover, Portsmouth, Gloucester, Worcester, Preston, and Leicester—a body of applications which put an end to the talk of universal resistance. While the Continent was "convulsed with questions of privilege and sentiment affecting the labouring classes, which will commonly make bad worse," he was sanguine that they would achieve striking results "by avoiding the metaphysical, and by pursuing a quiet but strong course of physical improvement (in which I would submit that it is most important that the Government, and the natural leaders should take and keep the lead)."[1] Eschew political metaphysics; aim at the practical in social reform; put your trust in Government —no better illustration than this recipe for English statesmen could be given of Chadwick's position in that current of thought which arises in Bentham at the beginning of the century and flows into Fabianism at its end.

For the next fifteen months, however, though the Inspectors pushed on steadily with their local inquiries, the main energies of the Board were directed towards the task of fighting, with limited powers and a handful of overworked officers, the epidemic which for the last year had been leisurely traversing the Continent. The cholera had marched from Moscow to the Danube as the Commons began to discuss the Public Health Bill; scattered cases were reported from Berlin as it passed the Lords. The dread shadow overcast the debates, and from time to time legislators threw uneasy glances over their shoulders at its steady advance. To meet the challenge the General Board had only the exiguous powers of the Nuisances Removal and Diseases Prevention Act, as amended in 1848 (11 & 12 Vict., c. 123); and before they could employ even this weapon they must wait until the Privy Council should deem the danger sufficiently acute, and issue an Order in Council permitting them to use these emergency powers for a period of six months. Not until such an Order was published could a medical member be added to the Board or directions be issued by them for the cleansing of streets and dwelling houses by the Guardians of the Poor. Another year elapsed, and the epidemic was nearing its height, before powers

[1] E. C. to Lord John Russell, 5 December 1848.

were granted to the Board and the Poor Law Guardians to institute prosecutions for violation or neglect of the Board's regulations (12 & 13 Vict., c. 111, ss. iii, iv). From the first, then, in
this important field of their activity, the one which for over
twelve months bulked largest in the public eye, the Board's
authority was circumscribed by an ancient jurisdiction stubbornly
maintained by the Privy Council Office.

Fearful and guilty local authorities could not at first bring
themselves to admit that the retribution they had seen approaching with a steady inevitability was now really upon them. The
earliest cases of cholera were hushed up or laid to the account of
some less dreaded malady. But by the end of September 1848 it
could not be concealed that the disease had begun its work in
England; and, as the Metropolitan Sanitary Commission had
predicted, it appeared by a kind of hereditary succession in those
neglected districts where plagues and fevers were bred anew for
each generation. In Leith the first case was in the same house in
1848 as in 1832. In Bermondsey it was near the same ditch. In
Pollokshaws the first victim died in the same room and even the
same bed as sixteen years before.[1] Amongst the earliest places
attacked in London was Fore Street, Lambeth, where "the
miserable inhabitants look more like ghouls and maniacs than
human beings," where the doorways at high tide were blocked
with boards and plaster to prevent the river getting in, and the
surgeon made his way to his patients along planks laid over two
feet of water.[2]

The two sailors from the Hamburg vessel at Horsleydown had
undoubtedly died of Asiatic cholera, Chadwick informed the
editor of *The Times* on 6 October. There had been two more
undeniable cases in Lambeth, two in Sunderland, five in Edinburgh.[3] The ripples of the epidemic were beginning to widen.
Sitting in the midst of their cesspools and dungheaps, the local
authorities were fluttering in apprehension. The Sheerness
Guardians were in a panic, reported *The Times*. They had
reason to be. "The offal of a population of eight thousand lies
upon the surface of the streets and alleys in its most disgusting
form. The only resemblance to a drain is a ditch which surrounds

[1] *Report on the Epidemic Cholera of 1848 and 1849*, p. 18; *P.P.*, 1850 vol. xxi, p. 3.
[2] *Times*, 28 October 1848.   [3] E. C. to J. T. Delane, 6 October 1848.

the town, full of black and stagnant matter, and forms the last receptacle for all the carrion that is too bulky and offensive to wither in the streets."[1]

On 2 October an Order in Council gave the Board powers for six months under the Nuisances Act, and three days later they published their first Notification in the *London Gazette*. To understand the administrative measures that it prescribed it must be remembered that the Board had no conception that the causal agent of cholera was a self-propagating micro-organism, discharged in the evacuations of the sufferer, and borne to the next victim in contaminated water or on the feet of that filthy feeder, the house-fly. They were not even aware that cholera was a specific infection, as distinct in its nature from plague and typhus as the elephant from the giraffe and camel. The plague of Alexandria, in their view, was the typhus of Whitechapel; yellow fever differed from ordinary fever only in intensity; and the cholera also was no more than a virulent form of those familiar crowd diseases which killed thousands every year in the slums of the great towns. The doctrine that one epidemic differed essentially from another Southwood Smith wrote off as an eighteenth-century error. Under the influence of the "epidemic atmosphere" it was possible for mild indigenous fever to develop into the most deadly of plagues; and, in support of this, Southwood Smith claimed that, six months before the cholera epidemic broke out in 1832, he had observed that cases of typhus in London were taking on characteristics approximating to cholera.[2] The Board were convinced therefore, that every case of diarrhœa—resembling as it did the first onset of the epidemic—was potentially a case of cholera. There is a consequent confusion, both in the methods of treatment they advised and in their accounts of the progress of the epidemic. The medicines prescribed in their Notifications were directed at the symptoms of diarrhœa, and the medical visitors were instructed to seek out all cases of looseness of the bowels. If any such cases did not pass into developed cholera, they were acclaimed as victories of medical science. Hence, since they found sixty cases of diarrhœa, the great majority of which were amenable

[1] *Times*, 24 October 1848.
[2] *Report of the General Board of Health on Quarantine*, p. 12; *P.P.*, 1849, vol. xxiv, p. 137.

to treatment, to every cholera death, the Board had a highly inflated opinion of the efficacy of their methods.

Opposed to the Board's theory was that of a large minority of the medical profession who retained the traditional belief in specific contagion. But if it were true, declared the Board, that anyone who touched a patient might himself develop the disease or transmit its *contagium vivum* to the next person with whom he shook hands, then the general practitioner on his rounds would leave a trail of death behind him; and every member of the General Board of Health must have fallen victim to cholera or typhus, since from morning to night they were receiving visits from medical inspectors just returned from the worst localities. Indeed, it was difficult to see how the human race had managed to survive so long, if every epidemic disease could thus propagate itself in all directions. Rejecting such absurdities, the Board directed attention towards those physical factors in the environment with which they believed disease to be associated. In the Report published in August 1850, in which they described their activity during the epidemic, they gave a list of ten of these "localising" or "predisposing" causes—overcrowding; filth; malaria from putrescent mud; dampness; want of drains and bad drains; graveyards; unwholesome water; food; fatigue; and purgatives.[1] The one "cause" on which the modern epidemiologist would fasten, unwholesome water, ranks seventh in the list, and is regarded, not as the vehicle for infection, but merely as a predisposing agent.

In the London of 1848 it was only too easy to point to some adjacent nastiness or offence to the nose to which a local outbreak could be attributed. "The epidemic was no respecter of classes, but was a great respecter of localities," wrote Dr. Sutherland, one of the Board's medical inspectors. "Rich and poor suffered alike or escaped alike, according as they lived in the observance or violation of the laws of their physical well-being."[2] They were attacked when they lived near the Regent's Canal, which had not been cleaned out for twenty-five years, or near the two acres of refuse accumulated in a suburb of Hull; when they lived in the Potteries with their three thousand pigs and their fat-boiling plant, or in the Taunton girls' school, where sixty-seven girls

[1] *Report of the General Board of Health on Quarantine*, pp. 37–67. [2] Ibid., p. 73.

were crowded into one sleeping room, with an average of sixty-eight cubic feet of breathing space each.[1] On the other hand, there were remarkable instances where the avoidance of filth had preserved lives as by a kind of providence. Hector Gavin reported the case of a well supplying a dozen houses, which was surrounded by four cesspools within a radius of twelve yards. The water was as thick as soup with seeping matter, and the landlord's agent was obliged to pump for an hour every morning before it ran clear enough for use. Of the eighty-five occupants of the houses, twenty-two did not use the well, and all escaped, while forty-six of the remaining sixty-three were attacked by choleraic diarrhœa.[2]

Under the terms of the Nuisances Act Chadwick's regulations were directed to the Poor Law Guardians, but he framed them avowedly with the object of concentrating power and responsibility in the hands of the Union medical officers. All places certified by them to be dangerous to health were to be cleansed every twenty-four hours; they were to inspect lodging-houses, and require the landlord to ventilate them; where a family inhabited a single room, they were empowered to order the removal of the patient or, alternatively, of as many as they deemed necessary of the other occupants. Dispensaries were to be opened at convenient stations, to supply remedies and advice on bowel complaints; and also "Houses of Refuge," to which endangered families might be removed. Believing as they did, that while the "epidemic atmosphere" prevailed, any case of diarrhœa might develop into cholera, the Board instructed the Guardians to have the infected districts combed out daily for such cases by a small squad of qualified officers. For the same reason they advised that all foods which tended to irritate the bowels should be avoided, every variety of green vegetables, for example, and all kinds of fruit; the diet should be solid rather than fluid, and animal rather than vege-table. They also placed a maternal insistence on the importance of warm clothing, and recommended the wearing of flannel next to the skin.[3] All such advice was rather remote from the actualities

---

[1] *Report of the General Board of Health on Quarantine*, pp. 49, 45–6, 43, 37–8.

[2] Seventh Notification, *London Gazette*, p. 2683.

[3] Notification in respect to Nuisances Removal and Diseases Prevention Act, *London Gazette*, 6 October 1848, pp. 3616–20. Second Notification, ibid., 31 October 1848, pp. 3875–84. Special Notification to Captains of Merchant Ships, Steamers and Colliers, 1 December 1848, pp. 4386–9.

of life in Whitechapel and Bethnal Green, where many thousands of those in the greatest danger were in no position to pick and choose their daily dietary or change their clothing to order.

Outside Gwydyr House, with its confidence and calm certainty, schism and dissension split the ranks of the medical profession. Cholera bewildered the doctors. "*Quot medici, tot sententiæ,*" observed *The Times*.[1] Theories as to its cause poured in to the *Lancet* and *The Times*, ranging from Budd's "Fungus Theory" and Snow's remarkable anticipations, to hypotheses thin spun by vast ingenuity from a handful of selected facts. Lea urged his "Geological Theory" that cholera miasm became toxic only when acted on by the calcareous and magnesium salts in water; while a Mr. Baggs lectured at the Polytechnic on "its dependence on the electric state of the atmosphere," stating that "this view of the subject is original."[2] One physician recommended a nostrum from an ancient Arabian manuscript;[3] another outlined how to treat a case on algebraic principles. "In our profession," commented Dr. Sutherland drily, "every new occurrence, an epidemic, or a new remedy, or an extraordinary case of disease, is attended by violent literary symptoms."[4]

While the doctors thus disagreed amongst themselves, it was inevitable that they should watch with jealous eyes the intrusion of a lay Board into their professional field. Chadwick had wanted his new department to be called "The General Board of Works and Health," or some such name, which would make it clear that its functions were chiefly in relation to those environmental factors which affected the public health. But a Board of Health it was, and presently it was being looked to for rulings on medical questions. The mutterings of the Colleges of Physicians and Surgeons grew louder. It was a strange Board of Health which occupied itself mainly with house-drains and water-pipes. Under it three laymen, two nobles and a lawyer, prescribed treatment, civil engineers analysed mortality rates, and a farmer (Smith of Deanston) conducted inquiries into the sources of disease—while the one medical member of the Board, added apparently as a kind of afterthought, drafted regulations for sweeping streets and emptying privies. Chadwick, with his oft-expressed desire to put

[1] *Times*, 1 September 1848.   [2] Ibid., 25 August 1848.
[3] Ibid., 14 September 1848.   [4] Dr. J. Sutherland to E. C., n.d. 1848.

O

doctors out of business, was the main target, and when the Treasury cut the allowances of the Board's medical inspectors to two guineas a day, there was an outcry against his "poor law parsimony" and "enmity to the profession."[1] The cholera notifi-cations led to open conflict between the Board and the two Royal Colleges. The *Lancet* sneered at the "extempore doctors" and the "zymotic gibberish of Dr. Southwood Smith."[2] The College of Physicians published a counter notification, which in contrast with the Board's warnings about fruit and vegetables imposed no restrictions on diet, and there was a brisk exchange on the subject of the cabbage as a predisponent to cholera. Though Morpeth congratulated Chadwick on having "cabbaged" the physicians,[3] the dispute did nothing to dissipate the impression that the Board was dominated by an unprofessional meddler.

It had been a mistake not to consult the medical corporations before issuing the cholera notification, a mistake which the Board tried to correct when an epidemic again threatened the country in 1853. Chadwick endeavoured to make his peace with the College of Physicians by a studiously courteous letter which he drafted for Morpeth's signature,[4] but he did not do so with a single mind. He was in no wise repentant. He had been criticised for his impertinence in offering a layman's judgment in technical questions; but his private (and far from silent) opinion was that the physicians were now seeking to annex as a medical province a field of investigation which he himself had opened up, and were presuming to set themselves up as the supreme authority on a subject about which most of them were grossly ignorant until the appearance of his *Sanitary Report*. He always doubted the "success of mere medicine,"[5] and tended to minimise the importance of the medical practitioner, whose training was to cure rather than to prevent. Medical men, he told Morpeth, were much divided amongst themselves; they distrusted each other; and the schools that distrusted medicine altogether were large and increasing.[6]

[1] E. C. to Sir George Grey, 18 October 1848.
[2] *Lancet*, 7 July and 9 August 1849.
[3] Lord Morpeth to E. C., 17 October 1848.
[4] E. C. to Lord Morpeth, 16 October 1848. The letter was published in the *Lancet* on 16 December 1848.
[5] E. C. to Lord Morpeth, 16 October 1848.
[6] E. C. to Lord Morpeth, 20 August 1848.

Clearly he conceived that the engineer, bringing abundant pure water to the poor and flushing away their refuse cleanly and expeditiously, and the architect, designing for them dry and airy dwellings, would between them throw out of employment a large proportion of the profession which lived on the ills of mankind.

Chadwick's scorn, it should be remembered, was directed at a profession which had yet to take itself in hand by the Medical Act of 1858. It should be remembered further that his narrow conception of the part the doctor was to play in public health administration was rooted in the theory that disease was a product of a deleterious environment. But whatever the reasons—and to those just noted we should undoubtedly add Chadwick's own superb self-confidence—his attitude crystallised into the principle that the professional medical expert should be subject to lay administrative control. For this he advanced two main arguments. First, no pharmacopœia could supply the preventive remedies he advised; they were to be dispensed, not by the apothecary, but by the engineer and the architect; while the prescriptions required must be written out in the form of Acts and regulations by the legal practitioner. Secondly, in the public interest the Board of Health must be quite free to adopt new views at once from whatever quarter they might come. Now the greatest obstacle to the progress of medical science was the "fixed professional opinion" of the medical men. They had ruined Harvey, and opposed Jenner. A lay Board, however, would not be held back from advocating new views by the fear that these would injure their practice or professional position. The same lesson was taught by experience in other fields. "It is a well known fact that in the church the brightest ornaments owe their elevation not to episcopal but to lay patronage. Nelson would never have got forward with a Board of Old Admirals."[1] Chadwick thus inaugurated a debate on the relations between medical officers and administrative civil servants which continued for more than half a century after the fall of the General Board; and which was not finally resolved until by a Minute of August 1919 the Chief Medical Officer of the Ministry of Health was given the pay and status of a Permanent Secretary, and permitted direct access to the

[1] "Notes on the hostile attitude of the College of Physicians to the preventive work of the Board of Health," MS., n.d.

Minister in order to submit proposals and discuss matters falling within his responsibility.

Meanwhile, leaving Morpeth to soothe the offended physicians, Chadwick was deploying his slender forces to meet the attack of the cholera. The appointment of two medical inspectors, Dr. John Sutherland and Dr. R. D. Grainger, had been sanctioned by the Treasury, and of these one, Sutherland, was immediately ordered to Edinburgh to aid and encourage the Scottish towns.[1] The police and the Poor Law Board were warned. A circular to the Bishops suggested that the clergy take the lead in calling the attention of the parochial authorities to the need for preventive measures. Chadwick was busy preparing regulations for the medical inspection and purifying of suspected vessels, when without warning Sir William Pym, the arch-contagionist at the Privy Council Office, clamped down a quarantine. Was this, fumed Chadwick, how a new department, whose influence was moral rather than legal, should be ushered in—by public contempt of one of its fundamental propositions?[2] The quarantine was so much ink on paper; as in 1831, when almost the only ships put under restraint by the cordon on the Wear had sailed from Dutch ports where no cholera cases had occurred. Even if it were not so ineffective in its administration, it was too late. The shipping interests appealed to the Board to intervene, and the medical officer of the Customs called on Chadwick to confide his own private opinion of its flagrant absurdity. But no answer came from the Privy Council to the Board's remonstrance,[3] though in the end, when it could no longer be denied that cholera was already busy in both England and Scotland, Pym agreed to lift his quarantine.

The Poor Law Unions, with their surgeons and fever wards, were better equipped to fight an epidemic than the vestry committees and volunteer bodies of sixteen years before. But Chadwick, who a month before the cholera broke out had complacently reassured Lord Lansdowne of the strength of this new machinery

---

[1] E. C. to Lord Morpeth, 5 October 1848.
[2] E. C. to Lord ? , 10 October 1848.
[3] Minute, undated, of October 1848. Also "Notes on the Privy Council administration on quarantine and other Laws," MS., n.d.

of his designing,[1] soon perceived that the legislature had committed a grave error in entrusting the execution of the Diseases Prevention Act to the Guardians. From their Board rooms the Guardians viewed the needs of one class only, the destitute; they were now called upon to meet a collective emergency which threatened all classes, the ratepayer as much as the pauper, without any consideration for that important if indistinct line which marked off the respectable and self-supporting from the disreputable and dependent. They were set up as a breakwater to protect property against the rising tide of pauperism, and the master principle of their administration was "to do nothing except on application, and then only upon proof given of the urgency of the case."[2] They were now asked to forget their rate books, and take the initiative in seeking out opportunities for the exercise of their new powers. Most of them stuck in their Poor Law rut. "They could not comprehend the duty of *searching for* objects of relief."[3] Preventive measures were regarded as common medical relief, to be given only upon the order of the medical officer, issued after inquiry and adjudication. Where a portion of the workhouse was set apart as a "House of Refuge," the workhouse test was applied to those who sought admission. "The majority of the Guardians," Dr. Sutherland reported after a visit to the Sculcoates Union, "consists of country people who would meet as often as you like, discuss for ever, and agree to nothing."[4] In the towns the Guardians were usually too fully occupied with their existing functions to find time to master these new and unusual duties. When they did act, they did so on the narrowest view of the situation. Not until cholera had unmistakably appeared in a district would they order whitewashing and cesspool cleansing, and strengthen the hands of their medical officers. Execution of the General Board's orders was generally postponed until the Guardians held their regular weekly meetings, the only motive for delay that the Inspectors could discover being "the hope on the part of the Guardians that the epidemic would have passed before the orders were executed, and that therefore the expense

[1] E. C. to Lord Lansdowne, 29 August 1848.
[2] *Report on the Epidemic Cholera of 1848 and 1849*, p. 138.
[3] Seventh Notification, *London Gazette*, 18 September 1849, p. 2863.
[4] Dr. J. Sutherland to E. C., 2 October 1848.

might possibly be saved."[1] When, for example, the Board ordered the Guardians of St. George the Martyr, Southwark (where more had died from cholera than in any district except Lambeth) to appoint three extra medical assistants, consideration of the order was put off from one weekly meeting to the next; twelve days passed; and then the Guardians resolved not to comply.[2] It was in vain that the Board urged that expense could not be avoided in time of public calamity; that "in this case economy is on the side of humanity, and the most expensive of all things is to do nothing." It was in vain that they pointed out that if money were not spent in saving life, it must be spent in maintaining pauper widows and orphans; that the funerals of cholera victims in London had already cost £50,000; that Lambeth must for years support 61 cholera widows and 226 cholera orphans; that from one small court, Pea-hen Court, had come one widow and 12 orphans, whose support would cost the parish of St. Ethelburga not less than £420—which might have been saved if £30 had been spent in putting the court in a proper sanitary condition.[3] Closing their eyes to Chadwick's figures, the Guardians of the Poor continued to regard themselves as the guardians of the rates.

In many places Town Councils and Improvement Commissioners pressed forward to take over duties from the paralysed hands of Union and parochial boards. The result of their zeal, however, was that powers and responsibilities were split between a number of rival authorities; and cholera sufferers died while their cases were being referred from one body to another. The first and most obvious necessity, cried Chadwick, was unity of action, and the first and most obvious defect of the law was that such unity of action was impossible. Four months before the epidemic broke out, he had suggested that the terms of the Diseases Prevention Act would surely permit the General Board to set up special Boards to take charge of preventive measures in the localities, as had been done in 1831–2.[4] The Law Officers had refused to sanction this "large remedial interpretation";[5] and the result was now plain in the reports of delay, expense, and loss of life

---

[1] Seventh Notification, p. 2682.   [2] Ibid., p. 2682.   [3] Ibid., p. 2863.
[4] "Memorandum as to provisions for the Cholera," MS., 24 May 1848.
[5] Minutes of General Board of Health, 1 August 1850.

coming in from all over the country. At Edinburgh Sutherland found five organisations doing the work of one. At Hull two Boards of Guardians, a Cleansing Board and two bodies of Sewage Commissioners shared duties which could be efficiently carried out only by a single authority. At Bristol part of the borough was under a Local Act, part was in the Clifton Union, part in the Bedminster Union; and the whole was under a Mayor and Corporation. "Who are the authorities in such a case, who are responsible for carrying out your regulations?" Chadwick was asked, "—and to whom am I to apply and urge forward in the good work?"[1] The weakness of divided command extended also to the centre. The Board's regulations went out to local bodies accustomed to look for their orders to another department of the central Government. At Sunderland Dr. Sutherland was not listened to because it was believed that the Poor Law Inspector was the proper person to advise on such matters. Chadwick at once wrote a letter of protest to Viscount Ebrington, sharp but "not undeservedly so," Morpeth agreed.[2] "In strict duty and in cases of emergency there ought to be no waiting for consultations of intermediate authorities who have and ought to have on such extraordinary occasions any intermediate discretion. People must not die that official forms may be gone through which are of no use."[3]

Scotland, which suffered the heaviest onslaught in the early months, possessed neither Boards of Guardians nor a General Board of Health. Chadwick proposed that while the epidemic raged the administration of health measures should be centralised in Edinburgh—and promptly brought down upon his head a storm of local jealousies. "Glasgow positively refused: they would not be placed below Edinburgh—not they! Aberdeen refused subjection to it in terms of violent abuse: if they communicated at all it should be direct with London."[4] A quaking deputation from Dumfries, where in the previous three weeks there had been 219 cases of cholera and 78 deaths, waited on the Board in London to ask for the assistance of a medical inspector;[5] yet,

[1] E. Gulson to E. C., 4 October 1848.
[2] Lord Morpeth to E. C., 13 October 1848.
[3] E. C. to Lord Ebrington, 13 October 1848.
[4] E. C. to Andrew Boardman, n.d. [5] Minutes, 5 December 1848.

returning home, they immediately fell to bickering with the medical men of the town over the fees to be paid for their extra-ordinary cholera services. Ashley was for sending a peremptory demand that medical assistants should be appointed without too close a scrutiny of the bill. Chadwick decided on a more concilia-tory course, and despatched his best man, John Sutherland, to talk some sense into the benighted parochialists. "My very spirit is crushed at the want of action of the people," he wrote to Chad-wick after his first day in the town. "In all my experience I have met nothing like it. Fair to look at and full of promises but no talk can be more empty. Anything but doing. The regulations of the Board appear to be so much waste paper." No dispen-saries, no House of Refuge, no house to house visitation! But after a week of Sutherland's drive and force of character, the parochial board, deflated but thankful, saw the cholera retreating from the town. "At the first effort everything looks well. Our cleansing is going on and our cholera cases are diminishing. The Committee of the Parochial Board will now do anything and I believe that both the General Board and I have their entire confidence and approval (with the exception of a recusant or two)."[1]

For fifteen months the tale of local inadequacy and short-sightedness went on. The medical officer of Cumnock complained that the parochial board refused to pay his charges for attendance on cholera cases. The Kingston Union declined point blank to appoint medical assistants or to publish notices of the provisions of the Public Health Act. The medical officer of Culross, who had urged the parochial board to take steps to carry out the Nuisances Act and the regulations of the General Board, was dismissed for his pains. The Guardians of Redruth refused to reimburse their Treasurer for paying District Visitors during the outbreak.[2] Summing up his experience in fighting cholera and ignorance in a score of towns in England and Scotland, Dr. Sutherland declared that the Sanitary Committee of Sheffield was "the only body in the country which had the enlightenment to perceive the full extent of their duty, and the courage and

---

[1] Dr. J. Sutherland to E. C., 7 December and 14 December 1848.

[2] Minutes, 23 January 1849; 3 February 1849; 12 January 1850; 25 February 1850.

energy to perform it. This, I believe, was done without regard
to expense, and in the firm conviction that apart altogether from
the humanity of the course they had taken, the ratepayers would
be large gainers in the ultimate saving of widowhood and orphanage which was, without doubt, effected."[1] The Committee began
to prepare as soon as cholera was reported in the country; taking
the Board's notifications as their guide, they embarked on a campaign of public cleansing, and consulted their medical officers
about the preventive measures desirable. To this Sutherland
attributes the fact that only seventy-six cases of cholera occurred
in the town, though 5,519 cases of "premonitory diarrhœa" were
discovered.

As the epidemic developed Chadwick became, as one friend
described him, "the busyest and necessarily most inaccessible man
in the empire."[2] Hardly a day passed without a meeting with
Southwood Smith and Ashley at Gwydyr House. There were
deputations to be cajoled and hectored, notifications to be drafted
for the *London Gazette*, orders to be telegraphed to Sutherland and
Grainger, the Poor Law Board to be spurred to further efforts,
the pretensions of Sir William Pym to be combated, another fat
Report to be prepared to condemn root and branch that relic of
pre-Chadwickian superstition, the quarantine system. And when
he had finished at Gwydyr House, he hurried round to the offices
of the Metropolitan Sewers Commission in Greek Street, and
there plunged into the great debate on the sewerage of London.
On 22 November 1848, Austin, the Secretary, told the Board,
in explanation of a gap of a month in the Minutes, that the pressure of business in drafting instructions, issuing forms, and attending to personal callers, equally numerous and more pressing
than the written applications, had made it impracticable to keep
the Board's records in order. In January 1849 Chadwick informed Lord John Russell that Austin was "overdone with work"
and Bain was "knocked up"; one Inspector had the premonitory
symptoms of cholera and another was down with fever; Lord
Ashley was away to recruit; "and Lord Carlisle excepted, it may
be said the Board of Health is very unwell."[3]

[1] *Report on the Epidemic Cholera of 1848 and 1849*, p. 107.
[2] J. H. Burton to E. C., 23 October 1848.
[3] E. C. to Lord John Russell, January 1849.

But the most severe test was yet to come. During the winter of 1848–9 the most violent outbreaks had occurred in Scotland, England escaping comparatively lightly—perhaps, as Snow ingeniously argued, because the English were not accustomed to drink much unboiled water in cold weather, while the Scots used it freely at all seasons to mix with spirits.[1] As the weather grew warmer, however, the figures for cholera deaths in London began to mount. Every day the excrement of a population of two millions poured into the Thames, the scouring force of whose current was checked by Teddington Lock; and with the ebb and flow of the tide, the stale water passed back and forth through London as the river regurgitated its filth. To protect the Londoner from this poisonous mass no defence was raised except the half-hearted filter systems adopted by some of the water companies. The situation was not improved when the Metropolitan Sewers Commission, acting on Chadwick's belief that filth in the river was less dangerous than filth in the sewers, recommended that the sewers be flushed regularly into the Thames. The low districts of the capital might have been constructed by design to serve as a culture medium for the breeding and nourishing of the germs of the epidemic.

The cholera broke over London in two waves. The first curve of mortality extended from the end of September 1848 to the end of March 1849, with 988 deaths, the highest point being 94 in the week ending 13 January 1849. Throughout April and May the epidemic was dormant, though every week recorded its deaths. In June it gathered strength, and the figures began to rise, the highest weekly mortality being 2,298 in the week ending 8 September 1849.[2]

Early in the spring of 1848 the Whitechapel Guardians had warned the landlords of their district in letters and personal interviews of the precautions which should be taken to meet the advancing cholera. The landlords weighed the cost against their tenants' risk, and decided to let the tenants take their chance. In December cholera crept into a dark hole of a cul-de-sac, called Hairbrain Court, which lodged 157 people in the thirty-two rooms of its thirteen houses. "In one house on the right side,"

---

[1] *On the Mode of Communication of Cholera* (1849), pp. 117–18.
[2] *Report on the Epidemic Cholera of 1848 and 1849*, pp. 12–13.

reported the Union Medical Officer, "a grandmother and grand-
child were laid out with the funeral paraphernalia of Roman
Catholics, while a husband, wife, and two children lay side by
side in the same room suffering from cholera. In the next house
a woman was lying in the last stage of the disease, who died a few
hours after. . . . There is a common privy at the end, and a
channel runs down the middle of the court, under which is a
drain, with branches right and left to the doors of the houses;
but these, not communicating with any sinks, serve as receptacles
for the filth which flows over from the privy, as appeared by one
of these branches then laid open for the purpose of being cleaned
out. Many of the children were dancing about on the heaps of
filth taken out of it. There is no supply of water for any of the
houses in this court, and the inhabitants have none but what they
can 'beg, borrow, and steal' from the neighbouring courts belonging to other landlords,"[1] Seven years before the New River
Company had driven a main through the court, but the landlords had ignored repeated pleas from the inhabitants to connect
their houses to it. "In another court, where the houses are in
better condition and are supplied with water, were found—a
man lying dead in one house, a girl dead in the next, and a man
dying in the cellar. This last poor creature was lying on a heap
of chips and dirt in one corner, close to the foot of the steps
leading down to it from the court, and his wife sat by his side or
leaned over him. He had been taken, last night, from a wretched
lodging-house in Hairbrain Court to St. Thomas's Hospital.
There he was refused admission, and being unwilling to go to the
workhouse could find no place but a cellar, without door or
window. No persuasion could prevail upon his wife to suffer him
to be removed. She said, while leaning over the body of her
husband, 'Give me some relief to-day and a coffin for him to-
morrow.' "[2]

A fortnight later John Liddle, the medical officer who made
these revelations, wrote frankly to *The Times*: "Under the present
arrangement, it is almost impossible for a union medical officer,
subject as he is to an annual election, faithfully to discharge his
duties as an officer of health, in endeavouring to prevent disease
by urging the adoption of sanitary measures, and at the same time

[1] *Times*, 16 December 1848.   [2] Ibid.

maintain his independence. He must either be silent upon the subject of the physical sufferings of the poor, and allow the most disgusting and degrading state of things to continue, without raising his voice to ameliorate them, or he must resign his appointment."[1] In making the Union surgeon the key to their administrative arrangements, the Board of Health had rightly turned to the one local officer with the necessary knowledge and skill, thereby earning for their decision the rare commendation of the *Lancet*. But the Union surgeon took his orders from the men who paid his salary, and his usefulness was limited by the intelligence with which they directed his activities, and the willingness with which they provided additional assistance during the period of emergency. Between the intentions of the Board and the will of the local authorities stretched a chasm which was not bridged either by the slender powers which the Board exercised under the Nuisances Act or by the good sense and public spirit of the Guardians. In the worst districts the Union surgeon struggled to stem the mounting flood of cholera and diarrhœa cases, and was lucky if he could get his masters to appoint an assistant or two to dose the sufferers. After eighteen years of service the medical officer of Lambeth sent in his resignation in disgust, and then sat down at two o'clock in the morning to write to *The Times*: "During the week ending July 31, I and my two assistants, appointed under direction of the Board of Guardians, from an order received from the Board of Health, have attended 322 cases of illness among the poor of my district, requiring 1,028 attendances to be given at the houses of the poor, and at my own surgery; 59 of the cases were cases of Asiatic cholera in its different stages, and 141 were cases of diarrhœa and ordinary cholera; for this duty my salary amounts to 39s., or £100 a year, which is not quite three-halfpence for the medicines required by each case and my own services."[2]

House to house visitation, Houses of Refuge, home nursing, remained luxurious refinements, which, since the Guardians refused to vote the necessary money and assistance, were introduced into no more than a few districts. With rare exceptions, the London Guardians neglected to make a list of the localities in their parishes which had been attacked by epidemic and endemic

[1] *Times*, 29 December 1848.   [2] *Ibid.*, 4 August 1849.

disease. On the very evening that cholera broke out in White-chapel, the Guardians resolved that the Board's order "need not be acted on in this Union";[1] and three days later, when their Clerk laid before them a list of the places where zymotic disease was then prevalent, they resolved further, "That the Clerk forward such particulars to the various local boards in the Union, but that the medical officers be not called upon to visit the places in question."[2] When the Board ordered the St. Pancras Guardians to appoint four medical visitors, they were met by a flat refusal, the Chairman observing that house to house visitation "was calculated to do more harm than good, from the alarm it created."[3] Receiving from Bethnal Green returns showing 125 deaths in the week ending 18 August and 127 in the following week, they promptly issued a special order directing the provision of a dispensary and adequate hospital accommodation, and the appointment without delay of four medical visitors, an additional medical officer to help in the infirmary, a sufficient number of nurses, two inspectors of nuisances, and a staff of lime-washers. Despite the emergency, the Bethnal Green Guardians waited five days before appointing a medical visitor; they opened neither dispensary nor hospital, and undertook no limewashing; and they appointed only one inspector of nuisances instead of two, and no nurses at all.[4]

Nothing showed up more starkly the crass negligence of the Poor Law authorities than the outbreak at the Tooting child farm. Here nearly fourteen hundred children were housed in a building which half that number would have filled. Cholera swept through the close-packed pauper children like fire across a dried prairie. Three hundred had been attacked, and 180 were dead, before the Guardians listened to the Board and withdrew their children from the plague spot. Eight days after the epidemic had broken out no steps had yet been taken to separate the healthy from the sick; the children still slept three or four to a bed, infection spreading from one to the other by the involuntary discharges of the cholera sufferers; medical supplies were short and medical

[1] *Report on . . . the Nuisances Removal and Diseases Prevention Act*, p. 28; *P.P.*, 1849, vol. xxiv, p. 1.
[2] *Lancet*, 8 September 1849.   [3] *Times*, 26 September 1849.
[4] *Report on the Epidemic Cholera of 1848 and 1849*, pp. 111–12.

attendance unequal to the task, there were no nurses, and hardly sufficient assistance to remove the corpses. Chadwick sent one of the medical inspectors (R. D. Grainger) to investigate; and as soon as it was reported to him that the cottages used as the boys' dormitories were built over a stagnant ditch which served as a sewer for the whole establishment, he dispatched an expeditionary force of fifty navvies armed with pickaxes and scoops. Wakley, the Finsbury Radical and proprietor of the *Lancet*, conducted an able and exhaustive inquest, which lasted three weeks, and laid bare a scandal which did almost as much as the green bones of Andover to discredit the Poor Law administration. A pathetic procession of child witnesses testified that they wore the same scanty clothing in summer and winter alike; that (though Drouet, the contractor, received 4s. 6d. a week for each of them) the ration of bread was inadequate, and such meat as was provided went to those who were strong enough to fight for it; that hunger sometimes drove them to climb the fence and steal food scraps from the hog-tub.[1] The medical inquirers found that many of the children were big-bellied with scrofula, and covered with the scabs of impetigo and the itch. The verdict declared that the victims were "suffering from the effects of insufficient diet, deficient warmth of clothing, and impure air." This was an indictment less of the cholera than of the Poor Law authorities, and in contrast the Board of Health, with their energetic promptness and their prescription of a meat diet, came well out of the affair.

In the City of London itself, with its devoted garrison sworn to the defence of local self-government, the Board were fortunate to find one powerful ally. In January 1849 the recently elected Medical Officer of Health, John Simon, read his first report to the City Commission of Sewers, assuring them that their new Act gave them as good an antidote for the spread of fever as vaccination for the infection of smallpox.[2] When the City of London Union refused to obey the Board's order to appoint nine additional officers, Simon persuaded the Health Committee of the Corporation to set up a board of inspectors to conduct house-to-house visitations. In their first round they discovered the bodies of six cholera victims who had died without any medical attendance

[1] *Times*, 20 January 1849.   [2] Ibid., 24 January 1849.

whatever. But opposition was strong on the Court of Common Council, and *The Times* believed that portions of Simon's reports were suppressed. The City should be proclaimed safe, Alderman Sidney maintained, because all this talk about cholera had caused thousands of families to flee in panic, and in consequence shopkeepers were "paying hundreds a year for their premises, and only earning 6d. *per diem* by their trade."[1] One member of the City Commission of Sewers objected to the "spicy, unctuous articles" in *The Times*, while another was annoyed by the practice of "handing over a heap of complaints to the press."[2]

Lacking the co-operation of the Metropolitan Guardians, the General Board, with two medical inspectors to cover the whole of England and Scotland, were helpless. Without the power to originate prosecutions for neglect or violation of their orders, the Board had no direct control over the Guardians, and it was only indirectly through the uncertain result of a coroner's inquest, such as that conducted by Wakley at the Tooting institution, that they could bring pressure to bear on the Poor Law authorities. In vain the Board lectured the Guardians on their responsibilities under the Common Law, warning them that they were legally accountable for neglect involving injury to health and life. They debated the advisability of prosecuting the more flagrant offenders. The powers of the Board of Health, argued Chadwick, were in fact a continuation of the authority of the Privy Council to take all necessary precautions in times of public danger. The authorities, from Blackstone to Professor Lang, were clear that the Poor Law Guardians as a corporation were not immune from punishment for infractions of the law.[3] But Carlisle advocated caution. Boards of Guardians were rather impalpable bodies, unpaid, and quite likely to throw up their appointments if prosecuted; their liability might still remain, but the result could only be great confusion[4]

Eventually, however, they determined to test their strength before the courts, taking a stand on their decision to close the worst of the overcrowded graveyards. The amended Nuisances Act of August 1849 empowered the Board to inquire into the state

---

[1] *Times*, 8 October 1849.   [2] Ibid., 10 October 1849.
[3] Minutes, 24 August 1849.
[4] Lord Carlisle [Morpeth] to E. C., 25 August 1849.

of the metropolitan burial grounds and to direct the managers to take such measures of precaution as were necessary for the public safety.[1] The Board at once sent out the medical inspectors, and by the second week of September burial had been interdicted in half a dozen of the worst grounds. The orders aroused violent opposition. Why, they might as well direct that no more people should die in the parish, as attempt to close these grounds, declared the Chairman of the Guardians of St. George the Martyr, Southwark; the obvious result would be that all the poor people would come to the parish to bury their friends, as they would be unable to afford their removal to a distant extramural cemetery.[2] A tumultuous vestry meeting in St. Saviour's, Southwark, resolved that the closing of their churchyard would be a hardship to the poor, who would have to pay double the fees to be buried in a cemetery. "Why did they not commence at the right end, and before closing one place point out another in which these poor people could be buried?" asked the Chairman, while another speaker "deprecated the meddling of a Whig Government, and indeed of any Government, in their local affairs."[3]

Convinced that it was less consideration for the poor than for the poor rates that agitated the vestries, the General Board stiffened themselves to meet the protests of the indignant parochialists. "We must not parley," Ashley told Chadwick; "the necessity of action is immediate, urgent, paramount to all law, right or interest. At once refuse to receive Deputations, and direct Law to act instantly. I will take any amount of responsibility."[4] A general Minute on Interments recorded their intention to act solely on the reports of their inspectors. They could not permit the delays of a renewed discussion on each case; it was their duty to give summary decisions, which must be delivered with promptitude if they were to accomplish their object.[5] "I am amazingly pleased with our Resolution. I chuckle over its Stile," wrote Ashley.[6] Proceedings were taken immediately against the rebellious parish of St. Saviour's, but the magistrates

---

[1] 12 & 13 Vict. c. 111, s. ix.   [2] *Times*, 21 September 1849.
[3] Ibid., 12 September 1849.   [4] Lord Ashley to E.C., 12 September 1849.
[5] Minutes, 13 September 1849.
[6] Lord Ashley to E. C., 14 September 1849.

upheld the churchwardens' contention that the Act did not empower the Board to close their burial ground. "Nevertheless we have acted rightly, boldly, wisely," Ashley maintained. "I never thought that our interpretation of the Law would stand before a Magistrate. But public opinion and feeling demanded such an act of Heroism on our part. We can and must urge very strongly the public overruling necessity of our course."[1] A second time the Board went to law, summoning the managers of the Whitefield Chapel burial ground before the Bow Street magistrate. The summons was again dismissed, the magistrate giving his opinion that the measures of precaution contemplated by the Act must be such as burying deeper in the ground or using lead coffins; they could not, at any rate, be held to imply the destruction of the property altogether, which would be the effect of enforcing the closure order. The two counsel and the magistrate united in condemning the new Act as one of the most lamentable instances of legislative bungling they had ever met.[2] In this way the local authorities wriggled through the wide meshes of an Act whose indefiniteness of phrasing had been intended to broaden the discretion of the Board. "This is intolerable," cried Ashley, after reading the magistrate's decision, "—public property must not be turned to public injury."[3]

The Board were now driven to issue regulations prescribing the use of quicklime at each interment. It was the only disinfectant available, and it had objectionable associations, Chadwick confided to an unusually sympathetic Delane. "At this time the population we know are peculiarly excitable, the poor Irish especially. The belief has now gone out, that the doctors are poisoning the wells.[4] At St. Andrews the other day there was a disposition to riot on this ground; that the doctors were poisoning them to diminish the population, and that the Government had sent down an Inspector with the beneficent object of preventing the victims being carelessly or wantonly chosen." It was a feeling that was not likely to be restrained by the parish gravediggers and sextons, who felt their livelihood to be in jeopardy; the danger was plain; but the Board, with their small force of

[1] Lord Ashley to E. C., 13 September 1849.
[2] *Times*, 28 September 1849. [3] Lord Ashley to E. C., 1 October 1849.
[4] As in the epidemic of 1831–2; see above, p. 51.

P

overburdened officers, had no choice but to work through these ignorant and unwilling agents.[1]

In the middle of the long vacation, with Parliament and the Courts in recess and the Ministers out of town, the Board were fighting a pestilence single-handed, with an ill-drawn Act and a scanty, inadequate staff. "Our affairs are coming to a crisis," wrote Ashley in the second week of September. "The Magistrates against us, no Courts sitting, the Treasury backward. . . . It will be necessary to report to the Government that the Board has no power equal to the terrible Exigency of the times."[2] Under the pressure of those heavy and anxious months, the secretary, the assistant secretary, and Southwood Smith fell ill in turn, and finally even Chadwick went down with suspected cholera. For a week or two at the height of the epidemic Ashley continued the fight alone, wrestling in prayer with God and the Government. "Labour and anxiety at the Board of Health very great," he noted in his diary on 7 September. "We are now in the City of the Plague, and still by God's love under his shield and buckler. He hears our prayers, and defends against the 'Pestilence that walketh in darkness.' Disorder increasing; close of last week showed a mortality trebling the average of London; 1,881 victims of this awful scourge! Yesterday showed for the metropolis alone, a return of 345 in one day. . . ." "London is emptied," he wrote two days later. "Cholera worse than ever; returns of yesterday quite appalling, and yet manifest that we do not receive more than two-thirds of the truth."[3]

The inactivity of the clergy dismayed Ashley. Whitewashing and opiates and strict temperance were all very well, but surely this was a time when the pious example of the Ninevites in proclaiming a fast and putting on sackcloth—which had such excellent results—might be profitably followed. In the Bishops' professional judgment, however, the emergency, grave as it was, did not call for measures of this drastic nature. However, a special prayer was read on 16 September, and the clergy of London united in exhorting their congregations to assist in delivering their fellow-men from the bondage of dirt. "A poor substitute for a

[1] E. C. to J. T. Delane, 15 September 1849.
[2] Lord Ashley to E. C., 13 September 1849.
[3] E. Hodder, op. cit., vol. ii, pp. 295, 296.

day of repentance and humiliation," grumbled Ashley;[1] but there was a gratifying decline in the mortality in the ensuing weeks. It was a curious survival of the ancient belief that plague was the direct action of deity, visiting the wicked with misfortune and disease. Sinful man could always think of some perfectly good reason why he should be so punished.

If ever a Government department was in need of prayer it was the Treasury in the black weeks of that September when the cholera score in the capital was mounting daily by hundreds. Sir Charles Wood was a timid Chancellor of the Exchequer, whose dread of expenditure was almost pathological. The paralysis of his inhibition spread downwards to the permanent officials who conducted Treasury diplomacy with the minor departments, and the wide vision of an England clean and healthy soon contracted in the tortuous channels of Treasury accountancy. At Somerset House Chadwick had already had experience of the obstructive tactics of the Treasury, but he was startled by the extent and nature of the obstacles which were now thrown in the path of the new department. This was the moment, when the staff was depleted and engrossed in the public emergency, that the Treasury chose to demand that the Board send in its accounts, adding that until they were made up the quarterly payment of their Parliamentary grant would be suspended. Chadwick and Southwood Smith were obliged to pool their salaries to pay office expenses,[2] while Ashley was furious that the reward for all their labour was "to be treated as Swindlers and Vagabonds."[3]

When an urgent appeal for a medical inspector was received from Newtown, Montgomeryshire, the Board replied that they had so many demands for aid that they were obliged to take them in rotation according to the priority of application.[4] Yet a fortnight later the Treasury refused to sanction the appointment of additional inspectors. The proposal should first be submitted to the Home Secretary, said Sir Charles Trevelyan. The Board replied firmly that the Public Health Act gave no jurisdiction over their proceedings to the Home Secretary. What if the Home

[1] Ibid., p. 300.
[2] E. C., "Administrative. Relations of the General Board of Health with the Treasury. Minutes for a paper on," MS., n.d.
[3] Lord Ashley to E. C., 25 October 1849.   [4] Minutes, 6 August 1849.

Secretary expressed the opinion that certain measures recommended by the Board were inexpedient, and the Board, in deference to that opinion, refrained from executing them? If loss of life were to ensue, would the opinion of the Home Secretary exonerate the Board from responsibility? The Board felt that it would not. Again, in the emergency now facing them, it was essential for the sake of promptitude to avoid multiplied references; divided responsibility was detrimental to the public service—especially if reference were made from a body with specialised knowledge to one possessing no special information on the subject.[1] This was unanswerable, and the Treasury now agreed to sanction the appointment of one medical inspector and four assistants in London—for a fortnight only.[2] On 7 September Bain had an interview with Hayter, the Parliamentary Secretary to the Treasury, in an attempt to secure approval for the employment of additional District Medical Superintendents in London; Hayter doubted whether the Board had the power under the Nuisances Act to make such appointments, and declined to give any answer until he had consulted the Chancellor of the Exchequer. The deaths in London were then approaching five hundred a day. Ashley, the only member of the Board still on his feet, went over to the Treasury to request an immediate consent to the appointments, but he could find no one there. Returning to Gwydyr House, he recorded in the Minutes that since the smallest delay must result in serious injury and loss of life, the appointments should now be made, in the hope that the Treasury would see fit to sanction them later.[3] He notified the Treasury immediately by letter of his action, but no reply came—till six months later, when the Board were reproved in strong terms for making appointments not only without the consent of the Treasury but without previously informing them.[4]

Thus, eleven months after the cholera had appeared in London, the Board of Health in exasperation threw off the reins of Treasury restraint, and on their own responsibility engaged the services of a sufficient number of medical men to comb out the stricken

[1] Minutes, 23 August 1849.   [2] Ibid., 24 August 1849.
[3] Ibid., 7 September 1849.
[4] E. C., "Administrative. Relations of the General Board of Health with the Treasury. Minutes for a paper on," MS., n.d.

districts. At the beginning of September, when the weekly total of cholera deaths had reached 2,026, the system of house-to-house visitation at last came into operation, with a staff of eight medical superintendents aided by such medical visitors as the Guardians could be persuaded to pay for. In the first week the four visitors in Bethnal Green discovered 1,571 cases of diarrhœa and 69 of cholera, every one of which had been without any medical assistance previous to the visitation. Altogether, in the eight weeks the system was in operation, the Board's officers discovered and treated over 45,000 cases of diarrhœa and cholera.[1]

With the diminution of cholera in London, the daily agenda of the Board gradually lost its atmosphere of fearful urgency. It had been a sharper lesson than that of sixteen years before. In London in 1831-2, out of a population of 1,681,641, 14,144 had been attacked and 6,729 had died; in 1848-9, out of a population of 2,206,076, the attacks numbered 30,000 and the deaths 14,601. Over the whole country one in 250 had been attacked in the first epidemic, one in 151 in the second. In England and Wales in 1831-2 the attacks had numbered 71,606, the deaths 16,437; in 1848-9 the deaths alone from cholera and diarrhœa were 72,180 and Scotland contributed a further seven or eight thousand.[2] Human efforts had done little to arrest or divert the onrush of the epidemic. Hippocrates flattered himself that he had brought the plague of Athens under control by burning fires in the streets. There is the same confusion of *post* and *propter* in the General Board's appraisal of the methods they adopted against the cholera. Lime-washing, cesspool cleansing, all the Board's earnest exhortations to shun filth, did not deny access to a water-borne microbe. In the perspective of later knowledge, it is easy to see that the Board, instead of prosecuting reluctant church-wardens and Guardians before unhelpful magistrates, would have been better employed in circularising the public on the need to boil their water, and in ensuring that the companies filtered their supplies. Not until their seventh and last Notification, published on 18 September 1849, did they suggest that water suspected of containing impurities should be boiled. In London they did probably more harm than good by their advocacy of regular flush-

[1] *Report on the Epidemic Cholera of 1848 and 1849*, pp. 110-11.
[2] Ibid., pp. 11-12.

ing of the sewers into the Thames. Belief in the spontaneous generation of epidemics from dirt, and in the fundamental identity of the diseases so generated—these twin medical heresies were propagated by the Board through the medium of their Reports and their energetic Inspectors, leaving an impression on professional opinion which was still strong forty years later. John Simon refused to accept Koch's germ theory till 1890. Florence Nightingale thought that continued fever might develop into smallpox. Chadwick dismissed with scorn the possibility of the existence of "diseased germs, a mere hypothesis";[1] and a few months before his death he told a newspaper reporter, "I cannot tell you how strongly I believe in soap and water as a preventive of epidemics."[2] It is easy to multiply examples of the wrong-headedness of the public health reformers; but in recognising their errors we must not undervalue the empirical sanitation which they championed. Unable to confront an enemy they could not see, whose real nature indeed they did not suspect, Chadwick and his engineers were well occupied in cutting his lines of communication.

Within the limits of their science and their power the General Board did what they could in 1848–9, and they would have done much more if the Treasury had let them. In many of the dark places of the capital, in Hairbrain Court and Slater's Court and Rosemary Lane, jets of water from the parish fire-engine, or from a hose attached to the nearest stand-pipe, played on walls and pavements, and purged away their scurf of filth. Grainger and Sutherland, the medical Inspectors, were enthusiastic about the results of the house-to-house visitation, which they considered had proved so effective a safeguard of the poor that "several lamentable instances occurred in which the wealthier classes perished while the poor were saved."[3] The Government undoubtedly gave the problem up, and its members remained in the country until the epidemic was spent. The Board stayed in London to fight; and at the least their activity did something to spread the belief that epidemics could be halted if energy and knowledge were applied to the task. The working classes—who, according to all the medical visitors, were well aware of the connection between their insanitary dwellings and the diseases which

[1] MS. memorandum, n.d.   [2] *Weekly Dispatch*, 13 July 1890.
[3] *Report on the Epidemic Cholera of 1848 and 1849*, p. 103.

afflicted them—revealed a touching gratitude, not unmingled with astonishment, at receiving visits of succour from the bustling, efficient officers of the Board. "The Board of Health may hope little, and perhaps desire little, for the applause of men," wrote Ashley in his diary, after reading an approving article in the *Observer*, "but I do much deplore that our anxieties and labours should be thrown away, and we be told that we have done nothing, attempted nothing, imagined nothing, wished nothing. Our diligence and zeal are mentioned in the article; yet it is less than justice. We have indeed toiled unceasingly, and not as mere officials, but with earnestness and feeling. Chadwick and Smith are men who may feel, but who show not fatigue or satiety in business, where necessity urges, or duty calls. As for the staff of the Board, miserably paid as they are, with scanty hopes of preferment, or even of continued employment, I am unable to speak with adequate praise. They have laboured even to sickness, and when struck down by the disease, have hastened back to their work, not for emolument (for they receive fixed salaries), but for conscience' sake. And such are the men whose scanty recompense certain gentry would reduce by 10 per cent. Out upon this disgusting economy!"[1]

The crisis had revealed sharply the weaknesses and anomalies of the Board's position. For all that their enemies protested, they were no Inquisition with supreme powers to reclaim an insanitary population. They did not possess the aggressive weapons needed to combat local privileges and property rights. It was unfortunate for the Board that the pestilence was in full retreat long before Parliament reassembled. "We must, if we can, keep up the spirit of physical reform," Ashley told Chadwick. "The Cholera, thank God, has passed—is not the wholesome fear passing also?"[2] The transitory fears of the majority had been the force which drove the public health measures through Parliament; the permanent and implacable interests of minorities now opposed their application and extension. In the days of security men forgot their tremors and the old errors which had brought disaster upon them, and few remembered the exertions of a hard-pressed Board save the grateful dwellers in the back streets, who were inarticulate, and the outraged parochialists, who were far too vocal.

[1] E. Hodder, op. cit., vol. ii, p. 296.　　[2] Lord Ashley to E. C., 29 October 1849.

CHAPTER X

GREEK STREET, 1848-9

HERE in London, Chadwick felt, at the very doorstep of Gwydyr House, was the tough centre of the sanitary problem. If life in the towns of the industrial north was even more squalid, and health, as the mortality rates showed, suffered even more, it was in London that the evils which he had indicted were massed and concentrated on the largest scale in the physical discomfort of a population of two millions; and the greatest strength of the opposition, the alliance of property and particularism, of shareholders and vestry politicians, was here entrenched. Before the end of 1849 the General Board of Health had in hand two major measures, for regulating the interments and the water supply of the capital, the story of which will be told in later chapters. From his other base, at the office of the Metropolitan Commission of Sewers in Greek Street, Soho, Chadwick since 1847 had been attacking a further aspect of the metropolitan problem—the main sewerage of London's 170 parishes and the domestic drainage of its 300,000 houses.

Throughout the 1848 session, at the same time that he had been guiding the Public Health Bill through Parliament, Chadwick had pressed forward with another important sanitary measure, a Metropolitan Sewers Bill, to give statutory recognition to the consolidated Commission set up in the previous December. By this Bill he hoped to recast the Commission more to his liking, and to rid it of the weaknesses which had already made themselves apparent in its structure and personnel. He had wanted, as we have seen, a small sanitary executive for London, composed of men carefully selected for their knowledge and enthusiasm for the work, to give close day-to-day supervision to the technical details. The Commission of twenty-three he considered too numerous and fissile for the task. They included a strong contingent from the Metropolitan Sanitary Association, Lord Ashley,

216

Lord Ebrington, R. A. Slaney and Dr. Southwood Smith; the physiologist, Professor Richard Owen, one of Chadwick's closest friends; the geologist, Sir Henry de la Beche; and two distinguished physicians, Neil Arnott and Sir James Clark. These could certainly be expected to follow Chadwick's lead; and in addition he could count upon the support of the chairman, Lord Morpeth, the First Commissioner of Woods and Forests, so long as he did not race too far ahead of the Whig Government. But four of the old district Commissioners had also been nominated, and with one of them, John Leslie, a vestry politician from the parish of St. George's, Chadwick at once found himself engaged in the bitterest of conflicts.

To his consternation he found that Morpeth was contemplating a step which would add strength to this dissident minority. Fearing an outcry if the Bill did not embrace the principle of representation, Morpeth was leaning to the view that each Union and select vestry should elect a member to a Metropolitan Board of Sewers, the right of the City to nominate its due proportion being of course reserved. Chadwick rejected with scorn the idea of such a "Sewers Parliament," where the ignorant delegates of Marylebone and St. Pancras would debate scientific principles of drainage, a subject as unsuited as chemistry or surgery for the discussion and voting of popular assemblies.[1] Bad as the works of the superseded Sewers Commissions had been, he told Morpeth, they were better than those of the parishes.[2] His own preference was indicated by the approval he gave to a suggestion of the Lord Chancellor's, that the Commission should be confined as far as possible to Government subordinates. "At this time," he urged, "we might with such subordinates give evidence of political importance: that it was possible for such subordinates to carry out a reform such as local representative bodies had never dreamed of: to beat commercial companies in efficiency, and even private builders in respect to the economy of works, and win the approbation of the public to the extension of new power without the ordinary cumbersome machinery."[3] In the event, however,

[1] "Metropolitan Special Commission. Notes on the Evidence examined," MS., 7 October 1847.
[2] E. C. to Morpeth, 4 August 1848.
[3] E. C. to Morpeth, 11 September 1848.

neither Morpeth's parliament of parochialists nor Chadwick's select Board of civil servants found favour with the Government, and it was decided that the Metropolitan Sewers Commission should remain substantially unaltered, apart from the introduction of five representatives of the Common Council.

Chadwick failed also in his efforts to bring the enclave of the City within the jurisdiction of the consolidated Commission. The Health of Towns Association published a sensational report on the state of the City, based on facts he had supplied. Both sides circulated petitions for signature among the parishes. Pamphlets and articles in the *Morning Chronicle* were addressed by City aldermen to other local authorities in the provinces to stir opinion against sanitary centralisation. Toulmin Smith appeared before the Metropolitan Sanitary Commission, and Chadwick put him through a "stout cross-examination";[1] a few weeks later the irascible antiquarian was accusing Chadwick of refusing him the opportunity to revise the notes of his evidence, and Morpeth implored his colleague not to give him the opportunity of "kicking up a dust."[2] In the public controversy the Corporation were worsted, but the "soup interest" prevailed as usual in the lobbies. The Health of Towns Association, believing that their agitation had stopped the separate Sewers Bill promoted by the City, were amazed to find that somehow it had got into the Lords. The Metropolitan Sewers Act of September 1848 (11 & 12 Vict., c. 112) was thus obliged to recognise the conjoint authority of the Metropolitan and the City Commissions of Sewers. The defences of the City garrison were still proof against the drive towards consolidation.

His hands tied by this division of powers, and by a growing rebellion in the ranks of the Metropolitan Commission itself, Chadwick opened his campaign for the cleansing of the capital. The first necessity was a general survey, without which the main arteries of London's drainage could not safely be laid down. No such survey could be pieced together from the materials in the offices of the old Sewers Commissions, and the surveyors' astonishing ignorance of the subterranean geography of their districts constituted perhaps the most damning indictment of their casual, rule of thumb methods. They had, Chadwick told Sir James

[1] E. C. to Morpeth, 29 April 1848.   [2] Morpeth to E. C., 29 May 1848.

Graham, only the longitudinal sections and heights of their lines of sewers; "if they deviate from them, they know not whether it be into a pit or upon a hill"; in fact, the Westminster Commission had granted a licence for laying down a sewer "in a direction in which it was found when the builder came to examine the spot, the water would have to run uphill."[1] When Chadwick's men, probing the cause of a violent outbreak of fever in Westminster School, opened up a great sewer running beneath the Abbey Precinct, the Clerk of the Works was amazed. "It is all a mystery," he murmured, "drains being things he never troubled himself with, so long as the water went off."[2] It was less than five years before that Chadwick had been asked by Butler Williams, Professor of Geodesy at the Putney College of Civil Engineers, to describe how a sanitary survey should be conducted. The idea was as new as that; and it was with some misgivings that he now put the survey of London into the hands of the Board of Ordnance, then engaged on a survey of all towns with a population of 4,000 or more on a scale of five feet to the mile. The Ordnance, whose officers had been busy over a period of years in the work of self-reform, was a department of which Gregory Hardlines, the Civil Service Pharisee, might well approve, but its pace was too leisurely and its departmental habits too rigid for the task now demanded of it. Patiently Chadwick and Sir Henry de la Beche explained their views on sanitary cartography to Colonel Hall, the Superintendent of the Survey. All that was immediately wanted was the triangulation and the levelling, which need occupy six N.C.O.s no more than eight months. There was no need to delay drainage works while the Ordnance, intent on making a plan which would be "a credit to them," marked gardens and flower beds, trees and lamp-posts—and even the number of steps before every house door—as they had in their recent map of Dublin. A block plan, at a cost of £37,000, of London and its suburbs for eight miles around St. Paul's would be quite sufficient.[3]

[1] E. C. to Sir James Graham, 27 March 1843.
[2] *Metropolitan Sanitary Commission, Third Report*, p. 14; *P.P.*,1847–8, vol. xxxii, p. 339.
[3] E. C. to Lord Morpeth, 4 January 1848; E. C. and Sir Henry de la Beche, *Report on Proposed Ordnance Survey of the Metropolis and Suburbs*, 10 January 1848. *Orders of Court*, vol. i, pp. 24–6, 13 January 1848.

Chadwick had good reason for his delight when the military surveyors hung up their "cat's cradle" on St. Paul's in January 1848, and people were astonished at the sight of common soldiers using theodolites in the street. But in two months the work came to an abrupt halt. Why should the whole country bear the expense of a survey of London, the Commons were asking, a survey which was quite unnecessary in any case?[1] Faced by a combination of provincial jealousy and metropolitan hostility, the Government declined to sanction any further advances from the Treasury. Lord Morpeth, who had assured the Sewers Commission of the Government's support, offered to resign from all his official positions,[2] but was talked out of it by Chadwick; and eventually it was agreed that the cost should be borne on the metropolitan sewers rates.[3]

Three months had been wasted by the political manœuvring of the Whigs, and it now seemed likely that the survey, stripped though it was to bare essentials, must take at least another year. How was the Sewers Commission to occupy itself in the meantime? In two ways, thought Chadwick: first, in experiment, for in sanitary works no authorities existed who could safely be followed; secondly, in creating house drainage where it did not exist, and in reorganising it where it did. The lines and outfall of the main drainage could not be settled until the survey was complete, but, after all, the combined area of the smaller conduits of the system of sewerage was greater than that of the trunks, as the area of the capillaries of the body was greater than that of the main arteries. The cesspools and house-drains formed three-fourths of the evaporating surface, the sewers only one-fourth. If the Commissioners busied themselves in replacing cesspools by water-closets, in taking up the badly levelled brick drains and laying in their stead earthenware pipes cleansed by adequate supplies of water, the noxious exhalations which offended the noses and depressed the health of Londoners would largely disappear. In short, they should aim first at "the complete drainage and purification of the dwelling-house, next of the street, and lastly of the river."[4] What this meant in concrete terms of human com-

---

[1] *Hansard*, vol. xcvii, pp. 1014–17, 2 March 1848.
[2] Lord Morpeth to E. C., 28 March 1848.
[3] *Orders of Court*, vol. i, pp. 49–51, 1 April 1848.   [4] *Times*, 4 October 1849.

fort may be illustrated from the example of the cleansing of Church Lane and Carrier Street, a part of the former "Rookery" of St. Giles's, where 2,850 people were crammed into ninety-five houses on a space of little more than an acre. Amongst the genteel correspondence of *The Times* there appeared one morning a crude, misspelt letter:

"The Editur of the Times Paper.
"Sur,
  "May we beg and beseach your proteckshion and power, We are Sur, as it may be, livin in a Wilderniss, so far as the rest of London knows anything of us, or as the rich and great people care about. We live in muck and filthe. We aint got no priviz, no dust bins, no drains, no water splies, and no drain or suer in the whole place. The Suer Company, in Greek Street, Soho Square, all great, rich and powerfool men, take no notice watsomedever of our cumplaints. The Stenche of a Gully-hole is disgustin. We al of us suffur, and numbers are ill, and if the Colera comes Lord help us.
  "Some gentlemans comed yesterday, and we thought they was comishoners from the suer Company, but they was complaining of the noosance and stenche our lanes and corts was to them in New Oxforde Street. They was much surprized to see the seller in Number 12, Carrier Street, in our lane, where a child was dyin from fever, and would not beleave that Sixty persons sleep in it every night. This here seller you couldent swing a cat in, and the rent is five shilling a week; but theare are greate many sich deare sellers. Sur, we hope you will let us have our cumplaints put into your hinfluenshall paper, and make these landlords of our houses and these comishoners (the freinds we spose of the landlords) make our houses decent for Christians to live in.
  "Preaye Sir com and see us, for we are livin like piggs, and it aint faire we shoulde be so ill treted.
  "We are your respeckfull servents in Church Lane, Carrier Street, and the other corts.
  "Teusday, Juley 3, 1849."[1]

The Times did go and see them; and as its reporter, at the protective elbow of a police sergeant, made his way from one human

[1] *Times*, 5 July 1849. The letter bore 54 signatures.

warren to another, his note-book filled with grimly pathetic details. The landlord of one of the better houses "pointed in triumph to a clock and some crockery in one of the rooms." One woman told him "they seldom tasted meat—hardly ever. They did not expect it. They were glad to get bread, and they had not often enough of that."[1] The assistant surveyor sent from Greek Street to inspect the area reported that the houses were let to a lessee for about £20 each per annum; each house was again underlet at £35 per annum; the single rooms were let at a highly remunerative rent; and finally the separate beds in the rooms were let to vagrants at about 3d. a night—bringing in, after deducting rates and other expenses, about £70 per house per annum. Yet in many of the houses, with their average of thirty or forty tenants each, the landlords had abolished the necessary conveniences because of the cost; and the occupants had to beg their supply of water from shopkeepers in the neighbourhood. The average annual outlay per house for emptying cesspools amounted to £1 10s., the water supply, miserably inadequate as it was, cost £1 10s., and the scavengers' charge, occasioned by the want of dustbins, came to a further £1—in all £4 per house per annum. For an improvement rate of £1 15s. the assistant surveyor estimated that the streets might be paved, tanks erected to furnish a constant water supply in every room, privies and cesspools replaced by water-closets and drains, a dustbin fixed in each yard and a common urinal in each court.[2]

In this and in similar reports by surveyors of the Sewers Commission, Chadwick worked out his interim plans for metropolitan drainage. A block of buildings, such as Goulston Street, Whitechapel, or Jennings' Buildings, Kensington, would be chosen, and would be examined by an officer of the Commission; and his report would indicate the measures needed, stressing the salutary fact that a comparison of annual costs proved that a clean dwelling was cheaper than a squalid one.

At the same time, to check jobbery, and to determine the details of domestic drainage, Chadwick set going a series of experiments and trial works. In his various reports he had con-

---

[1] *Times*, 9 July 1849.
[2] E. Gotto, *Report on Church Lane and Carrier Street, St. Giles*, 7 July 1849. *Orders of the Court*, vol. ii, p. 135, 12 July 1849.

demned the work of engineers of the highest reputation, of Rendel and Wicksteed and even of the great Robert Stephenson. Gwilt, the author of the standard *Encyclopædia of Architecture* advised for a moderate-sized country mansion a drain of an area of five square feet, with a capacity large enough to discharge 2,000 cubic feet of water a minute. In this sphere of disputed principles and contradictory practice, the public were at the mercy of the jobber—like the well-known architect whom Chadwick once reproached for putting in brick house-drains at half a crown a foot when for sixpence a foot he might have laid down superior earthenware pipes. "Oh, but you know, Mr. Chadwick," he was told, "we architects must live."[1] To the opposition on the Sewers Commission, when they questioned the value of his experiments, Chadwick declared that the disputed problems of drainage were a matter of gauging and measurement, which, if carefully conducted, would eventually remove all ground for differences of opinion. "Great was gravitation—it would not be diverted by passion or ignorance, and would prevail."[2] Earthenware pipes were brought from Switzerland and their prices and quality compared with home products. The production cost of bricks was analysed and the prices charged by contractors shown to be 60 per cent higher; whilst a subterranean survey revealed that the ruinous state of so many sewers was caused by the fact that the bricks supplied had been far inferior to the qualities contracted for at that very high rate of profit. The flow in the sewers was gauged, and it was demonstrated to the astonishment of the old officers that house-drains need not be larger than four inches in diameter, a pipe that size being sufficient to carry off the sewage from a thousand people or more. Tests were made to determine the quantity of water actually consumed in the metropolis, and the quantity which would be required for the new system of drainage. Trial surveys were made of suburban districts such as Richmond and Sydenham, and plans and estimates drawn up to show the practical advantages of the combination of water supply and drainage. Barges took out sewer water to enterprising farmers, and encouraging reports came in of double crops of grass and wheat. Chadwick pushed on quietly at the same

[1] E. C. to Lord Morpeth, 14 October 1848.
[2] *Times*, 24 July 1849.

time with preparations to dispossess the water companies. Explorers went out to test the quality of the surface and drainage water at Epping, Windsor, and Richmond. The specimens so far examined, he told Morpeth in June 1848, showed only six degrees of hardness, as compared with the twelve or fourteen degrees of Thames water; this would mean a saving in soap of £200,000 a year. For about £180,000, he calculated, they could drain a hundred square miles of land to give a completely new supply of up to a hundred gallons a day to each of the 300,000 houses of the capital.[1] If confirmed, these results spelt the doom of the companies, with their restricted supplies of dirty water. It was not surprising that he warned Morpeth that these researches should be kept quiet. What he feared most of all was that the companies, getting wind of his activities, would press for a Government pronouncement on "pre-appointed terms of compensation" which reflected their own inflated ideas of the value of their works.[2]

It was valuable work; it was necessary work; and in the interval until the completion of the general survey the officers of the Commission could hardly have been better employed than in conducting experiments and putting London's domestic drainage in order by blocks and districts. But the policy lacked that appeal to the interest and imagination of the ratepayers which a grand engineering feat like the main drainage of London would have provided. It was dullness unrelieved. Chadwick was a bad publicity agent both for himself and for the works of the Sewers Commission. In his speeches at Greek Street the noble theme of a capital freed from the burden of dirt and disease could scarcely be heard above the unending chatter about gully holes and dustbins and the flow of water through a four-inch pipe. *The Times*, which had smiled upon the Commission in its early months, fumed to see them dissipating their time and money in measuring house-drains and offering prizes for patent commodes.[3] By the middle of 1849 *The Times*, and the public, had lost all patience.

From the beginning Chadwick was convinced that the survey and the experimental works could not be supervised by an unwieldy body of twenty-three Commissioners, one section of whom

[1] E. C. to Lord Morpeth, 14 June 1848.
[2] E. C. to Lord Morpeth, 30 May, 31 July 1848.　　[3] *Times*, 2 July 1849.

never attended the monthly meetings at the rooms in Greek Street, while another section sat in permanent implacable opposition. In January 1849 he used his command over the majority of the active Commissioners to secure the appointment of a number of committees, one for Finance, another for Bye-laws, and, most important of all, a Works Committee, from which there branched sub-committees for the Ordnance Survey, the Trial Works, the Disposal of Refuse, and the Construction of Roads.[1] One object of this step was to carry on business in the intervals between the meetings of the full Commission; but it was Chadwick's aim also to ensure that scientific questions should be discussed in an atmosphere free from the friction, the delay, and the untidiness of disputation. He sought to "put a stop to the thirst for debates"[2] by withdrawing with companions of his own choice behind the doors of a committee room, where the merits of siphon traps and hollow bricks could be given the same calm deliberation as questions of surgery or physics. When he emerged from the committee room, however, he found himself in the less equable climate of an open assembly, where unfriendly Commissioners could attack him in ill-informed speeches half an hour in length, and where even friendly Commissioners in their ignorance could cause annoying delay. At his ease when making an exposition of principles to a sympathetic audience, Chadwick's temperature rose when he encountered the contrary pressure of a hostile mind. The anti-Chadwick party never numbered more than half a dozen, and its solid indissoluble nucleus was the little group of old Commissioners, Byng, Leslie, Jones, Bidwell. Chadwick left them in no doubt that he resented their presence. In their leader, John Leslie, a former member of the Westminster Commission, he discovered a man whose jaw was as firm as his own, and whose determination to expose error and point out true courses was just as great—with this difference: that Leslie was as set in the old ways as Chadwick in the new. Chadwick saw in Leslie the incarnation of that parochialism against which he had always

[1] *Orders of Court*, vol. ii, p. 8, 16 January 1849. The Committees were composed as follows: (1) General Committee, open to all members; (2) Finance (7 members); (3) Bye-Laws (6 members); (4) Works (13 members), with sub-committees for Ordnance Survey (4), Trial Works (3), Disposal of Refuse (3), Construction of Roads (2).

[2] *Times*, 3 August 1849.

contended, with its pig-headedness, its narrow horizons, and its clinging to exploded practices.

There seemed no end to Leslie's perversity. As soon as Chadwick heard that a number of the old Commissioners were to be transferred to the new body, he had immediately given them copies of the reports of the Metropolitan Sanitary Commission; and they had assured him that they heartily agreed with the principles he had laid down. Yet, hardly a week after the writs of supersedeas had been issued in November 1847, the old Commissioners, led by Leslie, were voicing views in plain contradiction of the new methods and in support of the practices which were to be abandoned. Assuming that they were not dishonest, concluded Chadwick, it followed that they did not understand the measures; and that what had really impressed them was the thought that their party foes were to be dismissed while they themselves gained positions of greater power.[1] At the very first meeting Leslie revealed how little he had grasped of the proposal to consolidate the works, when he contended that the two surveyors, Phillips and Roe, should be given equal status in charge of separate districts. A week or two later he stood alone, in defiance of the lawyers on the Commission, in questioning the legality of the general survey; he treated with the same contempt the opinion of the Law Officers, obtained after much expense and delay.[2] In meddling with house drainage, declared Leslie, the Commission were stepping beyond their proper function. They should content themselves with a simple declaration that cesspools ought to be abolished, leaving it to the individual citizen to find out how to do it; sewers should be driven up the streets, and then the occupiers left to form the junction as best they could. On the mysterious doings of the Trial Works sub-committee Leslie directed an angrily inquisitive gaze. Fourteen thousand warrants of distress for the non-payment of rates had already been issued, and the Commission should be more careful with the ratepayers' money than to spend it on gauging the run of the sewers and other profitless inquiries.

[1] "Memoranda in respect to the proceedings in the Sewers Commission," MS., n.d. E. C. to Morpeth, 30 December 1847.
[2] E C. to the Hon. Frederick Byng, 11 September 1848. *M.C.S. Minutes of the General Purposes Committee*, vol. ii, p. 55, 23 May 1848.

But the innovation which Leslie most detested was Chadwick's committee system.[1] He saw no reason why the old method should be changed of dealing with a miscellaneous assortment of business in open court, where all questions affecting the sewers administration could be discussed under the critical gaze of the ratepaying public. Had this been the only point at issue, Chadwick's case would have been incontrovertible. In so intricate a task as the administration of London's sewers—involving such diverse technical matters as the assessment of rates, the supervision of a large clerical and engineering establishment, the preparation of surveys and estimates, the trial of new materials and new devices—a subdivision into specialised committees was the only way to come to close grips with the details on which policy must be framed. It was in the committees, with their fingers on the pulse of business, that policy must be initiated; the open court, though it might influence its committees by criticism or encouragement, must in the main be content to ratify their decisions. But this was not all. No idea of composing the committees on representative lines seems to have entered Chadwick's head. From the all-important Works Committee the old Commissioners without exception were shut out.[2] He did not listen when Lord Carlisle (Morpeth), sensing the danger of an excluded, embittered minority, suggested that it might be prudent to occupy Leslie by putting him on a committee with three or four others of superior knowledge to report on the pollution of the Thames.[3] What could Leslie contribute to a scientific investigation beyond an ignorant obstructiveness? You might as well expect a vestry politician to design and construct a locomotive as to plan a scientific drainage system. It was hardly to be wondered at, therefore, that the decisions of the committees came in for a hotly jealous scrutiny when they were brought before the whole body of Commissioners in court or General Committee.

Inevitably the others fell under Chadwick's domination. It

---

[1] *M.C.S. Minutes of the General Purposes Committee*, vol. iv, pp. 38–40, 22 February 1849; pp. 59–60, 1 March 1849. *Orders of Court*, vol. ii, pp. 29–31, 15 March 1849.

[2] See the Protest signed by Byng, Leslie, Lawes, Bidwell, and Jones (*Orders of Court*, vol. ii, pp. 33–35, 22 March 1849).

[3] Lord Carlisle (Morpeth) to E. C., 16 April 1849.

was a benevolent despotism, working through the machinery of half a dozen committees, whose head and heart were Chadwick. As *The Times* objected, if the committees were filled by his nominees, and the Court was bound, as he insisted, to support the committees, it was only too clear that the Commission represented and registered the opinions of one man alone.[1] "Any Commissioner who did not belong to the Works Committee was perfectly useless," cried one critic. "Mr. Chadwick asked him why he did not attend; and he answered that the Works Committee governed the commission. All the rest were mere cyphers, and were treated with a degree of intemperance if, as commissioners, they came to the court to discharge their duty and do what they considered right. They were considered excessively impertinent if they asked a question, or alluded to any explanation that might do good to the commission."[2] The gulf between Chadwick and Leslie could not be bridged. The unhappy Carlisle found himself in the desperate dilemma of a man with one foot on each side of an ever-widening crevasse. Chadwick's last word was that "between good and bad sewers there can be no compromise"; there must be no "jobbery in urbanity," no "self-indulgence in kindly feeling at the expense of the public and of duty."[3] Carlisle was sympathetic when Chadwick, returning from another "dreadfully annoying day at Greek Street," cried that "the present state of things cannot, ought not to go on."[4] But not infrequently Chadwick, with his continual alarums, his protests and his fretting, strained the patience of the peace-loving nobleman. He could not endure bad blood and squabbles between the members of the Commission, he warned Chadwick, and if they continued he would run away from both Boards.[5]

When the time came in September 1848 for the reappointment of the consolidated Commission under the terms of the recently approved Sewers Act, Chadwick moved ponderously to shake off his Old Man of the Sea. It had been agreed that the original twenty-three Commissioners should continue in office unless they signified their own desire to retire, and when he found that Chadwick was trying to edge Leslie out of the Commission

---

[1] *Times*, 1 October 1849.   [2] Hon. Frederick Byng, *Times*, 3 August 1849.
[3] MS. fragment, n.d.   [4] E. C. to Lord Carlisle, 2 July 1849.
[5] Lord Carlisle to E. C., 26 January 1849.

Carlisle sent him a stiff note. "Now I am entirely convinced of the thoroughly *public-motived* spirit of all you do, and I can quite understand how particular people may thwart, annoy, offend, obstruct; but where is the work we can expect to do without a mixture of these elements? I sometimes think that people who have not been in Parliament are more intolerant of this species of opposition and obstruction than we who are more seasoned to it. We have enough of opposition and jealousy to deal with from *without*, to make it very unseasonable to excite and *create* them in fresh quarters. . . . So pray let there not be any more bad blood raised about it."[1] Earlier the same point had been urged by John Bullar, one of the lawyers on the Commission, whose good humour frequently cushioned the shock of the contending factions. There must be some opposition, and none was likely to be less effective than Leslie's; and "if you had not force of determination enough to master circumstances of annoying character, you ought to have been quietly buried in a cesspool some years ago, with a train of Assistant Commissioners following your funeral, and the pall borne by broken-hearted flushers!"[2]

If the cantankerous Leslie was the most irritating, he was not the most serious obstacle to the inauguration of the new order. Within six months of the consolidation Chadwick was complaining that the establishment in Greek Street was not running smoothly. The clerks and surveyors who had been inherited from the extinguished district Commissions were sensitive about their rights of precedence, and worked together with bad grace; and they were appalled when Chadwick introduced a regular working day of six hours from ten to four, in place of the carefree sloth of the old régime. Urgently needed was an engineer of commanding personality and advanced views to take charge of the works. On a proposal of John Leslie's the Commission had committed a cardinal error in dividing the metropolitan area into two districts, each under an engineer of equal status, with the result that the two officers, Roe and Phillips, pushed on with their separate programmes without consulting each other. They were both capable and well-disposed men, in Chadwick's judgment, but they needed to be watched; for it was a new system they were

[1] Lord Carlisle to E. C., 18 October 1848.
[2] John Bullar to E.C., 14 September 1848.

being asked to carry out, a system very different from that with which their experience had made them acquainted, "as widely different as a locomotive is from a common dung cart."[1] As morning after morning Chadwick was summoned to Greek Street to reprove the absurdities of the engineers and to smooth over their jealousies and disagreements, he recalled that Roe had been a reluctant witness in support of consolidation, and that Phillips' evidence before the Metropolitan Sanitary Commission had been given its edge by his resentment against his employers. Sir Henry de la Beche had been right, he began to think: the break with the old order should have been sharp and complete. The old officers could not adjust their mental habits, formed under the district commissions, to the wider outlook of the consolidated area, nor could they readily accept the new knowledge quarried by the Trial Works Committee which went against their professional practice for a quarter of a century. It was a fact, they agreed, when the demonstration took place before their eyes, that four-inch pipes kept clear whilst larger ones accumulated deposit; yet both continued to put down house-drains of double the size they admitted to be necessary. They had too much to unlearn, and though when pressed they might concur in the value of the new ideas, their vision was too obscured by old and accustomed practice to let them catch more than a fractional glimpse of Chadwick's grand design.

In his perplexity Chadwick turned more and more to the reliable Henry Austin, now the Secretary to the General Board of Health, who was acting as Consulting Engineer to the Commission. The introduction of his favourite strained and eventually shattered the surface agreement between the engineering officers of the Commission. Austin was unknown; quiet and modest, he lacked the authority and force of character which would have enabled him to dominate his two professional colleagues and to silence the clamorous minority in the courtroom. Roe remained faithful to Chadwick, but Phillips seceded to the side of Leslie and Byng.

The clash came in June 1849, when Austin and Phillips produced rival schemes for the disposal of London sewage. Instead of limiting the attention of the court to minor matters and piece-

---

[1] E. C. to the Hon. Frederick Byng, 11 September 1848.

meal work, said Phillips sharply—such as the drainage of a detached and separate district, the advantages of a three-inch over a four-inch pipe, or the shape of a water-closet pan—the energy of the Commission and its officers should have been concentrated in the first instance on the selection of a sound plan for providing an outfall independent of the Thames. Phillips' proposal, in its essentials, was the construction of about twenty miles of intercepting sewers from Kingston in the west to the Kent or Essex marshes in the east, following the course of the Thames and acting as a substitute for it, at a depth of some hundred feet below the bed of the river.[1] The idea was not new. It had already been examined and rejected several times; and in a modified form it was later to form the basis of Bazalgette's plans for metropolitan main drainage. Chadwick, his eyes still lovingly fixed on the mirage of gold from sewage, found it totally unacceptable. Far better was Austin's "converging system." By this plan London would be divided into districts, each having a sump, into which the refuse would be collected; from these reservoirs steam engines would eventually pump it out to the farmers through subterranean pipes. In any event, said Chadwick crushingly, whatever plan was adopted, tunnels or sumps, it must wait on the completion of the survey; and in the meantime the Commission must continue with its programme of experiment and preparation, remedying the domestic drainage wherever possible, and flushing the sewers regularly into the Thames.

In this policy he inevitably came into collision with those who held that the Thames was London's greatest nuisance and Londoners' greatest danger. As the summer stinks from the river were wafted through the windows of the office in Printing House Square, the leader writer of *The Times*, with handkerchief to his nose, poured out columns of protest. "Not a single cesspool to be found in the city—except one, reaching from Richmond to Gravesend, with an exposed surface averaging a quarter of a mile in breadth! No filth in the sewers—all in the river!"[2] The Sewers Commission relieved Church Lane and Carrier Street, but only by poisoning the water supply of the whole capital, a piece of devilry forbidden even by the rules of war.[3] It was only

[1] J. Phillips, "Letter to the Commission of Sewers on the Drainage of the Metropolis," 21 June 1849.
[2] *Times*, 7 October 1848.   [3] Ibid., 14 September 1848.

a choice of evils, replied Chadwick; to discharge noxious matter into the river was a lesser evil than to store it up in the midst of a dense population.[1] The flushing of the sewers he regarded as the greatest contribution the Commission could make to the defeat of the cholera. In their first month they flushed 22,400 feet of the Westminster sewers, with a deposit ranging from six inches to three feet six inches; their activity was intensified when the epidemic broke out; and in July 1849 an assistant surveyor reported that in each of the last six weeks the Commission had spent £150, every sixpence of which represented a load of filth carted away from the metropolis. The intention, and the energy displayed in its execution, were admirable; the results were not— for the hoarded refuse, including the fresh infected fæces of the cholera victims, was flushed into the Thames at a point opposite the main intake of London's water supply.

Judging the policy of the Commission from one aspect only— its effect upon the cleanliness of the river—*The Times* presently passed from occasional criticism to open and permanent hostility. John Walter began to suspect that he had been chosen as a Commissioner less on account of his interest in the sewers than of his influence with *The Times*;[2] which was only too true. His technical views he took from an aged engineer, Stewart, an old-fashioned empiric, who scorned the notion of waiting for the completion of the survey before beginning a general scheme of drainage, and favoured Phillips' plan of deep intercepting tunnels to divert sewage from the Thames. In a series of letters Chadwick attempted to turn *The Times* from its championship of Phillips. The intercepting sewer, he argued, was a reckless and uneco-nomical method of handling so valuable a commodity as town refuse; the plan amounted to throwing the sewage of London a hundred feet deep, only to pump it up again and send it back several miles in the direction whence it came, to be used as farm manure; it would occupy two or three years, cost two millions, and leave St. Giles's, Whitechapel, and Rotherhithe in much the same condition as at present. All this Chadwick explained to Walter and Delane, exuding a breezy confidence that after this exposure no one could possibly continue to countenance such

---

[1] *Times*, 14 January 1848.
[2] John Walter to E. C., 22 July 1849.

nonsense; but *The Times* still cheered for Phillips and intercepting sewers.[1]

Thus, in the summer of 1849 affairs at Greek Street came to a climax, and the Metropolitan Sewers Commission rushed with increasing velocity on its own destruction. Phillips and Austin exchanged broadsides, each deriding the other's scheme.[2] At the same time the chief clerk, Lewis C. Hertslet, after sternly reproving his employers for not laying down a definite course of action for their works, sent in his resignation[3]—and, so Chadwick alleged, promptly began to manufacture hollow bricks, £150,000 worth of which would be required for Phillips' tunnel[4] A curious little note reached Chadwick from one of the clerks: "Phillips says, and thinks that the Gentlemen comprising the Commission (useing his own words) are a lot of old Women or Muffs, and that the Commissioners will not get much out of him unless the Commissioners adopt his plans, for he will not be put down."[5] In the following month the debate begun by Phillips and Austin was thrown open to the whole profession, and engineers were invited to submit their plans for the sewerage of London.[6] It was a victory of *The Times* over Chadwick, who held that no comprehensive scheme could be laid down until the survey was completed, and was continually pointing out that, since the Commission were already engaged in undoing the work of civil engineers of the highest reputation, it was futile to seek in their ranks for the designer of London's main drainage. When the Court opened on 20 August to receive the plans, a crowd of excited engineers immediately surged into the room. The meeting was a tumultuous one, and the Commissioners present were startled by the numbers and rivalry of the competitors.[7] Sixty-two plans were submitted that morning, and another seventy-five before the competition

---

[1] E. C. to John Walter, J. T. Delane, n.d.

[2] *Orders of Court*, vol. ii, pp. 105–8, 21 June 1849. *M.C.S. Minutes of the General Purposes Committee*, vol. iv, pp. 72–91, 28 June 1849. J. Phillips, "Letter to Commission of Sewers on Drainage of the Metropolis," 21 June 1849. H. Austin, "Observations on Phillips' Letter," 29 June 1849.

[3] *Orders of Court*, vol. ii, pp. 103–4, 21 June 1849.

[4] "Notes of Information to Lord Palmerston on the foundations of hostility to sanitary measures," MS., *c.* August 1853.

[5] T. F. Greene to E. C., 7 July 1849.

[6] *Orders of Court*, vol. ii, p. 157, 23 July 1849.

[7] Ibid., pp. 220–223, 20 August 1849. *Times*, 22 August 1849.

was declared closed. All were useless, as Chadwick had predicted, being drawn up in ignorance of the findings of the surface and subterranean surveys.[1]

Every resolution was now becoming a battleground for the opposing parties, and at times the Court appeared "nothing better than a beargarden."[2] Should the Commission appoint two additional assistant surveyors? "Mr. Phillips, when appealed to, denied that more assistant surveyors were wanted; Mr. Austin as confidently asserted that they were indispensable. Mr. Chadwick spoke at some length on the point, seasoning his observations with further hits at the old commissioners."[3] When Chadwick remarked complacently that under the old Westminster Commission the cost of removing soil by hand labour amounted to seven shillings a cubic yard, while now it was flushed away for only sixpence, Leslie rose in a fury of denial and demanded a special meeting to go into the figures. On the appointed day only three members were present in the committee room to support Leslie. In an adjoining room Chadwick waited with a strong contingent of his friends, ready to enter and swamp the meeting if a quorum were formed; while a beadle stood at the door to intercept Commissioners who looked like straying into the rebels' camp.[4] It was a ludicrous situation which lost nothing in the telling in *The Times's* report.

As a gesture of appeasement the Works Committee was thrown open to all members in August 1849.[5] The move was a failure. The Committee was now in difficulties, cried Byng, and wished to involve others;[6] while Leslie pressed on his attack with a motion that the Trial Works sub-committee, on account of its cost and its small results, should be abolished.[7] In such wranglings and personalities the Sewers Commission was gasping out its life. "Mr. Leslie complained that other Commissioners were allowed to say what they pleased, but so soon as he spoke he was told that he was personal"; "Mr. Bullar . . . complained that the time

[1] *Report on Plans for the Drainage of London*, by J. F. Burgoyne, James Vetch, etc., 8 March 1850; in *P.P.*, 1854, vol. lxi, pp. 104–11.
[2] *Times*, 28 September 1849.   [3] Ibid., 3 August 1849.
[4] *Orders of Court*, vol. ii, pp. 225–6, 21 August 1849. *Times*, 22 August 1849.
[5] *Orders of Court*, vol. ii, p. 204, 9 August 1849.
[6] *Times*, 10 August 1849.
[7] *Orders of Court*, vol. ii, p. 281.

which should be given to business was wasted by Mr. Leslie in fruitless discussions."[1]

It could not continue. At the end of September 1849 Chadwick appealed to the Government to recast the Commission, in the hope of eliminating Leslie and his friends. The reply, conveyed in a letter from Lord Carlisle "under feelings of very great pain," gave him a severe jolt. Lord John Russell and the Lord Chancellor agreed to supersede the Commission—but only on condition that neither of the parties prominent in the recent disputes should be reappointed.[2] Chadwick was furious that this undiscerning Government should class him with Leslie as great and equal nuisances. For the second time in his career he felt that he was being made a scapegoat by the Russell Government, while the real culprits escaped uncensured. But the sentence could not be averted, and, despite the polite words of Russell[3] and Carlisle, he felt it to be another rebuff. The Board of Health put the best gloss they could on the affair, and in their Minutes passed off the defeat as a strategic withdrawal. Experience had shown, they declared, that membership of the Commission of Sewers was not compatible with their duties at the General Board: "Because as members of a local board, in which they can form only a minority, an undue weight and responsibility may be, and they believe has been, ascribed to their individual or personal influence with the majority;—And because as members of a local board they may be in a minority with reference to measures on which, from more enlarged information, they may not only take a different view, but with regard to which it may be their public duty to enforce on their responsibility an opposite course."[4]

It would have been well for Chadwick if this resolution, the argument of which is unexceptionable, had been passed a year earlier, and he had severed his connection with the Metropolitan Commission of Sewers the moment he was appointed to the General Board of Health. By September 1848 the large-scale survey, the essential preliminary to a metropolitan plan, was well in hand, and Chadwick might wisely have left to other men the task of building upon the foundation he had laid. There is a

[1] *Times*, 30 August 1849.   [2] Lord Carlisle to E. C., 29 September 1849.
[3] Lord John Russell to Carlisle, 24 September 1849.
[4] Minutes, 17 October 1849.

limit to the amount of work one man, whatever his resources of
energy and will-power, can profitably undertake. To establish a
great new department of the central Government, and to nurse it
through the dangerous years of its infancy, was a labour in which
he should have found ample room for the exercise of his abilities.
The trouble with Chadwick was that he felt himself to be indispensable. In this field of public health reform, where he had been
the pioneer, he placed no trust in the judgment of others, however
well-intentioned he knew them to be. Sir Henry de la Beche, the
geologist, Simon and Southwood Smith, the physicians, Roe,
Austin, Rawlinson, the engineers—all these and many other
friends of the cause saw clearly some fraction of the whole; but
none of them, Chadwick believed, saw the problem in all its bear-
ings so surely as himself. He hated to delegate his power, because
he could not at the same time delegate his knowledge and his
vision. It is a dilemma known to all benevolent despots.

What had he to show for his two years at Greek Street? In
the severe view of *The Times*—and *The Times* in this reflected the
opinions of the great mass of London ratepayers—his dictatorship
by committee had accomplished practically nothing. It was no
clearer now than in 1847 how the main drainage of London
should be carried out, whether by sump or tunnel or by continuing to use the Thames as a common sewer. All that Chadwick's Commission had done was to flush some thousands of tons
of refuse into the river, argue the advantages of four-inch capillaries, conduct a series of experiments of dubious value, and
cleanse a few blocks of forty or fifty houses. The responsibility for
this policy, misguided in its aim and unimaginative in its conception, concluded *The Times*, must rest on the man who had worked
himself into a monopoly of power.[1]

It was a heavy judgment, which hung around Chadwick's neck
to the end of his official career, and helped to drag him down at
the last. There was no denying that it had much substance. If
feelings had been sore at Greek Street, Chadwick's roughness in
dealing with the men and situations there had been largely to
blame. If the Commission had failed to come to grips with the
principles of metropolitan main drainage, it was partly because

[1] *Times*, 21 July, 21 September, 3 October 1849; 8 March 1850; 14 February
1851.

all his thinking about the subject was distorted by a false premiss
—his insistence that the sewage of London must be handled in
such a way that it produced a remunerating profit. That is the
weight of the judgment against him. But, on the large practical
issue, it was an ill-informed and partial judgment. The critics
cried out for immediate works, as if it were merely a matter of
sending out a gang of labourers with shovels and pickaxes to
trench and tunnel a passage for London's sewage. The problem
of metropolitan main drainage was not so simple as it appeared in
Printing House Square. The Commission of engineering experts
appointed in 1856 to consider the question took three years to
settle the principles, and a further seven years elapsed before
Bazalgette's scheme, with its eighty-three miles of intercepting
sewers at a cost of £4,600,000, was finally executed. Chadwick
himself had not foreseen how long and how expensive a business
it would be (he always insisted that he could have done it more
quickly and at less cost). But in one important respect he saw
further than his detractors. He had grasped the essential fact
that until a survey had been completed, however long that might
take, no general scheme of main drainage could be undertaken.
Bazalgette planned his sewers according to Chadwick's large-scale
survey.

CHAPTER XI

A NEW PRESIDENT

THE epidemic, which had put a severe additional strain upon the overcrowded burial grounds during the terrible months of 1849, had raised in an acute form the question of the accommodation for London's dead. By the amended Nuisances Act of August 1849[1] the General Board were empowered to inquire into the state of the metropolitan graveyards, and to prepare remedial measures for the next session of Parliament. The scheme which Chadwick laid before the Government in December followed closely the lines of his great report of 1843. Under it the burial of the dead, "a most unfit subject for commercial speculation," would become a public service, controlled by a small Board of qualified and responsible Commissioners, at least one of whom was to be paid. Parish churchyards, private burial grounds, and joint stock cemeteries would all be closed, and in future all interments without exception would take place in National Cemeteries managed by the Burial Commission. Funeral costs would be regulated according to a series of scales or classes; and Chadwick estimated that the consolidation of the services, together with the economy of large-scale contracts open to a Commission enjoying the monopoly of the 52,000 funerals annually occurring in the capital, would reduce the present bills of gentry and tradesmen by two-thirds and of artisans by one-half. To supervise the arrangements, to ensure that burial should be sanitary and decent and cheap, and to perform the other duties which Chadwick had sketched out in the papers submitted to the Health of Towns Commission, there was to be a paid permanent staff composed of one chief Officer of Health and eleven assistants.[2]

Such a scheme touched the interests of three main groups, the

[1] 12 & 13 Vict., c. 111.
[2] *Report on a General Scheme for Extramural Sepulture*, pp. 87-9, 113, 115. *P.P.*, 1850, vol. xxxi, p. 573.

Church, the Dissenters, and the cemetery shareholders. Parish incumbents would be paid compensation for the loss of their burial fees. Each of the National Cemeteries would have a consecrated portion with a church for conducting the Anglican burial service, and an unconsecrated portion with a chapel for the use of Dissenters. The eight joint stock cemeteries[1] must be compulsorily purchased, the award in each case being fixed by a jury. Only one of them, Kensal Green, possessed a site suitable for the purposes of the scheme, and this would be enlarged to form one of the National Cemeteries. At least one additional cemetery would be required, preferably on a site near the river; an average of ninety-six bodies a day would float along this "Silent Highway" from eight houses of reception established on either bank. Chadwick knew the ideal spot—Abbey Wood, part of an ancient monastic domain, a dry tract of gravel and firm sand rising gradually from the river's edge. The sum of £700,000 was immediately required for the construction of the new cemetery in the east, the enlargement of Kensal Green in the west, and the purchase of the joint stock burial grounds; and the annual expenditure on interest, establishment charges, and compensation would amount to £112,000. The money would be raised by a loan, payments on which would be defrayed from the receipts of the National Cemeteries. The Act would provide for a rate to make good any deficiency, but Chadwick was confident that, even with the burden of compensation and the reduction of the existing fees, no deficiency was to be expected.

In a series of remarkable papers, addressed to the Government and the Bishops, Chadwick gave his imagination full rein to fill in and colour the outlines of his scheme. Bentham, planning his Panopticon or working out to the last detail the equipment of a Government office, could not have been more patiently thorough than Chadwick as he laid down the design of his National Cemetery, the style of the church, the materials of its construction, the arrangements for the chaplain, the choir, the bearers, and the corpse. Lord Carlisle was staggered at the inventive ingenuity of his colleague as he described the Crystal Palace grandeur of the church, with its dome of stained glass ribbed with iron, and

[1] Kensal Green, Nunhead, Highgate, Norwood, Brompton, Abney Park, Tower Hamlets, and Victoria Park.

its floor of encaustic tiles; with its stalls for the mourners, walled with hollow bricks and hung with rich cloth, each distinguished by the arms of one of the metropolitan parishes or the terra cotta effigy of one of the apostles; with its approaches which might be covered with glass panels in wet weather, and its surrounding avenues lined with full-size or colossal statues.[1] It was a remarkable effort of constructive thought, but at the same time a grave imprudence. As Carlisle hastened to warn him, such papers were "apt to ooze out,"[2] and if that happened a storm of controversy and ridicule would burst over their heads.

The Cabinet considered the scheme on 12 December 1849 and shook their heads over the offensive tone of Chadwick's draft. The next day Carlisle and Ashley were summoned to the Home Office, when Sir George Grey apparently intimated that if the scheme was to have any chance of public support it must lose the peculiarly rigid cast in which Chadwick had shaped it.[3] Carlisle therefore redrafted the Report, and under his tactful pen Chadwick's attack on the undertakers and cemetery owners lost much of its rude directness. The Report appeared in February 1850, and two months later—most surprisingly in view of the attitude they were soon to adopt—the Government introduced a Metropolitan Interments Bill. "Panic has subsided; and Prejudices and selfish interests yield only to Fear in cases of this kind," wrote Sir James Graham. ". . . In the midst of the Cholera it might have been carried; I am not unwilling to hope, that with some modifications it may yet be found feasible."[4] It was something gained, at any rate, that the man who, as Home Secretary, had set his face against the scheme should now consider that it fell within the range of legislative possibilities.

A Crown-appointed Commission, with the power to levy rates, exercising functions which were now possessed by influential if sluggish vestries, threatening the existence of eight cemetery companies and three thousand undertakers, and treading the debatable ground between the Church and the sects, offered a very broad

---

[1] "Memoranda of draft instructions for consideration for designs in respect to the construction of a church for the celebration of Divine Service at the National Cemetery," MS., n.d.

[2] Lord Carlisle to E. C., 26 October 1849.   [3] Lord Carlisle to E. C., 12 December, 13 December 1849.

[4] Sir James Graham to E. C., 3 April 1850.

target in the Commons. The Bill was met by the unanimous opposition of the metropolitan members, who coupled Chadwick and the Bishop of London as objects of their boundless distrust: Chadwick for foisting upon the capital a huge job—"a board attended with its usual accompaniments of clerks, treasurers, secretaries, chaplains, and God knows what"[1]—which would put some scores of appointments within the gift of the Whigs; the Bishop for having browbeaten the Government into promising the clergy fees in perpetuity for services they would cease to render once their intramural churchyards were closed. The political economists argued against any interference with the machinery of supply and demand, but were blind to Chadwick's demonstration of the superior economy of large-scale Government contracts. The constitutionalists were shocked at the meddling with local self-government, but kept silent about the working of that admirable principle during the cholera epidemic. Dissenters were indignant that Christians who lived amicably side by side should be segregated at death, and protested that everybody, whatever his faith, would be mortgaged for all time to pay compensation to the Anglican clergy.[2] Outside, in the Press and in the lobbies of the House, the undertakers were raising an outcry, just as in 1831, *The Times* recalled,[3] the rag-pickers of Paris had threatened to riot if the French Government interfered with their vested interest in street garbage. But the Bill had won one powerful and unexpected ally. *The Times*, a little troubled at the condemnation of private enterprise, a little dubious of the proposal to control individual choice by Government officers, had yet decided that "the bodies of the dead and the tears of the living are subjects which may be withdrawn from trading speculations without violence to the maxims of political economy."[4]

Chadwick's scheme emerged from Parliament with substantially little change—save in one respect, and that, as it proved, a disastrous one both to the scheme itself and to the reputation of the General Board. He had recommended a special Burial Commission with four paid members appointed by the Home Secretary;

[1] T. Duncombe: *Hansard*, vol. cxi, p. 693, 3 June 1850.
[2] *Hansard*, vol. cxi, pp. 677–710, 3 June 1850; pp. 856–70, 6 June; pp. 903–31, 7 June; pp. 1068–78, 11 June; pp. 1286–92, 14 June; vol. cxii, pp. 122–4, 20 June.
[3] *Times*, 15 May 1850.   [4] Ibid., 17 April 1850.

R

the Government had decided instead that this new duty should be laid upon the Board of Health, reinforced by one paid member for the purposes of the Act. It was a further burden which Chadwick confidently assumed; but if the measure had been bedded out under a separate Commission, the General Board, its time already sufficiently occupied with the tutelage of the Local Boards which their Inspectors were calling into existence throughout the country, would have been saved two years of fruitless labour and anxiety and the discredit of the eventual failure.

In March 1850, at this delicate stage in the Board's history, when one intricate measure was about to be introduced into the Commons and another (the Bill for metropolitan water supply) was well advanced in preparation, the Earl of Carlisle was appointed Chancellor of the Duchy of Lancaster, and retired from the presidency. Ever since he had succeeded to his father's title, he explained to Chadwick, he had wanted more leisure for his own affairs. But the easy-going Carlisle turned his back without much real regret on Gwydyr House, with its earnest sanitary labours and its unsettled atmosphere of continual controversy. More than once he had threatened to "cut and run." He had supported Chadwick loyally, but with a sense of increasing strain, and though he remained friendly and helpful in the difficulties of the following years, he showed no willingness to take a full share of the odium which fell upon his former colleagues.

Chadwick could not conceal his alarm that the presidency was again at the disposal of the political chiefs. It had been a miracle that Lord Ashley and Lord Carlisle had been appointed to the Board in the first place, two noblemen sympathetic to the sanitary movement and willing to accept Chadwick's leadership with a good grace—a miracle unlikely to be repeated. Ashley also, he saw, was "discomposed and anxious," and might not co-operate cordially with a newcomer who had not shown zeal in the cause; and a change at the Board would be peculiarly hazardous at this very moment, when it was essential to retain undiminished the confidence of both churchmen and Dissenters. An old-established Board, with settled courses of action, might change its personnel without much danger; but at Gwydyr House, where all was new, it might be damaging to break up a partnership marked by "a perfect understanding, and reciprocity of feeling," in which "the public have confidence, as is most unequivocally shown by the extent of application to us."[1] Could not the presidency, he suggested to Lord John Russell, be attached to the office of the Duchy of Lancaster?[2] But Russell was unresponsive to his plea, and it was clear that the loss of Carlisle must be accepted. Chadwick wrote him a note of sincere regret, a farewell to the most understanding chief he had ever served under, a farewell at the same time, as his fears accurately divined, to the peace and unity which had been Carlisle's personal contribution to their common labours. "Whenever I have been deeply troubled in spirit and have received a note from you, it has produced a calming soothing effect, and helped me on in the course of duty; and so it is now, but it is the promise that tho' somewhat separated officially, you will be present and aiding us in our snubs which will be many. I have said amongst my friends that I have never served with any one whose motives I felt to be more pure and elevated and therefore kindly. I observed only that at times it seemed to me the kindliness was in excess for the rudeness, bad passion and sinister interests which were opposed to us. . . ."[3]

An even more serious blow to the Board of Health than the withdrawal of Carlisle was narrowly averted. Lord Ashley had counted upon having the honour of introducing the Interments Bill into the Commons ("Honour, in these matters, becomes *influence* and *power* to do more"), and when it was entrusted to other hands he sent in his resignation. He was given all the tedious details of the Provisional Orders to steer through the House, he grumbled, but any important measure the Government reserved for themselves; he was to be "reduced to the station of a senior clerk in the Home Office."[4] Hardly had he been talked out of his sulks when he heard that another man was to be appointed over his head as President of the Board of Health. Again his resignation went in; and he was persuaded to remain only by a promise from Russell that he should have the Bill for metropolitan water supply.[5]

If not Ashley, who was to take Carlisle's place at the head of

[1] E. C. to Carlisle, 6 March 1850.
[2] E. C. to Lord John Russell, n.d., *c*. 6 March 1850.
[3] E. C. to Carlisle, 27 March 1850.
[4] E. Hodder, op. cit., vol. ii, p. 318. [5] Ibid., p. 319.

the Board? Looking round for men of goodwill, Chadwick picked out Lord Ebrington, a member of the Poor Law Board, who had been active in the early public health campaigns and knew something about the subject; moreover, he assured Russell, employing a characteristic argument, the Poor Law Board could be worked just as well by three members as by four, and by transferring Ebrington the Government would save £1,500 a year.[1] Considerations of economy and aptitude, however, exerted no influence on the political dispositions of the Whig Government. Amongst the members of a deputation which had waited on Chadwick a few weeks earlier to oppose the application of the Public Health Act to Totnes was one who frankly confessed that he knew nothing about the measure and had never even read it.[2] It was Lord Seymour, heir to the Duke of Somerset—who now took his seat as First Commissioner of Woods and Forests and *ex officio* President of the Board of Health.

Seymour's coming fell like a chilling blast on the devoted company of Gwydyr House. At their first meeting he informed Chadwick and Southwood Smith that his rule of action in office was "never to act until he was obliged and then to do as little as he could." This, wrote the furious Chadwick, "to men who had explored the seats of fever and had each suffered by it, in a new department appointed to promote measures, for the reduction of preventible sickness and death by the wholesale, which they, from study, knew to be practicable!" Seymour, they heard, "was averse to all such interferences and his saying was that there must be poor"—"a pretty theory," commented Chadwick in disgust, "that physical degradation and misery were not only an irretrievable, but a proper necessity for the great mass of the population."[3] Seymour's shocked colleagues did not immediately challenge his statement of faith, "the policy of which for these times might be questioned for older departments" and which was particularly repugnant to the principle of the Public Health Act, "which is to do with the means granted to us, all the good in our power."[4] But the inevitable clash between Chadwick and

[1] E. C. to Russell, 7 March 1850.
[2] "Administrative. Notes of Objections to the course taken by Lord Seymour in respect to the Public Health Act," MS., n.d.
[3] E. C. to Lord John Russell, n.d.   [4] E. C. to Carlisle, n.d.

Seymour could not be long delayed. The new President soon made very plain the low value he set upon the activities of the Board. He openly declared that he wished to stop as much as he could. Deputations from local authorities and sanitary associations were given a cool reception, his Lordship listening to the details of their cases with unconcealed ill-humour; from members of Birmingham Town Council and from other sources complaints reached Chadwick that his whole bearing evinced hostility to the Public Health Act. His disapproval was vented on nearly every officer of the Board.

On three occasions only during the two years of his presidency did Seymour attend meetings of the Board, and since his colleagues were so rarely honoured by his presence difficulties soon arose over business which had been conducted in his absence. Not long after his appointment, Chadwick was summoned to the Woods and Forests. Seymour then laid before him a paper he had received from the Treasury, and asked "in a very unusual and unpleasant manner" why he had not been informed of it, and of the Board's proceedings in general. They had every wish to keep him informed, retorted Chadwick; but how could they supply full details of their manifold daily activities to a person who never came near them—unless he was prepared to listen for a period in proportion to the time which the Board took in transacting their business? And was it consonant with the Act for Seymour to conduct business, except at the Board and as a member of it? Such action was surely questionable in law and practice, and led to misunderstandings and unsatisfactory results. "For a new Board, jealously watched, surrounded by enemies," concluded Chadwick, "it was impolitic and unsafe to have any irregularities even in formal practice."[1]

Thus, the constitutional question, never raised while Carlisle was at the Woods and Forests, became acute under a less sympathetic régime. Had the three reformers now a colleague or a master?

On 5 August 1850 the Metropolitan Interments Act (13 & 14 Vict., c. 52) received the royal assent, and the General Board (with the exception of their President) held a special meeting to

_____
[1] E. C. to ? [probably Carlisle], n.d.

consider the steps necessary to execute its provisions. Southwood Smith, who had ceased to have official standing at the Board when the Order in Council under the Nuisances Act lapsed at the end of the epidemic, had been appointed additional member for the purposes of the Interments Act, and Charles Macaulay, nephew of Sir Charles Trevelyan, became assistant secretary. Alexander Bain, the assistant secretary appointed under the Public Health Act, had resigned six months before, worn out by the heavy pressure of business which the cholera had put upon the office. His place, in deference to the Treasury, had not been filled; and now Austin, "poor Austin" as Carlisle called him, who had struggled to cope single-handed with the ever-growing corres- pondence of the Board, threw up the task out of sheer exhaustion and became a Superintending Inspector. He was replaced by Tom Taylor, barrister-at-law and Fellow of Trinity College, Cambridge, but best known as a contributor to *Punch* and the author of popular farces.[1] At Gwydyr House, Chadwick decided before long, a man like Tom Taylor was playing out of character. He came late and left early, entertained actors and editors in the office, kept one messenger busy taking manuscripts to the theatre and the printers, and absented himself to attend rehearsals of his farces. The legal business was soon suffering from his cheerfully offhand attention.[2]

Was Chadwick's interment scheme workable? Was it prac- ticable for a public board to manage cemeteries, to monopolise burial, and to regulate the cost of funerals by large-scale contracts? To this question Chadwick's reply was to point out that in Frankfort, Munich, Berlin and elsewhere publicly-owned ceme- teries were in operation, while in Paris the *Service des Pompes Funèbres* worked to the general satisfaction; in short, that the measures which his critics asserted to be impracticable were at that very moment being put into practice abroad to the obvious benefit of the community. The only difference, in his view, was that his plan, which aroused the appreciative envy of Parisian administrators, was more thorough, showed a clearer recognition of the social objects involved, and provided a superior machinery for public control and instruction. Only the event could show whether he was right, and it might well have furnished him with

[1] Minutes, 18 March 1850.   [2] E. C. to Tom Taylor, 12 April 1852.

a conclusive reply to his critics. As it turned out, however, his scheme did not succeed; neither did it fail; it was merely not attempted. The General Board, in eighteen months, never got further than the preliminary skirmishing with the cemetery companies and the Treasury.

From the first it was made clear to the Board that the Treasury disliked the Interments Act, and distrusted the men who were to administer it. A week or two after it had been given the royal assent, Chadwick received an emphatic warning that the measure "would never be allowed to work."[1] The Chancellor of the Exchequer, Sir Charles Wood, had for years been dragged reluctantly at the rear of his party along the dangerous paths of social and economic reform. He had not accepted the necessity for the repeal of the Corn Laws until 1844; he had fought against Ashley's Bill to restrict the hours of women and children in factories; and the only remedy he could see for Ireland in 1847–8 was to wait with Malthusian resignation until famine and hunger had cut off the excessive numbers of Irishmen. Put in charge of the invalid Whig finances in 1846, he directed himself with single-minded devotion to the one object of cutting public expenditure. He had obliged the General Board to begin its task with a staff too small for efficiency, and he never forgot that during the epidemic they had defied the Treasury and appointed five temporary medical inspectors. His views were shared to the full by William Goodenough Hayter, who, as Parliamentary Secretary to the Treasury, was chief whip and paymaster to the Whigs, maintaining discipline and good humour in the party by the judicious dispensation of the loaves and fishes of patronage. He told Chadwick that he considered him and Lord Shaftesbury "no better than a pair of socialists," and frankly declared that he intended to do what he could to hinder them.[2] "Mr. Hayter has been sufficiently explicit to me on the subject," Chadwick remarked to Carlisle, as the Interments Act faltered to a standstill in the Treasury bog. "He has told me in so many words that he thought the whole measure entirely wrong; that he was opposed to our whole proceedings, that he thought it wrong to interfere with trading companies, that we were wrong in our measure as to water supply, that Government ought to have nothing to do

[1] E. C. to Russell, n.d. (1851).   [2] Ibid.

with these things: for Government did everything badly, or worse than other people. Certainly his own office has done nothing to reverse that dictum."[1] When the Russell Government fell in 1852, Hayter told Chadwick that he regretted quitting office since he would thus lose the opportunity of "working" the Board of Health.[2] Finally, Chadwick thought it was not without significance that the Treasury letters to the General Board bore the signature of George Cornewall Lewis, who had nearly succeeded in stopping the publication of the *Sanitary Report* in 1842.

It would be interesting to know how many legislative projects have been killed in embryo by over-cautious Chancellors and unsympathetic Financial Secretaries. The peculiar value of the Minutes of the General Board and Chadwick's memoranda and letters relating to the Interments Act, and to the Metropolitan Water Supply Bill which we shall consider later, lies in the fact that they reveal in detail how such an abortion was carried out, and light up the motives of those responsible.

The first step must be the immediate purchase of the eight metropolitan cemeteries, the soil of only one of which was suitable for burial; and the simultaneous closure of the overcrowded graveyards, which could be divided "only into such as are bad, and such as are extremely bad." The General Board must take possession at once of every cemetery and every graveyard. If only one district were selected for the introduction of the new scheme, bodies might be taken outside its boundaries to other grounds in just as bad a condition.[3] On 25 November 1850, therefore, after a careful examination of the sites by their Inspectors, the Board submitted an estimate of the value of the cemeteries to the Treasury, and requested permission to negotiate for their purchase. Two months elapsed before the Treasury replied. The Board's estimates, showing a valuation of £251,000, must have been framed on insufficient data, wrote George Lewis at last; the Treasury's own expert was of the opinion that the sites could not be acquired for less than their original cost, which might be as much as £750,000. The Board could not be permitted to enter into negotiations of such magnitude. The Treasury suggested an alternative course. The Board should buy up one

---

[1] E. C. to Carlisle, n.d.   [2] E. C. to Russell, n.d. (1851).
[3] Minutes, 21 November 1850.

or two of the cemeteries as a start, enabling them to close the worst of the graveyards; at the same time they might purchase land for a public cemetery, so showing the cemetery companies that they meant business and strengthening their hand in the negotiations.[1]

The Treasury thus recommended a half-and-half scheme such as the Board had all along opposed. The whole question of a burial monopoly under public management was reopened, and Chadwick found himself repeating once again his familiar arguments against leaving the interment of the dead to the anarchic, irresponsible competition of commercial companies. On 30 January 1851 Lord Seymour made one of his rare appearances at the Board. The reason was soon evident. He moved that the Board were ready to act on the Treasury suggestion, and would open a cemetery of their own to go into competition with the joint stock grounds. When his colleagues refused to adopt the Treasury's "absurd and destructive scheme," Seymour declared their attitude showed "most unwarrantable insubordination," and warned them "this would never be forgotten or forgiven by the Treasury."[2] The Board ignored his threats, and redefined their position in two uncompromising Minutes, the substance of which was embodied in letters to the Treasury.[3] Even if the juries awarded the full sum claimed by the companies, it would still be necessary to make the purchase—and it would still be consistent with the estimates laid before Parliament, which were based on the proprietors' own valuations of £400,000. If the Board attempted to carry out the Act without first securing possession of all the cemeteries, they would find themselves involved in a competition with the companies, unseemly and repugnant in itself, and leading to all the disorder and loss which were bound to result from the introduction of rival capitals into the same field of supply. In that contest the Board would be handicapped by the annual burden of compensation and interest; while their competitors, fighting "with a degree of virulence and desperation which has

[1] 22 January and 13 February 1851: *Second Annual Report of the General Board of Health under sec. 73 of the Metropolitan Interments Act,* pp. 109, 129–30. *P.P.,* 1852, vol. xx, p. 97.
[2] E.C. to Russell, n.d. (1851).
[3] Minutes, 30 January and 14 February 1851. Board to Treasury, 31 January and 15 February 1851: *Second Annual Report,* pp. 111–16.

not hitherto been witnessed," would enjoy two advantages—their sites would be closer to the capital; and they would feel no scruples about using such insanitary but profitable practices as pit burial.

Lord Seymour wrote at once to express his disapproval; the Treasury had refused to sanction the Board's scheme, and since on this point authority was given to the Treasury by the Act, the Board should submit to their decision. What would happen if all the other departments were to copy the Board's action, and argue with the Treasury instead of acting as they were required?[1] Chadwick in answer pointed out that the Treasury's proposal amounted to a suggestion that the Metropolitan Interments Act should be dispensed with, and another principle of action adopted, at variance with that laid down in the statute. The Act invested the Treasury with power to approve the appointments and the financial arrangements, but there the Treasury's responsibility ended. If the Board carried out the Treasury's scheme, and disaster befell them, it would be no defence to plead that they were acting on the advice of a body which had no legal standing in the matter. Parliament might well ask why the Board should have adopted a course flatly opposed to their own recommendations, a course they believed to be illegal as well as impolitic, on the suggestion of persons who had given no more than incidental attention to the measure and were not responsible for executing it.[2]

The Treasury could find no reply to this; and eventually—with the help, Chadwick believed, of some pressure from Sir George Grey—the Chancellor of the Exchequer was induced to allow the Board to proceed with the scheme sanctioned by Parliament. In March 1851, four months after the Board had made their original application, the Treasury authorised them to buy out the cemeteries.[3] Promptly they issued notices for the compulsory purchase of the Brompton and Nunhead grounds, and made an offer for the Abbey Wood estate at Erith, on which Chadwick planned to build his National Cemetery.[4] Now came further delays and embarrassments as the Board encountered the shareholders' invincible belief that their property was worth far more than the sum they were offered. Chadwick wished to compel a decision by the findings of a jury; as he pointed out to Lord Seymour, the

---

[1] 17 February 1851: *Second Annual Report*, pp. 132–3.   [2] MS. fragment, n.d.
[3] Minutes, 19 March 1851.   [4] Ibid., 21 March, 21 April, 8 May 1851.

experience of his own department, the Woods and Forests, proved how vain it was to expect to purchase land or property for public purposes by private agreement with the owners. The Treasury insisted, however, that the purchase should be made by a series of separate bargains; and the cemetery companies, unwilling to hasten their own destruction, claimed the right to submit their cases to the dilatory procedure of arbitration. Before the Board could enter into possession of the cemeteries they must await the adjudication of eight claims for compensation. By July 1851 the arbitration proceedings for the first two cemeteries had been in progress three months, and were still not complete. At this rate, their solicitors warned them, they would not get possession of all eight in less than a year.[1] Chadwick's exasperation mounted as the months went by; the Board had done their work in one-third of the time, the other two-thirds had been taken up by the Treasury and Lord Seymour, the "president who cannot preside."[2]

The heaviest blow was yet to fall. Chadwick now went into the City to raise money for the purchase. To his consternation the Guardian Assurance Company declined the loan on the legal ground that, the Board's life being limited by the Public Health Act to five years, it might not be in existence at the expiration of the loan. The Directors of the Royal Exchange Assurance Company, whom he next approached, examined the estimates of the amount to be expected from fees. They discovered the Act did not stipulate that all burials should be conducted by the Board; bodies might be taken to new and unconsecrated grounds outside the jurisdiction of the Metropolitan Interments Act, and, in consequence, no guarantee existed that the Board would have power over the whole of the burial fees.[3] A powerful reason for their doubts, Chadwick believed, was that the delay in executing the Act had encouraged speculators, and a Bill to establish a Metropolitan Necropolis at Woking was now being canvassed; its promoters claimed that they had the approval of the Government, and Chadwick discovered that the Solicitor-General, Sir

[1] Minutes, 1 July 1851.
[2] E. C. to Carlisle, 19 May 1851.
[3] Minutes, 22 April, 2 May, 24 May, 10 June, 17 June 1851. *Second Annual Report*, pp. 7–8.

Richard Bethel, was a large shareholder, while his brother-in-law was the architect.[1]

The Board now turned for help to the Treasury, suggesting that the measure should be financed with Exchequer Bills; this would save £17,500 a year on the estimated outlay of £700,000, since money-lending corporations demanded a profit of from 2 to 2¼ per cent more than the Government.[2] "See," exclaimed the Governor of the Bank of England to the Directors, when Chadwick consulted them about the loan, "see the way in which the Government manages these works, in placing the public at the mercy of money corporations like ours: putting the public at such an expense when it may upon a direct security, obtain the money by Exchequer Bills at so much less." Such Government assistance, argued Chadwick, was granted freely enough for other public purposes—the annual return listed advances for Harbours and Docks, for Railways, for Waterworks, for Collieries and Mines, for Lunatic Asylums, for the Improvement of Cities and Towns. Why not, therefore, an issue of Exchequer Bills for Metropolitan Interments?[3]

It was a test question for the good will of the Treasury, which now held the key to the situation. When Chadwick's solution was rejected, the Interments Act floundered to a halt. Despite the frequent, earnest meetings in Gwydyr House, the reports, the thousands of letters, the bustling activity of the Inspectors, the Board now found themselves hemmed in by a closed circle of perplexities. To shut the parish graveyards they must open new burial sites; to provide these and to buy out the cemetery companies they must have money; they could not borrow because of the legal flaw in their constitution—and to escape from this impasse they must seek the aid of the Treasury, an authority more anxious to restrict their activities than to see them extended. Chadwick was on edge with annoyance and the irritating sense of labour thrown away. Shaftesbury was on the point of resigning out of pique. Lord Carlisle seemed reluctant now to come out in support of the Board and the Report to which his name was attached—that amiable nobleman too easily took on the colour of the company he was in.

---

[1] E. C. to ? (Russell), n.d.   [2] Minutes, 1 July 1851.
[3] E. C. to Russell, 21 July 1851.

A last hope remained. Failing the issue of Exchequer Bills, there was still one way to make the Interments Act workable. Two clauses might be inserted into the Act: one providing that if the General Board ceased to exist some other body should assume their liabilities and duties under the Act; the other empowering the Board to levy their fees and impose their regulations on the burial of every person dying within the metropolitan area. That was all that was needed, thought Chadwick; that, and a disposition to help by the Treasury chiefs. Hopefully he prepared an amending Bill, and obtained the approval of the Assurance Companies to its terms.[1] After all, he thought, the "insuperable difficulties" of Sir Charles Wood were the merest oversights, which the Commons—who, in sanctioning the purchase of the metropolitan cemeteries, must have intended that the Board should have the means to do it—would rectify at once if the case were fairly put to them. Shaftesbury showed the two clauses to Sir Charles Wood, who said he had no objection, but did not think the House would pass them.[2]

The Chancellor, however, never laid the amending Bill before the House. "Instead of doing so," Chadwick complained to Carlisle, "Sir Charles Wood is reported to have represented that the Board had made some propositions which the Government could not assent to, as if it were something new and enormous that they required; whereas all they requested is comprehended in the scope of the act as it stands."[3] The Chancellor then introduced a Bill providing for the advance of £137,000 from the Consolidated Fund for the purchase of the Nunhead and Brompton cemeteries, and announced that in the next session the Board might be deprived of its executive powers and reduced to a Board of Control, burial being left to the parochial authorities or private parties.[4] It was clear that the Treasury had written off the Interments Act as a dead loss, and were now preparing to wind up its affairs. And worse was yet to be feared. Wood was openly coquetting with the wild men of the Marylebone and St. Pancras

[1] *Second Annual Report*, pp. 9–10. "Metropolitan Interments Act Amendment. Draft of a Bill to amend the "Metropolitan Interments Act, 1850," and to provide for the Regulation of Non-parochial Burial Grounds hereafter to be provided," 23 July 1851.
[2] E. C. to Carlisle, 22 July 1851.   [3] E. C. to Carlisle, 21 July 1851.
[4] *Hansard*, vol. cxviii, p. 1552, 25 July 1851.

vestries. Late one night in an emptying House he announced
that the Government intended to renew the Sewers Commission only temporarily, and to introduce a measure in the coming
session putting both the interments and the water supply under
parochial control; "Sir Charles made this statement, bowing to
Lord Dudley Stuart who forthwith thanked the Government."[1]
Shaftesbury, who saw him for a few minutes to convey the
Board's protest at this sudden change of front, reported that
nothing could have been more insolent than the manner with
which the Chancellor received him.[2]

For some months longer the Interments Act lingered on under
this suspended sentence. In October, after nine months of
haggling, the awards for the two cemeteries were promulgated at
last. The companies had failed so utterly to make out their case,
and the Board's offer was considered so liberal, that the umpire
declined to call evidence. The companies had claimed £268,111;
the Board had offered them £83,707; they were awarded
£117,105.[3] Though the rate of compensation was one-third
higher than the Board had intended to offer, cried Chadwick in
triumph, it would not make the total purchase price for the eight
cemeteries more than £350,000. What now of the £750,000
which the Treasury expert had estimated![4] Such facts, however,
had no power to shake Sir Charles Wood. He was satisfied, he
told a deputation from the Metropolitan Sanitary Association,
that the Board's estimates would be exceeded three or four times;
he added that in Edinburgh no one was buried within the city,
though the arrangements were in the hands of cemetery companies, so it did not seem so absolutely impossible for private
parties to do it.[5] The deputation left with the impression that
Lord John Russell, who was also present, did not know much
about the matter and Sir Charles knew very little more.[6]

In December the Treasury administered the *coup de grâce*. The
Board were instructed to abandon the awards for the Brompton
and Nunhead cemeteries, and informed that a new interments
measure was to be brought in,[7] framed on principles essentially

[1] E. C. to Lord ?, 23 July 1851.
[2] Shaftesbury to E. C., 28 July 1851.
[3] Minutes, 18 October 1851.   [4] E. C. to J. T. Delane, n.d.
[5] *Times*, 25 November 1851.   [6] E. C. to Lord ?, *c.* 25 November 1851.
[7] Minutes, 15 December 1851.

different from the existing Act. "There is no use, I am sure, in fighting against power, unless we have something on our side to appeal to," wrote Shaftesbury resignedly. "You particularly and the Doctor cannot *long* resist, and retain your positions; and we shall then lose *all* by endeavouring to save *half*."[1] A word from the Treasury, an additional clause or two, Chadwick reflected bitterly, would have saved the Interments Act and the Board of Health from the reproach of failure. Convinced as he was that "measures for the relief of pain and physical suffering should have the precedence over all others,"[2] he was perplexed and bewildered by this absence of good will. The more he thought of it the more incredible it seemed to him that "a matter of the most solemn moment, the horrors of a thousand agonising scenes to the population,"[3] should be so lightly dismissed by the Government. What had happened to show that his scheme was unworkable and wrong in principle? Nothing; yet the Government was now encouraging everything that the evidence had condemned, trading in burial, joint stock cemeteries, and parochial management.

Surveying the unhappy history of the Act, we can see that by the end of 1850 the Government had got over its cholera panic and had had time to think twice about metropolitan interments; and its second thoughts, coloured by a general suspicion of central Boards and interference with private enterprise, were against Chadwick's National Cemeteries. While still anxious to be rid of the indecencies of burial within the capital, and to find a remedy for a nuisance which inflicted itself on the eyes and noses of Members of Parliament every time they passed by St. Margaret's churchyard on their way to the House, it was not prepared to sanction the peremptory intervention of the Board of Health. In the Treasury view the enthusiasts at Gwydyr House were committing the Government to a vast undefined expenditure for a dubious object. Hayter told Chadwick in conversation that the cemeteries would never be bought for less than a million; to which Chadwick roundly returned that, if Hayter were not a shareholder himself, he was speaking in the interests of shareholders.[4] Certainly the Treasury produced no evidence to support Sir

---

[1] Shaftesbury to E. C., 7 December 1851.   [2] E. C. to Lord ?, n.d.
[3] E. C. to Lord?, *c.* 25 November 1851.   [4] E. C. to Russell, n.d.

Charles Wood's assertion that the purchase price would be three
or four times the amount stated by the Board; the arbitration
awards in the case of the Brompton and Nunhead grounds,
indeed, showed that Chadwick's figures were far more reliable,
and that the total cost of buying out the companies would be well
within the estimates which Parliament had before it when approval was given to the scheme. But behind this curtain of financial scruples the Treasury concealed a more powerful motive for
its opposition. Seymour (a former Secretary to the Treasury),
Wood, Hayter, Lewis, had all been trained in the negative traditions of the old administrative service, and all took the narrowest
views of the functions of Government. Their faith was in the
efficiency of private enterprise, and their principle of action was
to leave to the capitalist anything out of which he could make a
profit. They doubted the strength of Government to shoulder any
further burdens; and with good reason—Hayter, the Patronage
Secretary and "broker-general in offices," was well aware of the
quality of the placemen who were nominated by him, at the
instance of party supporters, to the departments of State. They
sighed with relief when they found that oversights in drafting had
rendered the Interments Act so imperfect as to be promptly
reversible. Thus, both the channels through which the Board
normally communicated with the Cabinet—the President who
was the interpreter of their views, the Treasury who acted as the
financial censor of their conduct—were openly hostile to the men
and measures of Gwydyr House. Disaster came, in Chadwick's
view, when no Minister high in responsible office could be induced
to find the time to approach the subject with a sincere desire to
surmount the difficulties. The Board's activities lay at the very
periphery of ministerial attention. Their scheme had been read
and studied in detail by no member of the Cabinet, except Sir
George Grey, who took little interest in the measure once it was
passed, and, of course, the Earl of Carlisle, who told Chadwick
regretfully that his representations had little effect "as I am
always rather considered to be still acting under your spell."[1]
As Chadwick foresaw, when he implored Carlisle not to leave the
Board in 1850, "half-knowledge would be continually finding
imaginary false difficulties and finding real ones insuperable."[2]

[1] Carlisle to E. C., 1 February 1851.   [2] E. C. to Lord ? (Carlisle), n.d.

The Metropolitan Interments Act, which had started on its way with such bright hope some eighteen months before, had now returned to lay its burden of discredit at the door of Gwydyr House. The common verdict was that the Board had failed. They had failed to close the overcrowded churchyards. They had devised an imperfect scheme, and to remove its imperfections had sought impossible powers over every corpse in London. They had annoyed everybody by their unaccountable delays, their quarrelsomeness, their absolute temper, their rudeness to parishes and cemetery owners. All this was the fault of the Board—but in particular of Edwin Chadwick. "That gentleman was no doubt very ingenious," cried John Bright, when the Commons were asked to vote the money for the purchase of the two cemeteries, "and whenever he had a board with such persons as Lord Shaftesbury sitting at it, he would be sure to pull the wire. And he did pull the wire, for if they granted the sum now asked for, Mr. Chadwick would become the arbitrary dispenser of more patronage than was in the gift of officers filling the highest situations in the Government."[1] In every clash of the Board of Health with their adversaries, the public now saw further evidence of the uncompromising harshness of his mind; in every suggested addition to the Board's functions, evidence of his ambition and love of power.

[1] *Hansard*, vol. cxviii, p. 367, 22 July 1851.

S

CHAPTER XII

LONDON'S WATER AND LONDON'S GOVERNMENT

THROUGHOUT 1850 and 1851, while the Board were making their fruitless effort to put into effect the provisions of the Interments Act, a greater project for improving the health of Londoners was pursuing a parallel course to disaster. In May 1850 Chadwick produced another bulky report, the *Report on the Supply of Water to the Metropolis*,[1] in which he once again trod that well-worn path of argument first traced eight years before. He had succeeded in consolidating seven of the Sewers Commissions; he now aimed to unify the nine companies which shared the water supply of London; and the final step he contemplated would be to bring water supply and drainage together in a combined service, administered by a single body for the whole of the metropolitan area. In short, he could see no reason why his principle of sanitary consolidation, the principle of the Public Health Act, should not be applied to the capital as much as to any provincial town.

The foulness of the dilute sewage which was pumped to the average Londoner as his domestic water supply was by now so clearly demonstrated that even a witness from one of the companies was prepared to admit that offensive matter made the water "not so pleasant"—though, Chadwick noted, he spoke as if "the water-drinkers are regarded as a small or eccentric set in the City, and that such pollutions of their beverage are things of no moment, calling for no remedy, and treated as a joke rather than otherwise."[2] But even if the Thames could be protected from contamination, asserted Chadwick, it would still remain an unsuitable source for London's water supply. It was too hard, twice as hard as the average for 150 rivers examined by the Board's Inspectors. Every day twenty-six tons of lime passed

[1] *P.P.*, 1850, vol. xxii, p. 1.   [2] Ibid. p. 45.

through the pipes of the water companies, coating the inside of kettles, baths, and boilers, and using up excessive quantities of tea and soap. The "washerwomen's interest," which in the aggregate was larger than that of all the cotton and linen manufacturers, demanded that the Thames, Lea, New River, Colne, Wandle, and other tributaries of a similar degree of hardness should all be abandoned as early as practicable. The weight of the evidence favoured "the principle of soft water supply by means of gathering grounds."[1] From 150 square miles of gathering grounds, from Richmond and the heaths of Bagshot and Farnham, London could derive a supply double that now furnished by the companies, and only a third or even a tenth as hard as the water of the Thames. An entirely new supply of the softest water, pure, filtered, and aerated, could be delivered on the constant system in unlimited quantity for drinking, cooking, washing, and all domestic purposes at an inclusive weekly rent-charge of 2d. a house. At the same time, since it was axiomatic that drainage and water supply were two inseparable aspects of a single problem, he sketched out a plan for the main drainage of London. Soil water should be expelled from the capital through pipes, skirting the cultivated lands where much could be retailed as manure, and the surplus discharged so far down the river that none of it could be brought back by the return tide. The gross outlay for water supply and drainage, he estimated, would be £2,142,000, necessitating an average weekly charge per house of 5d.—less than the present charge for a defective water supply alone.

In this scheme there was no place for the nine water companies.[2] The supply of a commodity which was absolutely essential to the health, physical and moral, of the people should not be governed by considerations of profit. Yet the companies proceeded on the principle of charging the consumer not according to the cost of the service, but according to their estimate of his necessities and his capacity to pay. The promises made by the companies when they were first established made ironic reading now. Sir William Clay, chairman of the Southwark and Vauxhall Company, had once observed indeed that they could not have kept

[1] Ibid. p. 113.
[2] New River, Hampstead, Chelsea, East London, Grand Junction, West Middlesex, Lambeth, Southwark and Vauxhall, and Kent.

their promises, and would have been fools if they had.[1] The Grand Junction Company had appeared forty years before with a programme of pure water, a constant supply, a high service free of extra charge, and lowered rates. Once its pipes were laid it had pumped its water from a point opposite the Ranelagh sewer; it had withdrawn its constant supply, and obliged its tenants to spend £50,000 on cisterns; and it had made its high service subject to a rate twenty times its actual cost.[2] Chadwick did not conceal his disgust at the bland inefficiency of the water companies, the costly inadequacy of their works, and their frankly predatory attitude to the public. He protested against the surrender of a public service to private enterprise. From earliest times the town water supply had been looked on as a municipal duty; it was only at a time when public administration was weak and public opinion ill-informed that the companies had gained their concessions. The State should now resume the rights which had fallen from its grasp in a period of debility, and which the companies were now so flagrantly abusing. Nor need it be gentle in doing so. Water flowing in a stream was *publici juris*, a commodity which no individual could claim as his property and of which everybody was free to make use. Since the companies could not lay claim to the Thames and its affluents, all the property they really possessed was their distributary apparatus— most of which, Chadwick privately declared, was scarcely worth more than the old iron of which the pipes were composed.[3]

Who then was to inherit the works and functions of the water companies, and combine them with the administration of the sewers for the execution of Chadwick's grand plan for the sanitary redemption of London? He dismissed brusquely the idea of a municipality. The administrative machinery suitable for a provincial town would be hardly appropriate for the metropolis of the whole empire, the seat of Parliament, and centre of law and commerce; an attempt to introduce it must open up large and new political questions the settlement of which would delay the remedies so urgently needed. Hence, in Chadwick's view, the

[1] E. C., "Notes of heads of remonstrance on the Metropolitan Water Bill," MS., n.d. (1852).
[2] E. C., "Promises held out in the prospectus of the Grand Junction Company," MS., n.d.
[3] E. C. to F. O. Ward, 6 October 1849.

task should be entrusted to a small Board of paid and skilled officials. Three competent officers, meeting daily and giving undivided attention to the subject, could push through business at six times the speed of the present thirteen Sewers Commissioners, who met only once a week or fortnight in committees of varying composition. Such a Board would be responsible to the Government, and through Parliament to the ratepayers; and in addition it would be surrounded with the guarantees set out in the provisions of the Public Health Act for explanatory reports and estimates, for public audit and the publication of accounts, and for the execution and maintenance of works on contract by open tender.

It was a bold, simple plan, argued with great power and at times with passion as Chadwick assailed the interests barring the way to a cleaner, healthier London. The Report, it must be emphasized, contains three distinct proposals: first, that the water supply of London should be derived from new sources; secondly, that the water companies should be bought out by the public, and their works consolidated; and thirdly, that an executive commission should be appointed to administer the combined service of water supply and drainage. By Chadwick these three proposals were regarded as inseparable elements in a single scheme; but in fact each of them—a soft-water supply, public ownership, an executive commission—was supported by an independent body of reasons, and might have been isolated for consideration on its own merits. A public monopoly of the water supply was the great object to be achieved. It would be better to dispossess the companies even if London continued to draw its supplies from the hard water of the Thames; it would be better to dispossess the companies even if their functions fell to some other authority than the executive commission that Chadwick desired. We may, at the outset, lay a finger on one reason for Chadwick's failure in this, as in so many other projects. Once he had arrived at a solution, after an exhaustive examination of the evidence, he committed himself to it wholeheartedly, bending to it all the energy of his emotions and his intellect. In that singleness of will and purpose there was too little room left for manœuvre, for modification, for compromise. He was incapable of cutting and moulding his schemes to fit the resistant pattern of other

minds, suppressing criticisms in detail so long as the main principle
were established, sacrificing with good will a lesser benefit that a
greater might be achieved. He had, as the Earl of Carlisle told
him, "possibly too ardent a strain after perfection which necessarily becomes one-sided in a world of so many mixed considerations."[1] It is to be regretted that Chadwick did not concentrate
his attention upon the primary task of buying out the companies
and consolidating the supply under public authority. Instead he
wandered off into the wilds of Surrey in search of the perfect
source, and the clear-cut administrative scheme of the Board
became entangled with disputed questions of chemical analysis
and hydraulic engineering. He was thus driven to extend his
lines to defend positions which were not vital, and to press
arguments which later scientific developments rendered largely
irrelevant.

Now that the scheme was before the public, Chadwick hoped
to get before the end of the 1850 session the Government's sanction
to take the preparatory steps for the consolidation of the water
works. Once again, however, he had fallen into the error of assuming that the hearty assent he heard in Gwydyr House would
find an echo in Downing Street; and that the Government, in
admitting the cogency of his arguments, were prepared to shape
their policy on his recommendations. The Treasury would be
very restive on the question, Carlisle warned him;[2] and two days
later Ashley added, "We must be very circumspect. I see clearly
that the parties are anything but friendly. Go forward very
gradually."[3] When Parliament went into recess, the Board had
secured their Interments Act, but the Government were still
avoiding a decision on the water-supply scheme. The Board must
get ready for an arduous November campaign, wrote Ashley,
when "we must pipe all hands, God helping us, for the water-
supply."[4]

The interval, as we saw in the previous chapter, was largely
spent in preparations for implementing the Interments Act; but
from ten o'clock to ten o'clock one late summer day the members
of the Board wandered over the wild heaths of Surrey, round
Farnham, in quest of gathering grounds. This preliminary survey

[1] Carlisle to E. C., 4 October 1848.   [2] Carlisle to E.C., 12 August 1850.
[3] Ashley to E. C., 14 August 1850.   [4] Ashley to E.C., 18 September 1850.

promised well, and Chadwick took immediate steps to have the results checked. For once he made an unfortunate choice of agent. The Honourable William Napier was a high-minded young man, who bore a burden of debt with the careless charm of good breeding and an aristocratic name. The combination of charm and family probably had its effect on Chadwick who, for all his scorn of the intellectual qualities of the upper classes, had a little of the snobbery of the man who has clambered several rungs up the social ladder. It is difficult to understand otherwise why he should have accepted so readily Napier's offer to make (for expenses only) a closer examination of the Farnham gathering grounds. He could have laid his hands on a dozen men better qualified for the task, whose reports would not have been so vulnerable to attack. Napier spent some six months in Farnham, but beyond underlining Chadwick's superlatives and feeding his faith in the soft sand springs, his researches did not amount to much. The water was undoubtedly there. "Gushes of water as big as one's waist," cried the enthusiastic John Simon, when he checked over the results, "with scarcely perceptible alteration by *any* reagent."[1] A few weeks' exploration of all the woods and valleys of the district revealed forty-four streams, with a yield sufficient for half a million houses; "the water being of its primitive purity; perfect as to aeration; brilliant in colour; soft almost as distilled water; of a grateful temperature, about 50°; and almost free from all mineral, animal, and vegetable impregnation."[2] The encouraging fact determined by Napier was that even in the unusually dry summer of 1850 the flow of these streams would suffice to furnish an increased supply to the whole of London.[3] More and more rosy grew Chadwick's hopes of collecting the spring water of the Surrey hills—a never failing source of 40,000,000 gallons at 1° of hardness—and pumping it from Farnham to the top floor of the highest house in the capital. With this amplified supply, he assured Prince Albert's secretary, they could wash the streets and houses of London in readiness for the Great Exhibition.[4]

[1] J. Simon to E. C., 21 October 1850.
[2] W. Napier, "Further Examination of the 'Gathering Grounds' for the proposed Government Water Supply to the metropolis," p. 6.
[3] *Memorandum. The plan of improved Water Supply of the Metropolis*, printed, 9 December 1850.   [4] E. C. to Col. Phipps, 19 October 1850.

When Ashley returned to London at the end of October, invigorated by a three months' holiday which had saved him from a breakdown, he was delighted to hear the results of Napier's researches. He would write at once to Grey, he said, for authority to prepare the Bill.[1] A week later he had been in touch with members of the Cabinet, and doubt was beginning to creep in. "Will our Government have courage and principle to carry the plan into effect?" he was wondering.[2] Then one day Lord Seymour came to the office, and to Chadwick's amazement demanded to know upon what authority the Board had investigated the water supply of London, and objected to any further proceedings on the matter. For answer Chadwick directed his attention to the recital in the opening paragraph of the Report.[3] With heavy foreboding, Ashley noted in his diary: "The Water Supply, for which alone I remained at the Board of Health will be set aside or emasculated by the Government; and yet I made this measure a condition of my stay there. The situation is painful, because it is become that of a clerk, and I am made, by Seymour and Grey, to feel it hourly. The Board has no free action, no power to effect any of its decisions, for the Treasury and the Home Office refuse, or thwart, every proposition."[4] On 19 December George Lewis informed the Board that the Treasury did not deem it expedient at present to incur the expense of a plan and levels of the district which Chadwick had indicated as the future gathering grounds for the capital.[5] And in the first month of 1851 the friction between the imperious Seymour and his imperious colleagues struck into flame. A curt note to the Secretary demanded to know who had authorised Napier to continue his inquiries at Farnham beyond the period sanctioned by the Treasury. The challenge was taken up by Ashley as the champion of the Board, and there was a sharp exchange of letters.

If Seymour thought he had ground to reprove his colleagues, demanded Ashley, would he not have done better to call them together and hear their explanations?[6] Seymour replied that the Board should have informed him of their action; "explicit direc-

---

[1] Ashley to E. C., 25 October 1850.   [2] Ashley to E. C., 2 November 1850.
[3] E. C. to Carlisle, n.d. (January 1851).
[4] 12 December 1850: E. Hodder, op. cit., vol. ii, p. 320.
[5] Minutes, 19 December 1850.   [6] Ashley to Seymour, 6 January 1851.

tions" had been sent by the Treasury to the Board that they should submit to him any proposal involving expenditure. Had he known of it, he would certainly have objected to any further investigation by Napier. Napier's report, with its account of the practice of the ancient Peruvians, the canals made by the Moors, the water-courses of Mesopotamia, and extracts from Sale's Koran, was "a paper suited only for a Monthly Magazine." If ever the Board initiated proceedings involving new expenditure in contravention of the Treasury directions, he would remonstrate again; he did not wish to lay himself open to censure such as the Treasury had passed on the Board before he came to office.[1] This was the first he had heard of "orders from the Treasury," replied Ashley. Seymour's right to find fault with his colleagues was unquestioned, but it would be more agreeable, and more consistent with the proper and necessary rules of Board operations, if he conveyed his differences of opinion in person. That had been Lord Carlisle's practice whenever he had any doubt or difficulty, and "the result was a most friendly and comfortable unanimity."[2]

Seymour, hearing of Carlisle's virtues, must have experienced something of the disagreeable feeling of a second husband whose wife sings the praises of his predecessor. He could have derived little more satisfaction from Ashley's next letter. The Board had no record of, nor could they or their officers remember, any "explicit directions" from the Treasury instructing them to submit to Seymour proposals involving expenditure; "and indeed the case is clear, for surely the Treasury would never have issued an Order which, in fact, would have been illegal, that, on a Board consisting of four Commissioners, three should be compelled to submit their proceedings to the fourth, who did not intend to take any share in the business, or even to be present at their deliberations."[3] At this Seymour proposed to appeal to the Chancellor of the Exchequer for a ruling as to his duties and responsibilities.[4] This did not answer the question, replied Ashley bluntly. "You charge the Board and me among the rest with neglect of duty and disobedience to 'explicit directions.' I asked you before, and I now ask you again, 'When was the Order given.

[1] Seymour to Ashley, 7 January 1851.
[2] Ashley to Seymour, 8 January 1851.   [3] Ashley to Seymour, 10 January 1851.
[4] Seymour to Ashley, 10 January 1851.

What was it; was it by word of mouth or in writing, where is it now to be found?' "[1] Pinned down at last, Seymour lamely confessed that he "understood" such directions had been given to the Board by the Treasury or the Chancellor of the Exchequer. [2] An "understanding," Ashley pointed out, was a weak foundation on which to reprimand his colleagues. The same day he wrote again to sweep away the last excuse for Seymour's querulous complaint. He forwarded copies of two letters, one dated 10 August 1850 informing Seymour of Napier's engagement, the second dated 12 August, from Seymour himself, recording "no objection." Napier's engagement did not begin till five days afterwards. "Such is the haste and want of consideration with which you attack your Colleagues."[3]

Lord Seymour had retreated discomfited behind the skirts of the Chancellor of the Exchequer, but in Gwydyr House there was dismay and a feeling that the Board had reached a crisis in their career. It would have been serious enough if the incident had merely revealed that the manners of their President were bad, his memory feeble, and his attention to the business of the Board neither regular nor sympathetic. The correspondence—taken in conjunction with the attitude which in this same month he adopted towards the Interments Act—showed in addition that he intended, in his own words, "to stop as much as he could" of the work of the sanitary reformers, and that in this policy of obstruction he was supported and incited by a powerful section of the Cabinet. Clearly he felt no loyalty either to the members or to the duties of the General Board. His allegiance was given wholeheartedly to the Lords of the Treasury, and he agreed with them that public health legislation meant finding money for busybodies to meddle with things which were better managed by Providence and the capitalist entrepreneur. To Ashley he was obliged to be outwardly polite; but Southwood Smith, Dr. Sutherland, Austin, all were treated to marks of his contempt; and Chadwick he loathed.

[1] Ashley to Seymour, 10 January 1851.
[2] Seymour to Ashley, 11 January 1851.
[3] Ashley to Seymour, 14 January 1851. There is no record of Seymour's reply to this. On 18 January Ashley told Chadwick, "Lord Seymour's reply is a becoming one. I hope for peace," which may indicate that he sent a note of apology.

One point was clearly illustrated by the Seymour–Ashley duel —the ambiguous nature of the President's status. Was he simply the first among his equals, or did he sit at the Board as a departmental chief with his subordinate advisers? By the Public Health Act he was on the same footing as the other three members of the Board; yet, as a Minister of the Crown, his shoulders carried more responsibility and his opinion had more weight. The Act, so Chadwick argued, directed the Treasury to make its decisions only upon the advice prepared by joint deliberation at a Board. The Treasury had no legal warrant to substitute for the collegiate responsibility of the Board action upon the responsibility of a single member of it—not even if he had taken part in the deliberations, and much less if he were absent and never listened to them. "It is rather hard in itself," Chadwick told Carlisle, "after having bestowed great labour in convincing the public, then the Government: then the parliament, and getting a measure passed, and then to have the whole measure subjected to gentlemen, who say that all are wrong and that they are hostile to the principles of the measure."[1] The question had another aspect. While the critics objected that the Board were independent and uncontrolled, Chadwick complained on the other hand that no Minister gave his full attention to the subject of public health. The Board shared with the Woods and Forests the time and labour of a minor Minister. Carlisle had attended carefully to his duties at Gwydyr House; with the result, since he could not be in two places at once, that he aroused dissatisfaction at the Woods and Forests. Even before his clash with Chadwick and Ashley, Seymour had declared, in conversation with Carlisle, that he would take little part in the Board's proceedings. It was obvious that, unlike his predecessor, he looked on the duties of the new department as of a very subordinate order indeed, and found the routine and atmosphere of the older office more congenial. In consequence, the whole business of the Public Health Act, as Chadwick protested, was subjected to a double or even a threefold procedure. After being passed at the Board, it was submitted to a President who never presided; and at the same time it was laid before the Treasury, whose officials had no resources of information to guide them on reaching decisions on sanitary policy. The business of

[1] E. C. to Carlisle, n.d. (January 1851).

the older departments kept to a well-trodden course, and could be understood by anyone of general intelligence; but the Board's business was new, and bristled with technicalities. A mastery of the new principles, Chadwick maintained, and regular attendance at the Board to discuss and observe their application in practice, were essential to the proper working of the Act.[1] If this proposition were accepted, the intrusion of the uninformed Seymour stood condemned for its arrogant impertinence.

The Board's position was further weakened in May 1851, when Ashley succeeded to his father's title. It was true, as Chadwick pointed out, that in the less sustained debates of the Upper House, his health would not have to bear the strain of late night sittings; and he would encounter less opposition from sinister interests than in the Commons.[2] Nevertheless, the removal of Ashley left the Board with Seymour as their only official spokesman in the Lower House—a champion unreliable in his loyalty, and more inclined to turn his weapons against the cause he was defending.

Despite Lord John Russell's promise to Ashley—which alone had persuaded him not to resign in March 1850—the Bill for metropolitan water supply was put in the hands of the Home Office. Not one member of the Board was consulted about the measure, except Lord Seymour, their *fainéant* President. The Government Bill, introduced on 29 April by the Home Secretary, Sir George Grey,[3] proposed that the stock of the existing companies should be valued, and that they should then be consolidated and placed under the supervision of Her Majesty's Principal Secretary of State. The dividends of the consolidated company would be limited to 5 per cent, any excess income being applied by the Treasury to the reduction of rates. As a sanction to ensure that the proprietors complied with the provisions of the Act, the Home Secretary would be empowered to stop dividends. Looking over the Bill with a discouraged eye, Chadwick must have felt that his Report might just as well have remained unwritten, Napier might have stayed in London, and the Board have saved

---

[1] "Administrative. Notes of Objections to the Course taken by Lord Seymour in respect to the Public Health Act," MS., n.d.
[2] E. C. to Ashley, 9 June 1851.　　　　[3] *Hansard*, vol. cxvi, p. 340.

themselves the laborious inquiries and preparations of the previous fifteen months. Grey's Bill, in fact, hardly noticed the findings of sanitary investigators over the last ten years. It did not provide for a constant service, for a filtered supply, nor for a resort to new and purer sources; these matters were left undecided, to be settled by the Home Secretary at some unspecified future date. It did not provide for a universal supply, so that nearly three-quarters of a million Londoners would still have to beg or steal their water, or catch it from a public stand-cock. It said nothing about the consolidation of water and drainage under a single authority, which had been recommended by three sanitary inquiries, in 1842, in 1845, and in 1850. Above all, it left the service in private hands, checked only by such supervision as could be expected from an overburdened Minister. The water traders remained—their virtual monopoly, based on a tacit agreement, now converted into a legal monopoly; guaranteed against competition and assured of a divided of 5 per cent on a capital whose value they placed at £4,800,000, a sum more than double the amount they had actually laid out.

The origin of the Government Bill was an open secret. Twelve months before Sir William Clay, chairman of the Southwark and Vauxhall Company, had addressed himself to Chadwick, declaring his hearty concurrence in the proposition that the waterworks should be consolidated and acquired by the public. The radical defect of the present system, he observed, was that the companies had no protection against the incursion of fresh competitors. Few years passed without new schemes being canvassed; the public were easily led astray by projectors who professed to be able to defeat the oppressive water monopoly; and the companies were thereby caused continual trouble, anxiety, and expense. For this reason, he believed, the proprietors would welcome a "water works annuity fund," created under the guarantee of Parliament, the amount of the fund to be determined by the actual net income of the companies; the annuities to be a first charge on the water rates, and transferable at the Bank like other Government annuities. In return, the whole property of the companies should be vested in the public. Both parties would gain by the change, the public by the economies of a unified administration, the companies by the increased value and security of their shares.[1] Clay's scheme was, in fact, an ingenious method of exchanging the precarious benefits of commercial freedom for the financial stability of a Government rentier. It sprang from an intelligent appreciation that the old order was passing, that— as the leaders of *The Times* unequivocally revealed—the weight of public opinion was against the companies, and that if they continued to resist they would exacerbate that opinion and open the way for a settlement on the ruthless lines indicated by Chadwick. But Clay, who wrote heartily that, if the companies and the Board of Health got together, they could come to an agreement in five minutes,[2] could have had no inkling of the depths of Chadwick's scorn for the claims of the water traders. Presently, finding Chadwick unresponsive, Sir William Clay diverted his stream of memoranda to the Home Office, where they were given a more sympathetic hearing.

In his acceptance of the principles of consolidation and public ownership, however, Clay—who confessed to be "tired of presiding over Directors' meetings"[3]—was far from typical of his class. There were others who retained their faith in private enterprise, who would rather keep their independent existence than be merged into either a consolidated company or a unified public service, and who were unwilling to exchange for a safe percentage the risks of the old order with its possibilities of greater profit. The majority of the directors were resolved to fight a delaying action as long as they could. A barrister friend of Chadwick's, engaged in auditing the accounts of the Chelsea Water Company, found a "good round sum" set down as a subscription towards fighting the Public Health Act.[4] When the Water Works Clauses Act of 1847 applied the first restraints to the trade in water, however, they realised that it was no longer sufficient to subsidise journalists and lecturers to talk darkly of French Centralisation and the invasion of property rights. They must make a show of accepting gracefully some part of the sanitary findings; and they calculated that if they did so they might be enabled, by virtue of their strength in the Commons and the respect accorded to them

---

[1] "Memoranda on the supply of water to the Metropolis. Sir W. Clay's paper," MS., n.d.

[2] Sir W. Clay to E. C., 8 April 1850.   [3] Sir W. Clay to E. C., 23 July 1850.

[4] E. C. to F. O. Ward, 6 October 1849. In another note, probably to Delane (28 July 1851), he gives the figure as £200 or £240.

by the Government as great nucleations of capital, to survive into
the brave new world of Chadwick and the Health of Towns
Association.

Each of the three solutions so far described—the Government-
appointed Commission urged by Chadwick, the statutory Company proposed by the Home Office Bill, the independent companies under certain minimum restrictions desired by most of the
proprietors—had its spokesmen in the debates of 1851. There
was a fourth party, however, more vocal than these, and commanding outside the House a wider measure of popular support.
If Sir William Clay, and beyond him the less accommodating
directors of the water companies, formed the right wing of the
opposition to Chadwick's scheme, the left wing was represented
by the advocates of parochial control. It was a confused, dis-
united, clamorous group, drawing its theoretical arguments from
Toulmin Smith, its members diverse in their aims and in the
quality of the motives which impelled them; a loose alliance of
the metropolitan M.P.s and the Common Council, of Guardians,
overseers, and churchwardens, the projectors of a dozen water-
supply schemes, and a dubious tail of contractors and jobbers;
some shouting for a municipality for the whole of London, others
hoping to obtain for the separate parishes of the capital the essential organs of urban government. The chief movers, Chadwick
was convinced, were a set of engineers and promoters who felt
that they had little or no chance with anything higher than a
parish vestry.[1] There was Mr. Taberner, for example, the
attorney's managing clerk who acted as spokesman for the Metropolitan Water Supply Association, and who was connected with
a scheme for supplying each parish separately by artesian wells.
He had the effrontery to call one day at Gwydyr House and offer
to direct the agitation according to the instructions of the Board,
on condition that they reimbursed him for the time and money
he had sacrificed. A similar suggestion came from the solicitor
of another scheme, which proposed to draw water from Henley
at an outlay of two millions and appoint a salaried Board or
Management costing £6,000 a year. "These overtures were made
on the most vulgar conception of the motives and desire of the

[1] E. C., "Water Supply: Central Establishment versus Parochial Establishment in the metropolis," MS., n.d.

members of the General Board to obtain mere power and patron-age; in which on the implied conditions that it was to be given to the promoters, unreserved support was promised, and hostility intimated if it were withheld."[1] But the scheme which was acclaimed in vestry after vestry from June to September 1851, and which enlisted the support of Delane of *The Times*, was a proposal by Francis Mowatt, member for Penryn and Falmouth, to vest the ownership and management of London's water supply in a representative body, comprising four members elected by the ratepayers for each of seventeen districts, together with four from the Common Council, and four nominated by the Government.[2]

In a series of lengthy letters and memoranda Chadwick com-bated the notion of creating a municipality for London. His argument followed two main lines. In the first place, the proposal stood condemned by all his experience of the corruption and interest-begotten prejudices of local representative bodies. He described in broad outline this gigantic new local authority, with a jurisdiction over two and a quarter million people, disposing of millions of pounds in rates, and faced with a complex of technical problems. Then, with a note of irony, he pointed to the products of vestry politics, and asked if men of this calibre could possibly grapple with so enormous a task. Could the small shopkeepers, who formed the majority of the metropolitan ratepayers, be expected to create a municipal council more intelligent and better disposed towards improvements than the Corporation of the City —a body whose ignorance, callousness, and susceptibility to sinister influences, were clearly shown by its defence of the cruelties and abominations of Smithfield Market? Secondly, shifting his ground, and aiming at the self-importance of national legislators, he urged that a unified municipality for the whole of London would be a formidable and independent power in the State, which would always be able, by the magnitude of its political influence, to procure the exemption of the capital from the opera-tion of the laws passed by the legislature. The administration of the metropolis, the seat of Government, was of national concern;

[1] E. C., MS. fragment, n.d.
[2] Mowatt attempted to introduce his Metropolitan Water Supply (Control of Representative Body) Bill on 24 June 1851 (*Hansard*, vol. cxvii, pp. 1140–9), and again on 6 February 1852 (*Hansard*, vol. cxix, pp. 220–31).

that was acknowledged by the special attention given to it by Government Commissions in the past. The two lines of argument thus converged in the proposition that the special nature of the problem presented by the capital city called for special administrative arrangements—in short, for the executive commission Chadwick had earlier indicated.[1]

If the Home Secretary read these memoranda, he did not allow himself to be swayed by their reasoning. Yet it was immediately evident that the Government's Bill stood no chance of success. Sir George Grey himself seemed to have no great confidence in the measure. The best plan if it were only practicable, he declared, would be to place the water supply in the hands of a municipal corporation or some analogous body. On the other hand, he confessed that if they were dealing with the subject as a new one, and could ignore long-established machinery and the aversion to Government interference in matters of daily and domestic concern, Parliament would do well to adopt the proposal made by the Board.[2] Hence, by the Home Secretary's own admission, his solution was only a bad third, and he laid himself open to attack from the one side by those who were not so easily persuaded that a municipality was impracticable, and from the other by those who believed that water supply was properly a subject for Government interference. The Bill was enfiladed from all quarters by a suspicious House. Why should Londoners pay £400,000 or £450,000 a year when a completely new and improved supply could be obtained for £2,000,000, demanded Viscount Ebrington, whose speech owed much to Gwydyr House.[3] Sir Benjamin Hall, the Member for Marylebone, prophesied that the Bill would boom the 3 per cent water shares to £130; seventy Members of Parliament, he was informed, held shares in the companies, and they were not likely to vote for any competition.[4] In his belief that the water companies were behind the Bill, however, Hall had misjudged their temper. They were far from willing, as we have seen, to forfeit their freedom of action to the extent contemplated by Sir William Clay; and the opinion of the

---

[1] See especially *Memorandum as to the Constitution of the Administrative Machinery for the erection of New Public Works*, printed, 24 January 1851.

[2] *Hansard*, vol. cxvi, p. 340, 29 April 1851.

[3] Ibid., vol. cxvii, p. 506, 5 June 1851.   [4] Ibid., p. 472.

T

majority of them was expressed by Sir John Johnstone, a former director of the New River Company, who could see no reason why the House should not pass a Bill tying down each company to certain rules and regulations, similar to those which would be applied to the proposed amalgamated body.[1]

The Bill passed its Second Reading by 95 votes to 79; but only two had risen to speak in its favour, Sir George Grey himself and Sir William Clay. On 5 June it was referred to a Select Committee, its defence being entrusted to three eminent counsel against the lawyers and engineers put into the field by the companies and the parochial party. The General Board were allowed no *locus standi* before the Committee, and their Inspectors were not called as witnesses; the most Chadwick could do was to send copies of his Report on Water Supply to members of the Committee. It was "really a very fearful thing," to refer such a question to a Committee of private and irresponsible members. "Should not they be reminded of their duties to those who are unrepresented; the vast mass of two millions of the population, and of the poorest?" "The private bill legislation is really in general the legislation of those who can pay for it. Where Hudson was unopposed he did as he liked, through these committees, with the legislature; and for railway purposes the committees, and through them Parliament itself, were the agency of the parliamentary agents. . . . There will be perhaps as much as three millions sterling in issue against the public for which there will be counsel. But the power of money in procuring the evidence of scientific witnesses is the most disgusting feature to be anticipated. Before the railway committees, men of science were got to swear against a rival line which had a tunnel, that the air of the tunnel would be dangerous to human life. Before the private committee of the River Lea Trust Bill, an eminent Chemist, who had given a certificate in favour of soft water for Liverpool, was got to express his horror at the proposal to supply [people] with soft water, as one for poisoning them. . . . In favour of the Thames water as it now is, the Companies obtained the strong certificates of men of science who had denounced it before the Board of Health. . . . Could not the inhabitants of Church Lane, St. Giles, or of Jacob's Island be advised to come *in forma pauperis*, and ask the committee

[1] *Hansard*, vol. cxvi, p. 322.

to assign counsel to them?"[1] With such reflections Chadwick looked on helplessly at the day-to-day clashes of the contending parties. He was cheered when Sir James Graham, who had no liking for the Government Bill, showed signs also of being impressed by the constitutional inconveniences of Mowatt's parish parliament.[2] But Graham had vagaries of his own, Chadwick noted disgustedly—some notion of supplying the north side from Watford and the south side from Farnham, and erecting a separate municipality on each bank; which would amount to having two hearts in one body.[3] Under cross-examination the parochialists made revealing admissions. But what was the use of bringing out the fact that the agitation was the product of a few interested individuals working on small minorities in the parishes, when the papers printed none of the proceedings?[4]

Between June and September 1851 one vestry after another condemned Grey's Bill and passed resolutions in favour of parochial control. Seven hundred ratepayers in Southwark signed the requisition for a public meeting against the Bill, the largest requisition ever known in the borough.[5] But the trading interests, Chadwick observed, seemed to be in complete possession of the papers, with the exception of *The Times*.[6] The secretary of one water company told him "they had got the *Economist*";[7] but opposition was only to be expected from a journal which had looked upon the Public Health Act as an unjustifiable meddling with natural law. More perturbing was the defection of the *Chronicle* and the *Daily News*, two newspapers distinguished hitherto for their advocacy of sanitary reform. Napier called on the editor of the *Chronicle* to complain of the way his views had been misrepresented, and discovered that the writer of the offending articles was Venables, the counsel for the Kent Water Company before the Select Committee. Chadwick was especially pained by the scurrility of the *Daily News*, which "has been introduced as a reformed newspaper and has been held up I believe by Bright and Cobden as an example of what a cheap Newspaper should

---

[1] E. C. to ? (Delane), 20 June 1851.
[2] F. O. Ward to E. C., 19 and 27 June 1851.
[3] E. C. to F. O. Ward, 3 July 1851.   [4] E. C. to F. O. Ward, 5 July 1851.
[5] *Minutes of Evidence taken before the Select Committee on the Metropolitan Water Bill*; *P.P.*, 1851, vol. xv, p. 1; Q. 4982, evidence of E. Collinson.
[6] E. C. to F. O. Ward, 28 July 1851.   [7] E. C. to Russell, n.d. (1851).

be." Crowe, the editor, was most respectable, and "it is most likely to be the affair of some mere capitalist." And so it turned out to be: Smith, the manager of the paper, appeared as the solicitor for the Hampstead Water Works, in which he was believed to have a large interest.[1] The *Daily News*, Chadwick recalled, had also been strongly opposed to the removal of Smith-field Market—the articles being written by one of the counsel engaged on its behalf. Chadwick wrote a public letter (which apparently remained in draft) to protest against a practice which must be conducive to the corruption of the Press, arguing that the retainer of a barrister who was an influential writer in a news-paper, perhaps even its proprietor, was in effect the retainer of the newspaper itself. He thought further of mentioning to the Attorney-General this new kind of huggery, which led to the employment of barristers not for their legal qualifications but for their secret services as writers in the newspapers.

The Times alone seemed not to speak with the voice of the hired hack. "Whatever bias I have heard imputed to the Times I have never heard it accused of a pecuniary bias. Indeed, although I largely differed from the late Mr. Walter, I always said that his integrity against every sort of sinister influence appeared to me to be most remarkable."[2] A tribute indeed from one so sharp to scent corruption! Shut out from the Select Committee on Grey's Water Bill, with the Government increasingly cold and unrespon-sive and the threatened interests ever more active and menacing, Chadwick made a bid for the alliance of the most powerful leader of opinion in the London Press, Delane of *The Times*. In Print-ing House Square unfortunately the name of Chadwick carried with it the odour of the polluted Thames; and he was driven therefore to make use of a stalking-horse, an eloquent and forceful journalist, F. O. Ward, who could put a more attractive colour on the sanitary case than could Chadwick with his desiccated English.[3] Delane had made it plain that he found more to recom-mend Chadwick's Government Board than Clay's statutory com-

---

[1] E. C. to F. O. Ward, 30 June 1851. [2] E. C. to ? (Delane), 28 July 1851.
[3] Ward made Chadwick's acquaintance towards the end of 1849. He had explained the Board's scheme in two articles in the *Quarterly Review*: (1) "Metropolitan Water Supply," vol. lxxxvii, pp. 468–502, September 1850; (2) "Sanitary Consolidation—Centralisation—Local Self-Government," vol. lxxxviii, pp. 435–92, March 1851.

pany; but in preference to either he wanted to see London's water supply in the hands of a municipality. To mature the municipal institutions demanded by *The Times*, argued Ward, would take a lifetime. The interval could best be bridged by a terminable Commission, small, paid, and removable, renewed at intervals of three years as an *ad interim* administrative expedient until the municipal reconstruction of London had been carried out. Ward addressed his letters to Chadwick, who forwarded them without comment to Delane; but *The Times* showed no signs of abandoning its campaign for the immediate establishment of representative government for London. Nor was Chadwick's assent ungrudging to the form in which Ward had shaped the Board's plan. He certainly did not concur with Ward's thesis that government by commission was no more than a temporary administrative device, to be replaced within a generation by a municipality. The feeling abroad in favour of representative control might be regretted, Ward urged on Chadwick, but it must be admitted, and their policy should be to modify it or mitigate it as best they could. All Chadwick's evidence that the parish agitators were interested men, and the vestry meetings but thinly attended, would not deter *The Times* and other journals from advocating ratepayers' control, which, "whether demanded by large meetings or small, is at all events the only principle that has in its favour *any popular meetings at all*."[1] This Chadwick must have felt was giving hostages to the enemy. Ward's letters acknowledged too much reasonableness in the ideas of the opposition for a controversialist of Chadwick's temper. After one or two of his letters had been held up by Chadwick's censorship, Ward ventured on a postscript of expostulation. It would weigh with Delane, he said, if all the letters were sent, "as this will show that independent views are taken and discussed, and that I am not a mere puppet reflecting your views and playing into your hands. (And, by the bye, let me mention that you are much weakened by the prevalence of a belief of this kind in many quarters—it is thought that the Engineers Inspectors and those who serve you, give in many cases opinions modelled in conformity with yours—which deprives the evidence, etc., of its cogency. Even *I* have been openly said to be 'in Chadwick's pay'! It is worth while to adopt

[1] F. O. Ward to E. C., 14 July, 31 July and 3 August 1851.

all reasonable means of mitigating the intensity of the dislike and opposition and mistrust occasioned by these unfounded ideas. Let my various letters, etc., go for what they are worth, for example —and be assured that, so far as they are wrong, they will not prevail, while the candour of giving fair play to opinions not *entirely* identical with yours will be much appreciated."[1]

Chadwick's irritability increased as the Select Committee ambled on through ten inconclusive weeks. Ward wrote to encourage him: "Above all keep our soldiers in good cheer— don't for heaven's sake talk about 'disasters' in the camp. I for one have not the slightest misgivings—and I promise you a bowl of Punch made with soft Gathering ground water delivered through my water-tap in Cork Street before two summers are over our heads."[2] The Committee closed the hearing of evidence at the beginning of August. No report was made. None was necessary. The case for consolidation was proved, but that was the one point on which agreement was reached by the unhappy Committee, bewildered by a confusion of issues—hard water against soft, constant supply against intermittent, Watford chalk against Surrey sand, Mowatt against Clay and the companies against them both. Russell had already announced that the Government did not intend to legislate on water supply during the present session. The water question had been put off for another year, as it was clear it must be the moment Grey introduced his ill-concocted Bill. The Treasury, which had refused to grant the Board £500 for a survey of the new sources, had spent £5,000 on the rejected measure.[3]

[1] F. O. Ward to E. C., 7 August 1851.
[2] F. O. Ward to E. C., 30 July 1851.   [3] E. C. to Russell, n.d.

CHAPTER XIII

THE INSPECTORS AT WORK

THE jealousy of the localities and the caution of the legislature had circumscribed the powers of the General Board of Health by the narrowest of boundaries. Their Inspectors could be summoned by a petition signed by one-tenth of the ratepayers; alternatively, the Board could hold an inquiry into the sanitary condition of any place with a death rate over 23 in the thousand, whether the inhabitants welcomed the investigation or not. But that was the sum total of what may be termed their initiatory or aggressive powers; and the wisdom of the Board held them back from pressing even these limited powers to their full stretch. As a rule of practice, they laid it down at the beginning that they would conduct no local inquiry unless they were assured of substantial local co-operation. They proceeded upon the authority of a return from the Registrar-General only after they had received solid evidence in the shape of some form of local representation—a resolution of the Town Council, a ratepayers' meeting, a petition from the doctors and clergy—that their Inspector would be kindly received by influential elements in the district. Sometimes they over-estimated the strength of the feeling in their favour; sometimes the swing of local politics put their friends out and their enemies in; sometimes a district which had at first seemed receptive was swept into opposition by the speeches and handbills of water company agents, Local Act attorneys, or the Anti-Centralisation League. This was only to be expected. The Inspectors' probe was bound at times to press on a tender spot. But the Board took up no intransigent attitude towards the localities, and they withdrew with admirable caution when the opposition seemed preponderant, regretting privately at the same time that they had no power to clean away such well defended dirt.

Nothing annoyed Chadwick more than the charge that the

Board of Health forced its way into a place and rode roughshod over the feelings and interests of its inhabitants. He would point in answer to the securities he had so carefully provided for sounding local opinion, consulting the wishes of the population, and preparing their minds for the responsibilities and benefits of the Public Health Act. A local examination was conducted by a specially qualified engineer, escorted by leading citizens of the district; a public interrogation of witnesses was held before the ratepayers; the Inspector explained the objects aimed at and the methods by which it was intended to achieve them; a report on the present state of the town was published locally, together with a description of the new public works proposed, and an estimate of their probable expense; and finally, in London, a responsible Public Board sat to review the contemplated measures, and to serve as a court of appeal to private parties. What more painless method could be devised of grafting the functions and powers of the Public Health Act on to the older machinery of local government?

How smoothly on occasion the method worked is illustrated in an entertaining account by Robert Rawlinson.

"On my arrival in Hexham, I found the town in a state of ferment as to the inquiry, the bell-man was perambulating the streets summonsing the ratepayers to a meeting to oppose the inquiry. This was repeated during the evening, one of the meetings being for the evening, the other for the morning. Several of the promoters called in upon me during the evening, evidently fearing the morning's meeting. I explained the Act to them, as the most absurd statements had been published and were believed. I learned that the leader of the opponents was a Local Solicitor. The promoters were most anxious to learn what course I should take, as they feared to come forward and support the measure in public. That is they would attend the meeting but wished to avoid taking an active part in the proceedings. I told them this was exactly the course I desired they should take—namely—let the opposition have all the talking to themselves, and so leave them to me as I was quite sure out of their own evidence I could convict, if not convince them. The inquiry had to be adjourned to a large room as there was a full and rather formidable attendance. The day being wet many workmen were there. I commenced the inquiry by a short statement of the proceedings which had brought me down—and then glanced rapidly over the powers contained in the Act—taking up one by one the objections which I had been informed the promoters of the opposition had made. I then requested any persons having evidence to offer either for or against to come forward and tender it. The opponents entered most resolutely into the arena, declaring that Hexham was well supplied with water; and was, in all other respects, a perfect town. I inquired for the return of the mortality, and found that, for the last seven years, it was actually some 29½ in the thousand, but with 'cooked' returns it was 24½ in the thousand. I then called the Medical Officers and the Relieving Officers and soon got amongst causes of fever, small-pox, and excessive money relief. I then traced disease to crowded room tenements, undrained streets, lanes, courts and crowded yards, foul middens, privies, and cesspools. The water I found was deficient in quantity and most objectionable in quality, dead dogs having to be lifted out of the reservoir. And though the opposition fought stoutly they were obliged publicly to acknowledge that improvement was needed—they, however, dreaded the General Board, and the Expense. I then explained the constitution of the Board and stated that their powers would be used to instruct, protect, and to check extravagant expenditure. By this time the eagerness of the opponents had somewhat subsided, the body of the meeting had come partially round, and so I entered into an examination of the promoters who came willingly forward. At the termination of the inquiry several of the opponents came forward and stated that I had removed their objections and they wished the Act could be applied immediately.

"Today I have inspected the town—and have found it as bad as any place I ever saw. I have had at least twenty gentlemen with me all day although it has rained most of the time. The town is old, and in as bad a condition as Whitehaven, and I don't know that I can say anything worse of it. I am staying at the best Hotel in the town, but there is no watercloset, only a filthy privy at some distance,—the way to it being past the kitchen. I have just been out in the dark and rain blundering and found some one in the place.

"I have inspected the sources of the present water supply, and find that the water is taken from an open brook, filthy and muddy in wet weather, and filthy and bright in dry weather. In the same districts I have found; or rather, been shewn, springs—pure and soft—and at a sufficient elevation, to give 150 foot pressure in the town—and in abundance for the whole population. The existing springs will be added to if requisite by deep drainage. Most complete water works might be formed at a cheap cost. And the town may be sewered and drained for nothing, as a Nursery Man adjoining has stated that he will give £100 a year for the refuse, if it is all collected by drains. There are many acres of market gardens and nursery grounds within reach of the outlet sewer and more than £100 a year will be obtained.

"Since the inspection today I have had parties from both sides with me, the opponents trying to explain away their opposition; the promoters to furnish information; and, at times, I have had nine or ten gentlemen at once, belonging to both parties. The leader of the opposition has made me a present of some Anglo-Saxon coins—called Stycus, which were found in Hexham Church Yard."[1]

The deft and tactful handling of a truculent opposition, leaving no scars of controversy, is an example of the Inspectors' diplomacy at its best. But not all inquiries ended so happily with a peace offering from the leader of the critics. When .T. W. Rammell invited the Corporation of Chipping Wycombe to accompany him on a tour of inspection, they refused point blank, "they having determined to give all attempts to saddle the town with the Act the bitterest opposition in their power."[2] Not infrequently pressure was brought to bear on witnesses to prevent inconvenient revelations. During the inquiry at High Wycombe, for example, the vicar produced a letter from one of his parishioners:

"Sir—If you send for me when you hare redy in the town hall, i will give a true statement of the newcence of the pigsties against my house belonging to Mr. Hunt. Mr. g. Hunt told Mr. J. Hunt that i told you about the sties. Mr. Jo Hunt asked Mr. g. Hunt if I hoed him any money, if I did he would demand it, and if i dint pay it he would have a warrant of distress and take my goods, that was the reson I was afraid to say the complaint, the

---

[1] R. Rawlinson to E. C., 30 September 1852.
[2] *Report on Chipping Wycombe.* p. 8 (March 1850).

Lord delievered daniel from the Lion paw, and that same god is
my god and he will deliever me from my henemys.

"i am your obdiet servent,

"John Pippin.

"the rev. Mr. Paddon, Wickham, Bucks."[1]

Many in the localities looked with suspicion on the tables of
mortality rates concocted in a distant London office, and called
on the evidence of "popular repute" or the "oldest living resident" to prove the healthiness of the district. At Merthyr Tydfil
Rammell met widespread resistance—and, in particular, from the
iron miners. They argued that the high death rate was caused by
their dangerous work underground and by lack of food. "What
they wanted was more meat," not sanitary regulations. One
miner put the point forcibly: "My reason is, that people have
not enough to buy food, and have nothing to spare for water.
The wives of many being barefoot, there is no expense of shoe-
leather." Rammell in reply demonstrated that, even if full credit
were given to pit accidents, 27·6 deaths out of each thousand were
still due to natural causes. By the end of the meeting the miners
had been induced to look at the question again in the light of the
evidence, and had agreed to send eight delegates, four against
and four in favour of the Act, from each of five districts, to accompany the Inspector on his round of inspection.[2]

Turning the pages of the Inspectors' reports, we become familiar
with a local drama, repeated in a hundred places, played sometimes as a comedy and sometimes as a tragedy, with innumerable
variations of plot and circumstance, but marked by a few constantly recurring themes. The stock characters appear again and
again—the landlords, who "would do that their neighbours did"
and refused to be "at the expense of making a drain";[3] the farmer,
frankly admitting, "I prefer cesspools to drains, and I should like
to stop drainage altogether";[4] the Improvement Commissioners,
defending their inactivity in the past with the argument, "Powers
are apt to go to sleep unless attention is called to them sometimes;
we don't claim perfection";[5] the local solicitor scornfully reject-

---

[1] *Report on High Wycombe*, p. 17.   [2] *Report on Merthyr Tydfil* (1850), pp. 4, 47.
[3] *Report on Wakefield* (W. Ranger, December 1851), pp. 11–12.
[4] *Report on Bangor* (T. W. Rammell, September 1852), p. 5.
[5] *Report on Chipping Wycombe*, p. 40.

ing the Inspector's statistics with the comment "the excess is but six-tenths, which is but half a man";[1] the Justice of the Peace, well-intentioned but knowing nothing of the provisions of the Public Health Act, demanding suspiciously, "Have not the Board of Health power to order what they please to be done? and can the inhabitants control the expenditure?"[2] Against this mass of interest, ignorance and apathy, the Inspector's strongest weapon was a general perambulation of the town. As he made his way through the courts and back streets, accompanied by a train of clergy, doctors, solicitors, Guardians, and Commissioners, the inhabitants crowded out of their wretched dwellings, crying out their complaints, in the belief that he was armed with power to give them immediate relief. One startling fact which these surveys revealed was that not only the higher but most of the middle classes also knew very little about the conditions in which the lower classes lived. The delegates of respectability often expressed astonishment and horror at what they saw, declaring how utterly strange it was to them, how unbelievable if they had not seen it with their own eyes. The plea of ignorance could no longer be maintained, however, after they had watched the Inspector put his questions and take down his notes in their uncomfortable presence. Here, for example, are the minutes made on such a tour by William Lee at Dudley:

"Patchett's-buildings.—All Irish. A court about eight feet wide, . . . with only surface drainage. No ventilation. A foul well used for cleaning the yard; most filthy privies are placed at the top, and as fast as the pots are emptied into the open receptacle, the fluid runs down the yard; the seats and passage covered with ordure, and the privies cannot be used. One case of cholera. The houses have water; the landlord would not lay it to them, but the water company did. One of the tenants says, 'He will not put a brick in, but if he is asked to do anything at the property, d— and b— us, and is often drunk.' Rent for house and chamber, 2/4d. *The whole of the medical evidence shows these yards to be among the worst localities of disease in the town.*

"Mr. Richard Fellows' property, and Thomas Williams, four houses.—Only one privy, without door, roof, or seat, and part

[1] *Report on Chipping Wycombe*, p. 6.
[2] *Report on King's Lynn* (W. Lee, September 1852), p. 9.

of the wall down. The tenant, Richard Roberts' wife, says: 'I cannot get him to even come and look at it. We pay 2/6d. per week. The back door is nearly down, and I am sure I expect it falling on the children. My husband is lame, or it would not be as it is. We cannot go into the privy. We have no water but the *cellar water*, which we use for slopping; we cannot get any other without either buying or stealing. The landlords ought to lay water on for all the houses.'

"William Cox's property.—Nine houses; no water; have to go half a mile for water. One of them says, 'We may as well talk to that,' stamping her foot on one of the bricks of the footpath, 'as talk to the landlord about having any water. He looks after the rent.'

"Badger-square.—Twenty-five houses. Very shocking privies. No water but from a draw-well. One of the tenants, who lent a rope and bucket, said, 'We have to steal water or do anything we can, and to drink the well water. There are dogs and cats in it, and sometimes we wind a cat up and cannot stomach it. . . .'

"The New Dock.—A street which is a perfect quagmire, even at this dry season, for want of pavement and drainage. The property is almost new, and yet everything connected with health is in the most wretched state.

"Birmingham-street, Vanes's-yard.—. . . The Inspector of Nuisances caused the owner of some property below this to erect a privy for some houses that were without; but the tenants pulled it down, because they said *they should have all the people in the district coming to it if they did not.* He then erected three others, and had locks put on, and they now stand.

"Bond-street, John Owen's property.—I asked, 'Where do you get water?' Answer—'We steal it. . . .'

"All the neighbours about this part of the town were calling my attention to the ills connected with drainage, privies, want of good water, and stench, etc., to such an extent, that I was compelled to refuse to take them down in my minutes, because I should have had to mention almost every house, and could never have used my remarks."[1]

So, in town after town, against the advocates of *laissez faire* and local self-government, the Inspectors argued Chadwick's

[1] *Report on Dudley* (W. Lee, 29 December 1851), pp. 77–85.

thesis that in matters of public health an impartial central authority must intervene to adjust the balance between the powerless masses and those of their betters who wanted privilege without responsibility. Meanwhile in Gwydyr House all the anxiety of decisions which they knew involved life and death to thousands crowded upon the Board as the time came round each session for the preparation of the Bills in which their Provisional Orders were confirmed by the legislature. Whitstable and Newton Abbot must be struck out of the schedule because strong local opposition had developed.[1] A deputation from the Leamington Commissioners asked that the application should be postponed for a session. Did they represent the real wishes of the ratepayers? wondered the Board; and their doubt was shown to have good grounds a few days later when they heard that the resolution of protest had been passed at a vestry meeting closed to the public.[2] Ryde took a poll on the Act, and two-thirds of the ratepayers voted against its application; a fortnight later the medical men of the town sent a deputation in favour of the Act, but the Board reluctantly refused to move against the majority of the inhabitants.[3] Deputations, friendly and hostile, waited on the Board, and counter-petitions poured in, from administrative bodies whose powers would pass to the Local Boards, from ratepayers who dreaded the expense of water and drainage schemes, from landlords who disliked regulation and office-holders who feared dismissal. Attempts were made to discredit the testimony of the Inspectors. A letter from the Commander of the Royal Engineers at Portsmouth attacked the reports of Grainger and Rawlinson as a "tissue of wilful misrepresentation," and declared they must have been imposed upon by interested persons.[4] Babbage's report on Bromyard was stated to be full of absurdities and lies; he had remarked, for example, that three funerals had taken place there on one day—but not that they were of three old women, aged seventy-two, ninety-two and ninety-five respectively.[5]

From Alfreton came a typical petition, signed by the Mayor and the largest ratepayers, and maintaining that the town had, "to the knowledge of the oldest inhabitant, been notoriously

[1] Minutes, 21 June, 27 July 1850.   [2] Ibid., 12 and 27 July 1850.
[3] Ibid., 26 March, 12 April 1853.   [4] Ibid., 21 August 1849.
[5] *Hansard*, vol. cxxiv, p. 1351, 9 March 1853.

remarkable for the health and longevity of the inhabitants." It went on to plead the case of the owners of lands and premises on whom the chief burden of the charges would fall, and forecast an exodus from the town to avoid the additional imposts, with the result that the property in Alfreton would be greatly reduced in value. The "gigantic machinery" and "numerous officers" were quite unnecessary, as the parts complained of had now been improved under the Nuisances Act. Those who signed the original petition had been deluded by the belief that the Act would involve an expense of no more than twopence a week.[1] At the subsequent inquiry at Alfreton a local clergyman informed the Inspector that he had been asked to "direct" his tenants to sign the counter-petition.[2] The Board had abundant reason to believe that landlords and other interested parties only too often employed threats and misrepresentations to stir opinion against the Public Health Act; and that where such tactics failed, counter-petitions were cooked up and signed with fictitious or forged names. The clash of local jealousies and interests may be illustrated by the case of Macclesfield, from which the Board received four memorials, one in favour originating from the Mayor and Corporation, three opposing the Act, promoted by the Police Commissioners of the town and the Highway Boards of Sutton and Hurdsfield. The motive of the Corporation in getting up the original petition, alleged the memorial from Hurdsfield, was certainly not the sanitary improvement of Macclesfield, but a desire to force all the other public bodies in the borough to surrender their functions and powers.[3] A letter from the Town Clerk of Macclesfield later informed the Board that out of the 4,132 signatures appended to the counter-petitions, only 1,421 could be identified as those of ratepayers; several of the signatures were not those of the persons they purported to be; many of the names were in the same handwriting, and some appeared fictitious; there were also frequent repetitions of the same name, and the names of persons not resident at all; and in several cases after the signature of the father those of the children were appended.[4] To

[1] *Report on Further Inquiry at Alfreton* (W. Lee, December 1850), p. 5.
[2] Ibid. (December 1850), p. 10.
[3] *Report on Macclesfield* (R. Rawlinson, February 1851), p.8.
[4] Minutes, 9 June 1851.

counter such trickery the Inspectors were later instructed to verify the genuineness of signatures by personal visits or by reference to the rate books;[1] and ultimately, in May 1853, the Board decided to request that in future the Clerk to the Guardians should attach to each petition a certificate showing the number of ratepayers and attesting the qualifications of those who had signed.[2]

From Great Yarmouth came an octavo pamphlet of fifty-eight pages, alleging that the evidence taken before the Inspector had been mutilated, falsified, and fabricated, defending the water supply which he had condemned as hard and impure, and advocating an alternative scheme of sewerage which would leave nearly 25,000 out of the 28,000 houses undrained. The application of the Act, "firstly, would destroy a large proportion of the value of real property; secondly, ruin whole families who are living upon the surplus income of mortgaged property; thirdly, drive from the town those owners of shipping property who, having no interest in the real property of the town, will be induced to reside where local taxation will be less oppressive; fourthly, by which means hundreds of poor will be thrown out of employ, and become chargeable upon the parochial rates; and fifthly, largely contribute towards the decay of a town once among the most flourishing seaports in the empire of Great Britain."[3] The Inspector, William Lee, reported to Chadwick that the death rate in the town was 24 in the thousand; and a Select Committee of the Lords which investigated the case decided that the mortality was so excessive that the General Board would have been justified in applying the Act without any petition from the locality. There was nearly half an ounce of saline and mineral matter to every gallon of the water supply. With the exception of the barracks, all the houses recently built had no means of drainage whatsoever; and all their privies and middens opened into dead wells, the seepage from which daily poisoned the water used by the nearby Military Lunatic Asylum. Local improvement was the responsibility of a body of 113 Commissioners appointed under an Act passed forty years before, and now altogether unequal to the requirements of the borough. "A flagrant instance of taxation without representation," concluded

---

[1] Minutes, 24 October 1851.   [2] Ibid., 26 May 1853.
[3] *Report on Memorial from Great Yarmouth* (W. Lee, October 1850), p. 27.

Lee. "A majority of the Commissioners are self-elected for life; . . . for a great number of years, until within the last few months, they had never published any accounts; . . . the Abstracts now published, with the Public Health Act impending, are so mystified that their Lordships could not understand them." One witness admitted that in order to obtain signatures against the Act he had told ratepayers that they would be compelled to pay 7s. 6d. to 10s. in the pound as rates.[1] The objections from Great Yarmouth were supported by Joseph Hume; but the case against the town was so overwhelming that the Board felt strong enough to defy the opposition.[2]

The hamlet of East Stockwith sent a memorial against being included within the district assigned to the Gainsborough Local Board:

"Worthy Sir,

"We the undersigned Being Princeable Rate Payers of the hamlett of East Stockwith do feel our Selves agrieved By your Saniture measure concerning the Plans Laid down of us haveing any thing to Do with gainsboro waterworks or any Part of the Dreaniage it Doth Require as we have a good Dreaniage of our own about 6 feet fole in 20 chean, wich falls Down into the Carr wich that Dreaniage is Verry good and hath Been greatly Improved at a Serious Expence by the Erection of a large Steam Engene at Ravensfleet which will Continually Bring Large Rates upon us for the Management and Repairs of the Same we have good Dreaniage and three Trustees Regularly Chosen to Enspect any Defisunces that may occor in our Dreans will not Lett any Stagnated water become a Nuoisance to hinger any thing and as to haveing any more Expence with New works it will be a burden more than we Can Bear as our Rates his Exceedingly heavy. Now we Sinceerly Beg of you to withdraw any Such mesure from us as it will be of No use what Ever to our Place with gratitude we are your Obt. Servants.

"(Signed) Robert Wildboar (and 50 others)."[3]

This was an anxiety felt by many small areas newly brought within the boundaries of a sanitary district; and the Board

---

[1] William Lee to E. C., 4 August 1851.   [2] Minutes, 15 April 1851.
[3] *Report on Further Inquiry at Gainsborough* (W. Lee, May 1851), p. 6.

U

returned their usual soothing answer—assuring Robert Wildboar and his fellow ratepayers that inclusion in the jurisdiction of the Gainsborough Local Board would not involve being burdened with the cost of the works, unless they received benefit from them.

The indifference of the absentee Presidents, who shared none of the enthusiasm of the Board and had no desire to share any of their labours, was another source of delay and difficulty. In June 1852, to take a notable instance, Lord John Manners, Seymour's successor, told the Board that he feared he would not be able to undertake the introduction of a second Confirming Bill that session. He gave no reason for this decision, which would have thrown away months of preparatory labour spent in investigation and the conciliation of local sentiment. The Board protested strongly. The towns in the schedule stood in urgent need of the powers of the Act, and postponement might occasion the loss of many lives; especially in Woolwich, in parts of which the death rate rose to 38 and even 40 in the thousand, Wisbech where the septennial average was 30 in the thousand, and Salisbury where it was a fraction higher.[1] Lord John then consented to introduce the Bill—on the understanding that, in the deliberate opinion of the Board, it was unlikely to arouse any delay or discussion in Parliament.[2] How the Board could be held answerable for the Bill's smooth passage through the House he did not make clear.

By February 1850 the Board had received applications from 192 places, with a total population of 1,969,915, ranging from Birmingham with its 182,922 to the Northamptonshire parish of Little Bowden with 439. The Public Health Act had been introduced at that date into thirty-two places.[3] After the initial impetus of the first eighteen months, however, the number of new applications slackened off to an average of just over twenty a year. In July 1853 a return of the Board showed that petitions had reached them from 255 places, 164 of which had been brought under the Act, 86 by Provisional Order, and 78 by Order in Council.[4] The power to act on the authority of a return from the Registrar-

---

[1] Minutes, 9 June 1852.   [2] Ibid., 9 June 1852.
[3] Return, 6 March 1850 (Commons); P.P., 1850 (110), xxxiii, 591.
[4] Return 1 July 1853; P.P., 1852-3, vol. xcvi, p. 1.

General had been exercised with the greatest caution. In the first five years the Board directed inquiries into only twenty-eight places from which they had not received a petition signed by at least one-tenth of the inhabitant ratepayers; and even in these places, as we have seen, they made no move until they had seen good evidence in the shape of influential local representations that their Inspector would be given strong support. In one place only did they institute an inquiry without any form of local requisition. A petition reached them from the parish of Walsoken, a suburb of Wisbech; in the view of the Inspector, William Lee, no effective sanitary works could be constructed for this parish without taking in the rest of the town. His report subsequently gained the unanimous approval of the inhabitants of Wisbech, the death rate of which was 30 per thousand. In other places, Alnwick, for example, the Board reluctantly decided not to incorporate within the boundaries of the Local Board certain districts where hostility to the Act was manifest, although their inclusion would have rounded off the natural area for drainage.[1] The drafting of a sanitary scheme was determined by physical facts, the line of a watershed and the delimitation of a natural drainage area. But across the physical face of the countryside, its rivers and hills and geological strata, earlier generations had traced the lines of their civil administration, cutting it into units which frequently bore little relation to the area within which the objects of the Public Health Act could be most economically and conveniently accomplished. Chadwick, much as he would no doubt have liked the task, could not sit down like Napoleon in council and redraw the administrative map of Great Britain. Some redrawing there must be: but the Inspectors were instructed to go beyond the existing civil boundaries only where the physical necessity could not be denied, or where it would be a manifest advantage to the occupiers and owners of the district to be included in the new jurisdiction. Commanding as they did a staff of Inspectors which was never more than seven in number, and for most of the period was only five, the Board had no strength to spare for protracted battles in the localities.

The critics in Parliament and the Press, who tried to make out that the Board's intervention was everywhere resented and that

[1] Minutes, 26 April 1850.

sanitary works meant enormous expense for a doubtful benefit, were amply rebutted by the evidence. The average cost of applying the Public Health Act by Provisional Order was little more than £136, by Order in Council still less, only £88. To obtain a grant of similar powers by Local, Improvement, or Waterworks Acts involved legal charges amounting to over £1,600; the average expense of even an unopposed Improvement Act was £600. The comparative costs of the two procedures were strikingly illustrated in the case of Reading, where a Local Act was promoted for the sanitary improvement of the town. A preliminary inquiry by the Department of Woods and Forests cost £900; and the expenses ran up to a total of £8,000—yet in the end the Bill was defeated by the opposition of the local water company. Subsequently a petition was sent to the Board of Health; their Inspector conducted his inquiry and survey for £140 19s. 3d.; and the works for which £60,000 had been estimated under the unsuccessful Local Act were executed for £25,000.[1]

In most places the Inspector of the General Board was the first to give serious and informed attention to the framing of a comprehensive scheme for supplying the inhabitants with water and relieving them of their refuse. He was ordered, in the set of instructions drawn up by Chadwick, to consider the threefold aspect of the problem: how water, pure and wholesome, from springs or rivers or upland gathering grounds, could be brought to the population; how it could be carried away again after use, bearing human wastes with it; and, finally, how the products of the sewers could be utilised to manure the neighbouring farm land.[2] The Inspector directed the attention of local authorities to sources of water which they had never suspected. At Ely William Lee suggested that the polluted Ouse should be abandoned, and the land-drainage water be collected instead from the tableland above the city.[3] At Alnwick Rawlinson proposed to get water from the moors, "not by impounding reservoirs, as would most certainly have been done by any Engineer not

[1] Return (Commons), 1 July 1853, pp. 23–4; *P.P.*, 1852–3, vol. xcvi, p. 1. *Report on administration of the Public Health Act . . . from 1848 to 1854*, p. 39; *P.P.*, 1854, vol xxxv, p. 1.
[2] *Report on . . . the Nuisances Removal and Diseases Prevention Act*, *P.P.*, 1849, vol. xxiv, p. 1. App. x, pp. 129–35.
[3] *Report on Ely* (11 January 1850), pp. 36–8.

educated in your school, but by deep drainage. The idea was of course new in the district, and the Local Board requested to *see* some of the water that they might be assured of its quality and have a guarantee as to quantity before being committed to the scheme."[1] Rawlinson made trial borings which revealed water four to ten feet below the surface, two degrees in hardness, and sufficient to furnish 84,000 gallons a day for the 7,000 inhabitants. Two years later Dr. Sutherland told Chadwick, "I have seen the Alnwick works. They are beautiful. I would rather have seen them than the finest temple in the Universe."[2]

Accounts of the progress of local schemes presently began to reach Gwydyr House. They made encouraging reading for men who had need of encouragement. At Barnard Castle, for example, four miles of pipe sewers, from four to fifteen inches in diameter, had been laid at a depth of seven or eight feet at a cost of 1s. 8d. a linear foot; the cost of main drainage falling on each house being only £2 6s. 10d., or ¾d. a week. The water supply, formerly derived from the River Tees, was now drawn from soft-water springs five miles away, and brought by an earthenware pipe to a covered reservoir, and thence by a seven-inch iron pipe to the town. "The water is only brought into the light in the room where it may be drawn, in a constant supply as fresh as at the spring-head," observed Chadwick with satisfaction. The supply for each house cost less than 1½d. a week, so that the total rate charge for the combined public works amounted to less than 2½d. a week for each householder.[3] When, early in 1853, Chadwick and Southwood Smith spent a pleasant day inspecting the recently completed works, they watched with benevolent approval while "an address was presented to the Local Board by several of the poorer classes expressing their gratitude for the improvements introduced into their dwellings."[4] Similar achievements were reported from other towns. At Ottery St. Mary, in Devon, combined works were constructed for less than a penny per house per week; at Tottenham and Ely for less than 1½d.; at Hitchin and Penrith for 1¾d.—all below the average rates charged by trading

---

[1] R. Rawlinson to E. C., 25 September 1852.
[2] J. Sutherland to E. C., 25 June 1854.
[3] *Minutes of information collected with reference to works for . . . drainage of dwelling-houses, etc.*, p. 134; *P.P.*, 1852, vol. xix, p. 307.
[4] Minutes, 6 January 1853.

companies for water supply alone. Even Sandgate, which had few houses, and those of a size and value above the average, paid less than 3d.[1] In the towns brought under the Public Health Act the total cost of combined public works for water supply and drainage averaged $2\frac{1}{2}$d. a week for each house; the private improvement works (such as filling up the cesspool and fitting sink and water-closet) amounted to a further $1\frac{1}{8}$d.; the total average weekly cost being thus $3\frac{5}{8}$d.[2]

These were arguments that a ratepayer could understand, and it was with such figures before him that Chadwick maintained that the question of the scale of sewers was far from being "merely big and little endian controversy"; on its correct answer depended the relief of an immense amount of sickness and the saving of many thousand lives.[3] If, as the engineers of the old school asserted, it was necessary to lay down in every street brick sewers large enough for a man to enter, the expense would prohibit complete drainage in many provincial towns. The smallest brick sewer recommended by the surveyors of the old Commissions of Sewers cost 11s. a foot, while the average cost of the entire public drainage at Rugby, Tottenham, Barnard Castle and Ottery St. Mary was no more than 1s. 9d. a foot. At Carlisle a leading railway engineer had estimated £70,000 for laying down street sewers of deposit on the old style; yet self-cleansing tubular sewers were put in for £23,000. In fourteen towns where pipe sewers were laid down the total outlay was £98,858, as compared with a probable cost of £249,394 for large brick sewers; and the average cost for each town was no more than £7,061 instead of £17,814.[4] Where properly laid, moreover, and adequately supplied with water, they involved no appreciable current expense whilst brick sewers demanded periodic cleansing by manual labour.

No part of Chadwick's theories, not even his highly coloured picture of the agricultural value of liquid sewage, aroused such violent opposition as his advocacy of pipe sewers. Captivated by the ingenuity of his "Quart into Pint" reasoning, it was said, he

[1] *Minutes of information collected with reference to works for . . . drainage of dwelling-houses, etc.*, p. 134; *P.P.*, 1852, vol. xix, p. 307.
[2] Return, 1 July 1853; *P.P.*, 1852–3, vol. xcvi, p. 1.　　[3] MS. fragment, n.d.
[4] *Report on administration of the Public Health Act . . . from 1848 to 1854*, pp. 39–40; *P.P.*, 1854, vol. xxxv, p. 1.

closed his eyes to the fact that pipes were frequently cracked or choked, while brick sewers as frequently performed their function efficiently. It was alleged that the evidence in support of his four-inch pipes came from unknown witnesses, all of whom he had later rewarded with appointments under the Sewers Commission; and from a Trial Works Committee, who had conducted experiments under the scientific supervision of a staff of bricklayers' foremen. And if Chadwick himself did not stand to make money out of earthenware tubes (his enemies paid him the compliment of not holding him guilty of any lesser corruption than the desire for universal power), the seven pipe manufacturers of Lambeth were suspected of subsidising F. O. Ward, the Press champion of the new system.[1] Tubular drainage, said the critics, was too delicate and sensitive for people so barbarous as the English working classes, who, as the sewer-men testified, had the habit of throwing away with their own excreta such unwanted articles as scrubbing-brushes, hearthstones, pig's entrails, nightcaps, and litters of kittens. Engineers shuddered at the thought of the intestinal troubles such carelessness must cause in a complex of narrow pipes, and the hundreds of miles of streets which must be torn up again and again to deal with them. "As the population cannot hastily be fitted for the sewerage," declared one, "the sewerage must be fitted in a degree for the population."[2]

Whenever failures occurred (and failures were naturally common in the early experimental days) a triumphant "We told you so!" went up from the Institute of Civil Engineers. To Chadwick's immense indignation the story was spread that the four-inch pipes he had fitted in his own house in Stanhope Street had choked up, and had been replaced by drains of a larger bore.[3] Pipes were frequently manufactured of unsuitable materials, thin and brittle, crudely fashioned, and so untrue in section that two pipes of twelve inches diameter when brought end to end might show an unnevenness of joint of more than an inch. A variety of joints—butt, socket, half-socket, rabbet—came into confusing use. To the faults of the pipe-makers were added those of the pipe-

[1] See, for this and similar charges, *Engineers and Officials* (anonymous pamphlet, 1856).

[2] Thomas Page; in *Reports on an inquiry relative to the prevalence of disease at Croydon*, p. 48; *P.P.*, 1852–3, vol. xcvi, p. 35.

[3] E. C. to ?, 28 August 1852.

layers. Pipes were laid in sandy soils without protection, their inlets were left unguarded, they were given insufficient fall; nine-inch pipes were connected to six-inch or four-inch, and at times a tubular sewer would be continued by a square sewer, larger in size and constructed of dry rubble or bricks.[1] But gradually pipes gained ground. Stronger materials were brought into use; improved machinery gave greater accuracy and uniformity of design; experience taught how best to lay and joint the pipes, how to inspect and ventilate them, and guard them against the entry of improper substances. Chadwick persuaded the Lambeth manufacturers to make pipes of superior strength and workmanship for towns under the Public Health Act. By 1852 one factory alone was turning out weekly ten or eleven miles of glazed earthenware pipes, and Chadwick estimated that not less than fifty miles of sewer and drain pipes were being produced each week. By the end of 1853, 27,000 houses in London, nearly a tenth of the total number, were being drained by some three or four hundred miles of pipes. Dr. Sutherland could write in February 1854, after a visit to Rochdale: "The result of the pipe drainage is that there have been no obstructions, no breakages and no cost of repairs. Some of the pipes were laid in 1846. They are laying down pipe sewers in some of the widest streets in Manchester, and I find pipes everywhere. Say what they like, the pipes will eventually gain the day."[2]

Chadwick's quarrel with the Institute of Civil Engineers went deeper, however, than a clash of technical opinions. The battle of the pipes was embittered by professional jealousy and personal pique. As scornful as their chief of the "Fossil or Gwilt School,"[3] Chadwick's bright young men cocked snooks at some of the most respected names in engineering, Stephenson, Rendel, Bazalgette. At Gwydyr House it was commonly said that, in the sanitary field at least, the eminent engineers had proved eminent failures; and outside Gwydyr House it was retorted that Chadwick excommunicated all engineers who did not blindly adhere to his small-pipe dogmas. Not least among the weaknesses of the Board's

---

[1] *Minutes of information collected with reference to works for . . . drainage of dwelling-houses, etc.*, p. 48; *P.P.*, 1852, vol. xix, p. 307.

[2] J. Sutherland to E. C., 2 February 1854.

[3] W. Lee to E. C., 9 March 1852.

constitution was the arrangement by which their Inspectors were paid by the day, and were free, once they had completed an engagement for the Board, to undertake private commissions. They might in their official capacity examine and report on the sanitary condition of a place under the Public Health Act, and then as private individuals put in a bid to carry out the works they had recommended. And very often the Local Board, as it nervously faced up to its programme of sanitary construction, sought the services of the Inspector, who had the advantage over his professional competitors that he had already surveyed the ground and had indicated authoritatively the works that would be required. Chadwick himself could see nothing wrong with this system. If the Inspector's plan were suitable, why should he not be allowed to execute it? His labours in preparing the ground had surely earned him the right to be employed; and it would scarcely make for economy and efficiency if the commission were withheld from engineers of the greatest experience in this kind of work, and given instead to those who might have everything to learn. They could be ill spared from their primary duty of conducting the local inquiries, but Chadwick, with his ingrained suspicion of all engineers who did not derive their practice from the principles of his sanitary reports, was delighted as one local scheme after another fell into the safe hands of the Inspectors, the only true and dependable apostles of pipe drainage.

Moreover, it was pleasant to be able to tell critics that, far from the Local Boards protesting against central interference, they often complained that the General Board had inadequate powers to assist sanitary authorities, fresh to their duties, in administering a novel and difficult measure. Gwydyr House, which had not sufficient staff even to draw up all the necessary bye-laws and legal forms, was kept busy enough without the further duty of tutoring Local Boards. When appeals came in, however, Chadwick felt he must draw upon his slender resources of men and time to find them an answer. By May 1853 Inspectors had been employed as engineers to carry out works under the Public Health Act at fifteen places, and at a further twenty-one places the works were being executed or about to be executed by them.[1] By 1854

[1] Return (Commons), 23 May 1853; *P.P.*, 1852–3, vol. xcvi, p. 27. Inspectors had been employed as engineers at: Rugby, Sandgate, Barnard

twenty-four towns had asked the General Board to name an engineer to plan their works; eleven had asked their advice on the appointment of surveyors; twenty-five surveyors had sought the advice of the Board's chief engineer, Henry Austin; and forty-four towns had engaged the Board's Inspectors.[1]

But it was not simply as privileged rivals, backed by the authority of the General Board, that the professional engineers had reason to fear the Inspectors. In conducting the local inquiry the Inspector brought under scrutiny any projected schemes for sanitary improvement, and his opinion naturally weighed heavily with the Board, who, under the 119th section of the Public Health Act, must give their sanction to any local plans before a loan could be raised on the mortgage of the rates. It was contended that this might mean, in effect, that an engineer was obliged to submit his plans for the approval of a man who might later put himself forward for the same engagement with the Local Board. At Durham, for example, a brush occurred between the Inspector, William Lee, and Chadwick's one-time favourite, Thomas Hawksley. Hawksley, whose more recent utterances sometimes contradicted his opinions of that earlier period when he had been looked to as the chief engineering hope of the Towns Improvement Company, was now completely out of favour at Gwydyr House. Lee, after an examination of his plans for the improvement of Durham, could see no reason why the works Hawksley estimated would cost £6,000 should not be done for £4,300. Charles May, Hawksley's Quaker partner, wrote to protest, Hawksley himself apparently refusing to have any personal communication with Chadwick. By what authority did the Board require engineers to submit details of their plans and estimates to other engineers, perhaps much their junior, who were their direct competitors? It was the general feeling in the

Castle, Southampton, Coventry, Newmarket (survey only), Ormskirk, Hitchin, Croydon (waterworks and plan only of drainage works), Penrith, Dartford, Launceston, Ashby-de-la-Zouche, Selby, Epsom.

Works were being executed or were about to be executed by them at: Lancaster, Alnwick, Morpeth, Nantwich, Rotherham and Kimberworth, Baildon, Altrincham, Berwick-upon-Tweed (works of sewerage only), Wigan, Knighton, Newcastle-under-Lyme, Burslem, Diss, Maidenhead, Gainsborough, Cardiff, Warwick, Dover, Gloucester, Salisbury, Woolwich.

[1] *Report on administration of the Public Health Act . . . from 1848 to 1854*, p. 44; *P.P.*, 1854, vol. xxxv, p. 1,

profession that this practice was "subversive of honourable competition and degrading in its character, as creating a repugnance in the mind of those best able to serve the public to such supervision."[1] Despite his experience as a waterworks engineer, replied Chadwick, Hawksley had never drained a town in his life, and had always averred that drainage was a separate branch of practice. "Why," he exclaimed, "the junior inspector has had far more practice in town drainage but more particularly improved town drainage than you both put together or any one of the engineers the most eminent you have named."[2] To the Dean of Durham he confided his belief that the whole affair was "utterly frivolous." "All this means as it seems that Mr. Hawksley objects to any examination of his plans or to such examinations only as he likes or by whom he likes. . . . I do not understand how professional engineers could get on if they are never to act, except when they are clear of rivalry."[3]

Hawksley subsequently published a pamphlet, alleging that another Inspector, Ranger, after condemning Hawksley's plans for the Darlington waterworks, which he had peremptorily demanded to see, had soon afterwards reproduced the specifications verbatim as his own work at Barnard Castle and Southampton. At Croydon Ranger had rejected plans submitted by two other engineers—and had then accepted the engagement himself. Chadwick personally had objected to the employment of Wicksteed by the Leicester Local Board, and had suggested to Great Grimsby that Rendel should be superseded by an Inspector.[4] These were grave charges, and for a time Chadwick thought of taking proceedings against their author, so that the Board and the Inspectors might deny the allegations on oath.[5]

Conscious of his own rectitude, and distrustful as ever of the motives of his opponents, Chadwick did not give full weight to their criticisms until it was too late. He was always prepared to agree that it was a sound principle to pay the Inspectors an annual salary. It would protect them from the suspicion that self-interest

[1] Charles May to E. C., 7 July 1852.   [2] E. C. to Charles May, 20 July 1852.
[3] E. C. to the Dean of Durham, 23 July 1852.
[4] T. Hawksley, *Letter to the Marquis of Chandos, M.P., in relation to the exercise of some of the extraordinary powers assumed by the General Board of Health, and the Superintending Inspectors,* 22 April 1853.
[5] E. C. to Lord ?, 7 June 1853.

dictated their attitude to the drainage schemes they examined, and relieve them from the invidious duty of passing judgment on the plans of professional rivals; and it would set free all their time and abilities for their public functions. The serious disadvantage, as it seemed to Chadwick, was that it would also deprive provincial towns of experienced sanitary engineers before the transition to the new system was safely accomplished. Approving the principle, therefore, he would nevertheless on this account have liked to put off its introduction till about sixty towns had been completed by the Board; supported by that body of successful experiment, they could discount the effect of the Croydon disaster and snap their fingers at the Institute of Civil Engineers. By the middle of 1853, however, a number of examples of the new works were in operation, and he consented, not without misgivings that the step was being taken prematurely, to a draft clause making it illegal for the Board to appoint an Inspector otherwise than at a fixed yearly salary. The damage by this time had been done, and the idea had become fixed in some influential heads that the Board of Health was an arrangement for the benefit of Chadwick's protégés. It afforded excellent material for Lord Seymour in the momentous debates which decided Chadwick's fate.

CHAPTER XIV

THE LOCAL BOARDS

THE constitution of the Local Boards was laid down in the schedules attached to the Confirming Acts and Orders in Council of the General Board, to whose discretion the Public Health Act had left the size of the new local authorities and the property qualifications of their members. The schedules were short and followed a simple, unvarying pattern. The Local Board was to consist of a certain number, one-third of whom were to retire each year. They must be resident, and must either possess real or personal estate, or both, to a certain minimum value, or be rated to the relief of the poor of some parish, township or place within the district upon a certain annual assessment. The date of the first election was fixed, and its conduct entrusted to some leading citizen, the Chairman of the Board of Guardians, the Union clerk, the vicar, the Lord of the Manor, a Justice of the Peace, a solicitor, or a banker. These provisions resulted inevitably, as Chadwick described it, in "the Local Government of a Class," and "that Class the well to do Class."[1] In twenty-nine out of seventy-eight places to which the Act was applied by Order in Council, the property qualification was put at £1,000; in three places at from £600 to £800; in thirty-one at £500; in twelve at £300 or £400; and in three only at less than £300, the lowest figure being £200. The alternative rating qualification tells the same story. In fifty places out of the seventy-eight it ranged from £20 to £30 per annum; in a further twenty-four from £10 to £20; and in four places only was it below £10.

From the same group of places may also be illustrated the trend of the Board's policy in fixing the size of the Local Board. In fifty-six places the number was put at nine; in a further eighteen at twelve; in two the number fell to six, in another two it rose to

[1] E. C. to I. P., 24 March 1848.

fifteen. The figures for the Provisional Orders give a similar picture, though here a few of the Boards were given eighteen members. When the Vestry Committee of Brighton asked for a Local Board of forty-two, the General Board opposed the demand with vigour. Their figure was twenty-four, but they expressed their willingness to compromise on thirty. The apprehension was groundless, they declared, that thirty was an inadequate number to supply committees. In large Boards responsibility was weakened and business impeded by irrelevant discussion and irregular attendance.[1] A compact executive of nine or twelve members, with the sound views of men of substance; elected on a property franchise by plural voting; holding power for a limited term of three years—this was the aim of the Board's policy in the localities.

Once a Local Board had been constituted, however, the members elected to it might well be adverse to the operation of the Act. They might be of the humour of the Local Board of Mileham, who declared that they "do not consider any Plans or Maps whatever will be required for the proper drainage of the District."[2] An unwilling Board might even commit suicide; the Bromyard Local Board, for example, who "not having elected a Chairman, held a meeting, or taken any other step in execution of the Act, and more than three months having elapsed since the election all the members of the Board have become disqualified and the Act has become a dead letter."[3] At Selby the opponents of the measure used bribery and corruption to get themselves elected to the Board, and then promptly passed a resolution announcing their intention to prevent the construction of the combined works to which the General Board had given their approval, following this action by reducing the salary of the surveyor from £150 to £75.[4] Sanitary powers might for years lie unused, until a more progressive Board came to office. Thus, at Sheerness the Local Board fell under the dominance of an adverse majority shortly after its establishment, and for three years after it had passed under the Public Health Act the town, which as a naval dockyard had close relations with the central Government, remained in its state of abject squalor. There was some sharp comment about the

[1] Minutes, 15 and 17 April 1852.   [2] Ibid., 26 October 1850.
[3] Ibid., 13 May 1853.   [4] Ibid., 13 and 29 April 1853.

delay, and Chadwick wrote in defence of the General Board: "A local Board is often several years in making up its mind; it then sends in its plans for examination in a hurry—often essentially imperfect. We have only one engineer available for the service of examination, who is worked night and day, and some *weeks* delay occurs,—as in a private, overworked professional office;— but the *years* of delay are laid to the door of the General Board."[1]

There were complaints—from Fareham, Epsom, Castleford, and Worcester, for example[2]—of the stupor and inefficiency of the Local Boards. The General Board could only reply that they had no power to compel the local authorities to carry out the requirements of the Act. When the Godmanchester Town Clerk reported that the Corporation, in accordance with the wishes of the inhabitants expressed at a public meeting, had determined not to put the provisions of the Act into force, the Board had no answer but to point out that they were thus violating an Act of Parliament.[3] The three reformers early decided "that they would not press the Act, because under the existing state of the law, it appears to them to be of no use to call into existence an administrative machinery or to impose responsibilities where there is no adequate authority, no efficient support, of means for public prosecution: and where the subject has no means to enforce them."[4] When so much of the sanitary legislation was discretionary, it was little use, they felt, to wave a writ of mandamus over the heads of recalcitrant authorities. In the emergency of the third cholera epidemic at the end of 1853 they considered whether in some of the more flagrant instances of neglect they should have recourse to the remedies of the Common Law. Homicide by "unlawful omission" might be committed by anyone who neglected a legal obligation to apply food, clothing or other necessaries required to sustain life or prevent injury. Now it was one duty of Local Boards to cause such sewers to be made as might be necessary for the purposes of the Public Health Act—and that duty was not discretionary but compulsory. They could therefore be held liable to penal consequences for the imperfect discharge or unlawful omission of this obligation. It might be

[1] E. C. to W. F. A. Delane, 9 June 1853.
[2] Minutes, 17 January 1850, 28 June 1851, 7 April 1853, 8 October 1853.
[3] Ibid., 14 November 1851.   [4] MS. fragment, n.d.

proved, for example, that many lives had been needlessly lost by cholera in Luton as a result of the inactivity of the Local Board. Against this charge it was no legal or moral defence that the Luton Board had only obeyed the instructions of their constituents; a majority could not dispense with Acts of Parliament—and, in any event, the ratepayers did not form the majority of the inhabitants. What would the working classes think if they saw that offences against their betters and against property, as in the Bristol riots, met severe punishment, while offences which spread disease and death among the poor and unrepresented classes went unpunished?[1]

But no swift punitive action followed this homily. The Board could only observe that the Luton case illustrated the need of greater security for unprotected populations, and then resolve that the facts should be laid before Lord Palmerston with a view to prosecution by the Law Officers. Drainage and water supply, however, were not subjects in which the Government felt that its prestige was involved, and, even in the midst of an epidemic, the Law Officers of the Crown regarded the struggles of the General Board with a detachment which reflected the lack of interest of the ruling classes.

Only half a dozen clauses of the Public Health Act gave the Board any real measure of control over the local authorities of their creation. Their consent was needed for the establishment of pleasure grounds, and for the closing of an old burial ground or the opening of a new. They could hear the appeals of parties who believed themselves aggrieved by the Private Improvement rates imposed by the Local Board. But their principal weapon was the power to sanction mortgages on local rates to supply the funds for works under the Public Health Act.[2] Here was the instrument by which Chadwick hoped to control the financing and planning of the new sanitary works. Before the Board would consider the sanctioning of a mortgage, they insisted on seeing a complete survey of the district, together with plans and estimates of the proposed works, and details of the charges to be laid on the ratepayers. If the works were too extravagant, or were designed on the old principles, or did not combine drainage and water supply

---

[1] Minutes, 7 December 1853.
[2] 11 & 12 Vict., c. 63, ss. 74, 82, 83, 120, 119.

under one administration; if the rates were not calculated according to Chadwick's principle that the charges should be spread over a period coextensive with the benefits derived from the works —then Austin, who acted as the Board's referee on engineering questions, invariably reported against the approval of the mortgage.[1] Thus, when the Local Board of Eton requested permission in April 1850 to raise a loan of £1,000, the General Board withheld their approval until plans, estimates, and particulars of the works were furnished; and in February 1852 they refused to sanction a plan for the drainage of Leicester for which a £35,000 loan was wanted, condemning "its imperfect, wasteful, and inefficient character."[2] But even this, their most salutary power, had its limits. They could not, for example, prevent the raising of money for a Local Act, much as they objected on principle to such a procedure. Regretfully they had to admit that under the terms of the Act they could not refuse their sanction to a loan of £4,000 for a Local Act for Bilston, "though they wish to record their sense of the impropriety and gross extravagance of such expenditure."[3]

In addition to this measure of control over the public loans of the local authorities, the Board had certain powers with respect to the officials appointed under the Act. The surveyor could not be dismissed without their consent, and their approval was necessary to both the appointment and the removal of the medical officer of health.[4] The intention was to interpose a shield of impartial and distant authority between these officers and the interested animosities which might secure a dominating position on the Local Board. As Austin told Chadwick of the surveyor at Hull: "He is doing his work well and with energy, but he has much to contend with. He told me that if it had not been for the protecting clause in the Act, he could not have kept his place for six months, that without it, his position would have been unbearable, and that he would not have remained for a thousand a year. It is certainly so with all the best men we have."[5] Even so, despite the safeguard against removal, the officers remained the creatures

---

[1] Minutes, 6 February 1851, 31 March 1852. *Report on . . . Nuisances Removal and Diseases Prevention Act*, p. 62; *P.P.*, 1849, vol. xxiv, p. 1.
[2] Minutes, 25 April 1850, 12 February 1852.   [3] Ibid., 16 May 1851.
[4] 11 & 12 Vict., c. 63, ss. 37, 40.   [5] Austin to E. C., 16 April 1853.

X

of the men who paid their salaries and fixed the conditions of their service. There was an illuminating clash with the Local Board of Clitheroe on this issue. On 20 March 1852 the General Board were informed that the Clitheroe surveyor had been dismissed, because of the determined opposition offered by an overwhelming majority of the ratepayers, property owners, and other interested persons, which made it utterly impossible to execute the provisions of the Act. They replied that, having no power to release the Local Board from the legal obligation to carry out the Act in the best way they could, they could not legally sanction the dismissal of a surveyor when the only reason alleged for it was the inability of the Local Board to fulfil its duties under the Act. Nevertheless although threatened by a writ of mandamus, the Clitheroe authorities resolved not to carry out the Act. The surveyor, backed by the General Board, stuck to his post; whereupon the Clitheroe Board reduced his salary to 25s. per annum, and he was obliged to resign.[1]

Any Local Board which began a scheme of public works must needs appoint a surveyor; but the necessity for an officer of health was less keenly felt, and the parsimony and shortsightedness of the local authorities prompted most of them to dispense with this appointment. The difficulties in the way of creating a permanent paid medical service were clearly illustrated when Bilston asked the Board to sanction the employment of an officer of health—at £20 a year.[2] When the Southampton Board expressed the view that it was not desirable that their officer of health should abstain from private practice, they were firmly told that his public duties were incompatible with the demands which private engagements would make upon his time.[3] But what answer could be returned to the medical officer of Darlington, who stated that he did not intend to relinquish his practice, since his salary was only twenty guineas a year?[4] The Board's solution, contained in a letter circulated to the local authorities (9 October 1850), was to suggest that, where any district was thought too small for the payment of a properly qualified officer of health, the best plan would be to appoint a single officer to act for several

[1] Minutes, 20 March, 8 May, 2 December 1852, 14 March, 4 April 1853.
[2] Ibid., 26 December 1850.　　　[3] Ibid., 14 November 1850.
[4] Ibid., 1 January 1851.

adjoining towns. It was not till 1872 that the appointment of a medical officer of health was made obligatory on the district Boards; and their security of tenure was eventually secured by the Public Health (Officers) Act of 1921. It had taken two generations, since that first sketch in the *Sanitary Report*, for Chadwick's conception of the nature and duties of an officer of health to realise itself in administrative practice.

When Chadwick began his public health inquiry in 1842, hardly a town in the kingdom had a publicly owned water supply, and few voices were raised against the dominant faith in profit and private enterprise. His reports had played a decisive part in developing among local authorities the self-confidence to take public utilities such as water and gas into their own hands. In the years between 1842 and 1848, however, as we have seen, he oscillated between advocacy of municipal trading and of large-scale private enterprise under Parliamentary regulation. The *Sanitary Report* and the Health of Towns Commission had been largely an inquest on the shortcomings of parochial and municipal bodies. In the first optimistic flush of the Towns Improvement Company, and despairing of action from a thankless and unenlightened Government, Chadwick had laid it down as a principle that in commercial agencies lay the only hope for sanitary reform. Much had happened to change that opinion. The golden prospects of the sewage manure project had faded. His railway inquiries had shattered for him the myth of capitalist efficiency, and contact with cemetery and water companies had shown him that to look to profit-making corporations to plan for the public interest was like putting the flock in the care of the wolf. The complete shifting of his ground was admitted and defended when the Board summed up their experience in their final report in 1854. The failures pointed out in the Health of Towns Report, they stated, had justified the presumption that local authorities were incompetent to provide water supplies; but the subsequent examination of trading companies had revealed no superiority in efficiency, economy, or management. Experience under the Public Health Act had shown that local authorities could supply the lower classes, who were generally neglected by the companies, for 1¾d. a week, and at the same time avoid the risks and losses of a trading body. Moreover, they were willing to undertake the construction of works for complex objects, such as combined works for drainage, water supply and sewage disposal, which the wary capitalist would rarely touch. The new works exonerated municipal corporations and Local Boards from the charge of incapacity levelled against them, and demonstrated that responsible public bodies could give cheaper and better service than companies actuated by the motive of a trading profit to be levied on individual necessities.[1]

Throughout its brief life, therefore, the General Board encouraged Local Boards to take public utilities into their own hands, ousting, forestalling, or combating as necessary the agents of private enterprise. At Carlisle, for example, Rawlinson recommended that the water company should be taken over by the Corporation. In constructing the works a company might be equally efficient as a public body, but in two respects it fell short—it could never have the same motives and interest to urge a general use of water for purely public objects, such as surface washing; nor could it possibly have the same means at its disposal to accomplish these purposes.[2] When a Reading deputation asked the Board whether they should oppose the Bill then before Parliament for extending the capital and powers of the water company, the Board agreed that it was contrary to public policy to allow the introduction of new capital by a trading company. "It was the duty of the Local Board to oppose the introduction of such new capital, and so to keep themselves free for the choice of any improved source of water supply for their district."[3] In March 1854, in an interview with the Clerk of the Local Board of Hull, they promised their support to a Bill which aimed at consolidating the Local Board's control over the gas works and the cemetery, both at present in the hands of trading companies. A week later they declared their intention to support a motion that a Water Works Bill for Southport should be postponed, in order to give the Local Board time to prepare a scheme which would put the supply under their own management.[4]

Chadwick's original intention had been that the Provisional

---

[1] *Report on administration of the Public Health Act . . . from 1848 to 1854,* pp. 24–6; *P.P.,* 1854, vol. xxxv, p. 1.
[2] *Report on Carlisle* (June 1850), pp. 79–80.
[3] Minutes, 13 February 1851.   [4] Ibid., 10 and 18 March 1854.

Orders should in effect be Local Acts, framed to cover, not only the narrowly interpreted objects of a sanitary measure, but also such other matters of local administration as paving, lighting, markets, and roads. In the first of the Confirming Acts (August 1849) he succeeded in inserting a clause which empowered Local Boards to enter into contracts for the supply of gas or oil or other means of lighting, and to provide lamps, lamp posts and other apparatus as necessary.[1] But the scrutiny of the Parliamentary critics proved too keen, and objection was promptly voiced to the introduction of these supplementary clauses. The absence of provisions of this nature was one strong reason why in some places, Newcastle and Birmingham for example, a Local Act was preferred to the simpler and cheaper procedure by Provisional Order. The Board regarded it as one of their most important duties to send their experts before the Private Bill Committees to oppose such Bills in principle or in detail.[2] Twice they succeeded in defeating a Local Act, and in others they secured the insertion of the mortgage clause from the Public Health Act, which brought the proposed works under their supervision; but they failed in other attempts because they lacked the means to bring up witnesses, and had no recognised *locus standi* before the Committees.

The immense output of instructional pamphlets from the Stationery Office of to-day would have delighted Chadwick. Throughout his official career he was engaged in cutting channels for the regular flow of information from the localities to the central departments, and thence—digested, tabulated, and illuminated by a wider experience and a deeper science—back again to the local authorities. As he always insisted, even if the powers of the General Board had been greater, he would still have preferred to proceed, whatever the extra labour, by persuasion, and to accompany every step by a full exposition of the reasons.

For the guidance of the inexperienced Local Boards the body of sanitary doctrine which Chadwick had built up on the results of his ten years of investigation was set out in three instructional pamphlets—on house drainage, land drainage, and the application of sewer manure.[3] In the first of these they were told that

[1] 12 & 13 Vict., c. 94, s. viii.
[2] Minutes, 9 March 1849 (Macclesfield Water Supply Bill); 7 March 1851 (Wrexham Local Bill).   [3] *P.P.*, 1852, vol. xix, pp. 307, 1, 133.

their primary duty was to abolish all cesspools and replace them by water-closets and tubular drainage; and for their information diagrams and descriptions were given of the improved appliances then gradually coming into use, such as screw-joints for earthen-ware pipes, movable dust bins, and a simpler form of water-closet. In the second pamphlet they were enjoined not to confine their attention to the drainage of houses and streets. It was equally a matter of concern to the sanitary economist to remove excess moisture from the site on which the town was built, the roads which connected it with other places, and the lands which fringed its suburbs. Chadwick recalled how a London medical officer had once taken him to a height overlooking his parish. "Those mists," he had said, pointing, "exactly mark out and cover the seats of disease for which my attendance is required. Beyond those mists I have rarely any cases to attend to but midwifery cases and accidents." Catarrh, rheumatism, scrofula, would all be decreased by an energetic policy of land drainage. Moreover, the value of the land would be enhanced; heath and moorland, for which 5s. an acre had once been a high price, had been sold for 30s. or £2 when thorough-drained, and clayey soils had risen in value from 7s. 6d. to £3 or £4 an acre. The trilogy of instruc-tional pamphlets was completed by the Minutes on Sewage Manure, which assured Local Boards that for an annual outlay of 6s. an acre for piping the liquid sewage to the fields a single farm might be made as fertile as three or four. The Local Boards must regard themselves as trustees for the inhabitants collectively in the management of this valuable public property, in which no private individual should be permitted to establish permanent proprietary rights.

As one fat Report followed another, and Gwydyr House poured out its Minutes of information and its sheaves of model bye-laws, it began to be said that the Board's printer must have a very lucrative business. The tracts were excellent, wrote J. R. McCulloch from the Stationery Office, but why were they dis-tributed free? If McCulloch were on the Board, Chadwick replied, he would vote for doing more rather than less in the way of distributing information to the Local Boards. The highest authorities had admonished the General Board to "conciliate public opinion"; and even without that admonition they would have felt themselves bound to do so. They had very little power, and in these times it was difficult to exercise any power whatsoever; and after all, it was better to proceed by the influence of instructions wherever they could. If as a result of their Minutes they could get improved works into operation in even a few towns, it would be worth not only the whole expense of the printing ten times over, but the whole expense of the General Board.[1]

It was not the first time that he had clashed with the Stationery Office. In 1849 McCulloch proposed to the Treasury, "for the sake of economy," that all reports and papers should be printed in folio. *Prima facie*, Chadwick at once objected, it was improbable that folio was cheaper than octavo; and his inquiries revealed in fact that if the whole of the Parliamentary printing were put in the convenient format adopted by everybody outside Her Majesty's Stationery Office, some £24,000 a year might be saved on the annual bill of £200,000. But this was far from being the most important aspect of the question. "Either the objects of the Board must be attained by the naked exercise of power—in which case it must have additional force of officers, which would be expensive, or it must act by persuasion, that is to say by the exposition of facts, and their influence on opinion."[2] Now to the latter course printing in folio would be fatal, since, as the printers confessed, 3,000 copies in folio would not be as much read as 1,000 in octavo. At Lord Brougham's suggestion the Poor Law Report of 1834, and the extracts from the evidence of the Assistant Commissioners, had been printed and circulated in octavo, the first official papers to be so published. The folio editions of those reports were now in the warehouse or had been disposed of as waste paper; of the handier edition nine or ten thousand copies had been distributed free of charge to the parishes and a further fifteen thousand had been sold.[3] Thus, in Chadwick's eyes, the whole question of the proper relationship between Government and public opinion, and in particular between the General Board and its local satellites, was one of the issues at stake in this "battle of books between official folios and official octavos, between big and little blue books."[4]

[1] E. C. to J. R. McCulloch, 24 February 1852.
[2] E. C., "Administrative. Relations of the General Board of Health with the Treasury. Minutes for a paper on," MS., n.d.
[3] E. C. to Lord Brougham, June 1849.   [4] E. C. to ?, 1 June 1849.

In 1852 Henry Austin, relieved of his anxieties as Engineering Secretary, was sent out as an emissary of Gwydyr House to make personal contact with the Local Boards. From time to time he reported to headquarters his impressions of his tour. At Derby, where no plan of the town drainage had previously existed, he found the Local Board actively engaged on improvement measures and delighted with the increased powers derived from the Public Health Act.[1] At Norwich, however, they were "fencing with the question of the Survey."[2] His intervention at Ely, where a majority of the Board had been hostile, cleared up a number of misconceptions and greatly helped the progress of the drainage scheme.[3] At other places, too, his assistance was welcomed.

"It is rather a melancholy case," he wrote from Towyn. "I have seen nothing out of Ireland, bearing the same deplorable appearance, or in an equally bad condition.

"Nearly the whole of the property is in the hands of Trustees for a Minor and is managed by an Agent, who, in opposing all improvements, forced the inhabitants to take refuge under the Public Health Act.

"The place is however far too small to support the Machinery of the Act, and is precisely one of those for which other provisions are urgently required.

"There are only about 150 houses in the town, and nine-tenths of those are under £5 rateable value. I need scarcely say that there is not a drain in the place, scarcely the luxury of a cess-pool, soil and refuse of every description strewing every spot, nearly, except the main street. There are two places from which the whole population has to fetch water.

"Accompanying this state of things is a corresponding condition of ignorance how to remedy it—although the Board, impressed with the magnitude of the evil, are most anxious to do so. Clark, unfortunately, not considering the character of the place, had recommended a scheme of drainage and water supply which would cost more than double the amount actually required for suitable works, and more than double indeed, the whole sum which they would be empowered to borrow—and therefore they had determined at last upon a defective scheme of partial drainage without water supply.

[1] Minutes, 12 July 1852.   [2] H. Austin to E. C., 28 February 1852.   [3] Ibid.

"They expressed themselves very gratefully towards the General Board for sending me to them, and were most thankful for the advice given. They will proceed at once to get out a plan of complete works, and as an example of economy and of the amount of improvement which may be effected for the money, I believe it will be a curiosity."[1]

"Brynmawr," he wrote a few days later, "has been to me the most satisfactory case I have yet visited. It is a wretched place wholly dependent upon the iron works there. The mortality is frightfully high, but I was assured that they would do nothing but carry out a most objectionable plan of drainage for which they had applied to the General Board to sanction a mortgage of £1,500—which, if not granted, they intended to levy at once by rates. It certainly did appear a hopeless case, and the more so because they had actually entered into contracts and had commenced the works. I am happy to say however that I was enabled to induce them to stop the works and give up the contract, and begin *de novo* to lay out a proper plan of drainage and water supply, for which they will apply to the Board for a mortgage of between £4,000 and £5,000. It will be the more important case as an example to the large populated districts here engaged for miles around on the iron works—all of the same miserable kind."[2]

Inexperienced Local Boards, struggling with their novel duties, received with thankfulness the instructional Minutes of the General Board and the advice of their Inspectors. At more than one place votes of thanks were passed or grateful letters addressed to Gwydyr House. The arguments of Toulmin Smith here fell on unbelieving ears. The application of the Act had not deprived them of local self-government, declared a report of the Worthing Sanitary Committee; for their former Commissioners held office for life, while one-third of the Local Board must retire every year, and no member could remain in office more than three years without re-election. The Local Act under which the district had been governed hitherto had been quite inadequate, since it gave no power to provide a supply of water, while such powers as it did confer upon the Commissioners could not be used until they had liquidated their debt. As for the necessity of seeking the General Board's sanction to local schemes, "we look upon this

[1] H. Austin to E. C., 7 October 1852.   [2] H. Austin to E.C., 18 October 1852.

restriction as affording the very best possible protection to the ratepayers against having their money fooled away upon useless works."[1]

From the chairman of the Ormskirk Local Board came an account of the benefits which had resulted from the application of the Public Health Act in 1850, an account which might have been paralleled in a score of other places:

"The population of the Town is 6,200, of whom one third at least are Irish, and the majority of the Inhabitants are poor Cottagers, crowded in Courts and Yards at the back of the principal Streets.

"Previous to the Act, no Sewerage Works of any moment existed, nor was there any supply of Water. The Lodging Houses, especially those frequented by Irish labourers, were crowded to excess: fever was seldom absent from certain quarters of the Town, and a high rate of mortality existed.

"Since the introduction of the Act a complete system of Sewerage and of Water Supply has been effected, for which we are largely indebted to the valuable services of Mr. Rawlinson. The Works have been in full operation since the summer of 1853, and already, out of an aggregate amount of 1,000 dwelling-houses, 700 are thoroughly drained and supplied with Water, and it is worthy of remark that although in the onset a strong opposition was expressed against the Act, yet, in consequence of the mind of the Inhabitants becoming reconciled to its establishment, the private Works have with few exceptions been carried out voluntarily, and with hearty good will. Cottagers are furnished with an unlimited supply of good water at the rate of 1d. per Week. A more efficient supervision of the Lodging Houses has been obtained, of which there are 120 in the registry.

"Without entering into the experience of other Towns, I am enabled to speak in behalf of myself and Colleagues . . . that we have met with no undue interference from the General Board of Health, nor have we any accusations to bring against that body, of arbitrary treatment: on the contrary, our communications have been uniformly received with a spirit of fairness, and from the advice and co-operation afforded, a more efficient scheme of Works has been executed than otherwise would have been, had

[1] W. H. Dennett, *Report to the Sanitary Committee, Worthing*, August 1851.

we been left to our own resources. Were we called upon to give evidence, our testimony would be unanimous, that in our case, the Public Health Act has proved to be a wise, salutary, useful, and benevolent provision of the Legislature."[1]

Quiet progress such as this, however, attracted less attention in the Press and House of Commons than the noisy resistance of some half a dozen of the Local Boards; and the steady improvement of conditions, the cumulative effect of which must be awaited with patience over a long period, caught the eye less arrestingly than a sudden and startling catastrophe, such as the Croydon epidemic in the last months of 1852.

The outbreak at Croydon was one of the earliest and most striking examples of a phenomenon which was to occur from time to time during the latter half of the century in the new residential districts of the growing towns, bringing perplexity to sanitary reformers despite the stoutness of their confidence—an explosion of typhoid fever following the introduction of the new pipe sewerage which it was claimed would put an end to the causes of zymotic disease. Croydon had been brought under the Public Health Act in August 1849, and by December 1851 combined works of drainage and water supply had been installed in most parts of the town. Typhoid appears to have been imported in September 1852, on the person of a villager from Oxted, twelve miles away, where an epidemic was already raging. It spread along the lines of the new sewers, which, as Budd later explained in his classic treatise, acted as an extension of the diseased intestine of the typhoid sufferer; and, filtering through the cracks and leaks of a most defective pipe system, it contaminated the water supply. In a population of 16,000, there were by December 1852 1,800 cases of fever with a mortality of about sixty, and numerous cases of diarrhœa and dysentery with a mortality of about ten. Croydon was, though its respectable and well-housed citizens could not credit it, one of the most unhealthy places in Surrey. But the town had experienced nothing so dramatic as this epidemic of typhoid; an epidemic, moreover, which attacked chiefly members of the middle and upper classes, who had been the first

---

[1] J. A. Kershaw to Lord ? (Palmerston), 20 July 1854. This was one of the testimonials received by the General Board at the time of the debates in 1854 which decided their fate. For other references, see pp. 364–5.

to benefit from the new drainage and water system. It was noted that all the cases had occurred during and since the execution of the new works, and people reminded each other of the nuisance when the Local Board filled in the cesspools and open ditches throughout the town, so disturbing earth saturated with the accumulated filth of years. The outbreak, it was promptly alleged, must be due to the new pipe sewers and the activities of the Local Board.

The Board's investigators, Southwood Smith, Sutherland, Austin, and Grainger, were already in the field, when they were informed in January 1853 that the Government had appointed Dr. Neil Arnott and Thomas Page, an engineer from the Board of Works, as an independent Commission of Inquiry. The appointment reflected the general suspicion which now attached to the Board's every act, and Chadwick realised at once that at Croydon Gwydyr House and its works were in the dock. The Croydon Local Board, under its vigorous chairman, Cuthbert Johnson, was regarded as one of the most progressive and successful of the General Board's satellite authorities. Little more than a year before, Chadwick and Southwood Smith had attended a pleasant and heartening ceremony at the opening of the combined works. They had looked on benevolently as the Archbishop of Canterbury lifted the valve of the great steam engine which pumped water to the high-level reservoir; and at a civic dinner in the evening Chadwick had gone into his familiar, well-loved statistics, and congratulated the householders of Croydon on obtaining the benefits of pure spring water and self-cleansing sewers for 5¼d. a week.[1] It is easy to understand his annoyance and anxiety when Neil Arnott, one of his earliest allies, informed him that the report had been obliged "to speak of faults and failures in works which you had hoped were to be deemed perfect."[2]

Since both the Board and its critics accepted the prevailing pythogenic theory, the Croydon investigation developed into a hunt for stinks and an inquest on some very bad pipe-laying. There were some sharp exchanges on the question whether unventilated pipe sewers or brick sewers of deposit were the most foul-smelling, but the purity of the water supply, which was

---

[1] *Times*, 13 December 1851.   [2] N. Arnott to E. C., 27 April 1853.

really to blame, was attested by both sides. The investigators, in fact, were looking for the wrong thing in the wrong place, and most of the points made would be ruled out of court by a modern scientific inquiry. However, if the dialectical limitations of the contestants are accepted, the Board had much the better case. Before the introduction of the Public Health Act Croydon had been similar to scores of other towns, honeycombed with cess-pools, and drawing its water from wells. Vilely as the works had been carried out by the local contractors, they had reduced the sewer emanations and the potential foci of disease. Faults in the design and construction of the Croydon drains, however, were treated by the Government Commission as faults inherent in the system of tubular drainage, and Page made plain his opinion that four-inch and six-inch pipes were too delicate to stand up to the rough domestic habits of the lower classes. Chadwick in vain urged Arnott to visit Tottenham, Rugby, Hitchin, or some other place where such works were in successful operation, so that he might judge for himself whether the blunders committed at Croydon were unavoidable or not.[1] The Report of Arnott and Page, published in April 1853, indicted the pipe sewers and house drains of Croydon, and by implication censured the engineering theories of the General Board. "Such events occurring in a place like Croydon, with an intelligent Local Board of honourable men eager to perform any amount of gratuitous service which promised advantage to their town, and who were near the Central Board in London, for easy conferences, prove the desirable securities for the efficient performance of such works are not yet possessed and further show that some of the anticipated advantages of the pipes have not yet been obtained, and some of the drawbacks connected with the employment of them had not been foreseen."[2]

Chadwick spent some months in preparing, in collaboration with the chairman of the Local Board, a massive counter-attack, but his reply to the allegations of Page and Arnott remains in wordy and argumentative manuscript fragments. For once Shaftesbury refused to follow his truculent colleague into the battle. Chadwick's report was so strongly personal in tone, he

[1] E. C. to N. Arnott, 14 and 26 March 1853.
[2] *Reports on an inquiry relative to the prevalence of disease at Croydon*, p. 7 (Arnott); *P.P.*, 1852–3, vol. xcvi, p. 35.

wrote, that "if sent forth as I have before me in MS.," "it would be absolutely the ruin of the Board." "You, I, and the Doctor, we three, should *by our own act and deed*, be cast down, bound hand and foot, into the burning fiery furnace."[1] The Board's best defence was slow to come, but unanswerable when it came. Five years later the Chairman of the Local Board was able to send Chadwick the quarterly tables of mortality for Croydon with the comment, "You will see that the sanitary condition of the Parish for the year 1857 has been singularly good—and that instead of our Deaths having been 22 per thousand per annum as they have averaged for the nine years ending Christmas 1856, they have only been 15·92 per thousand per annum. And as Dr. Farr in his tables called 17 per thousand per annum the 0 of his Scale of Insalubrity we may rejoice at being thus below his Zero. . . . As to returning to Cesspools all classes now know what a comfort and advantage it is to be free from the Nuisance of Cesspools and would not return to the system if it were possible to avoid doing so."[2]

[1] Shaftesbury to E. C., 15 October 1853.
[2] William Drummond to E. C., 10 May 1858.

CHAPTER XV

REACTION, 1852–1853

It was in 1852 that the current of events turned decisively against
the men and principles of Gwydyr House. For over three years
the General Board had been spreading the doctrine that in certain
spheres the play of competition should be checked in the interests
of society, and that in those spheres enterprise, though it might
remain in private hands, should at all events be planned with an
eye to economy and the public benefit. Was Chadwick an enemy
of private enterprise and free competition? Was he a socialist?
He strenuously defended himself against so terrible a charge. But
it was surely possible to retain those principles, to which English
capitalism ascribed its rude health, without falling into the moral
and economic quagmire of *laissez faire*. His Interments Act, for
example, was based on just those "wholesome and eminently
English principles"—with this difference: that the aim was to
bring them "to bear *for* instead of *against* the public interest." A
district was marked out, and private enterprise invited to compete
freely by open tenders to perform the requisite service. It must, of
course, engage itself to act in accordance with prescribed regulations, designed to secure proper solemnity and greatly improved
arrangements; and to impose a scale of charges fixed at the lower
level that would become possible if only one capital, one management and one set of officers were employed in the service.[1] What
objection could there be to that? So Chadwick argued, endeavouring to show that the method of public contract would leave ample
elbow-room for legitimate private enterprise. But his disarming
explanation failed to carry conviction to the capitalists to whom it
was addressed, who saw that if they accepted his reasoning they
could no longer proceed whither they wished and how they wished
under the influence of the push and pull of profit, but must put

[1] MS. fragment, n.d. E. C. to Russell, 4 November 1851.

themselves under the dictates of a conscious social purpose. If they could find it possible to breathe the rarefied atmosphere of Gwydyr House—if they were prepared to allow their profits to be limited, their budgets scrutinised, their activities regulated and the minimum standards of their service defined—the companies might still remain. But if not, if they declined to bind themselves by contract to public service, then their work could be done as well, or better, by civil servants of the Chadwick school or by local authorities tutored by his Inspectors. The outline of Chadwick's ideal State was becoming clearer: a State where collective utilities, such as water, gas, and means of communication, were owned by the public, though they might be constructed and maintained by contract; where charges were fixed not with an eye to shareholders' dividends, but merely to defray the cost of service; where units of administration were cut to the size calculated to give the best technical and economic results.

Against this conception there set in during 1852 a powerful and many-sided reaction. It was the reaction of local authorities, wary of rearrangements of ancient boundaries and of encroachments on their traditional independence; of governing oligarchies, who saw in the extension of the central power an end to their patronage and perquisites; of property owners who reckoned that the fever tax would bear less heavily upon them than the cost of new drains; of engineers whose professional standing and rules of practice were endangered by the Board's Inspectors, and of Parliamentary agents whose fees were threatened by the expeditious procedure of the Provisional Order. It was the reaction of commercial companies who saw in the advance of gas and water socialism an invasion of the sphere of profit, and of manufacturers who found that sanitary regulations would add to their costs and close to them modes of working that had been profitable in the past. "There was no end to such kind of legislation," cried one, "and, if persevered in, there might, in time, be a Bill to prevent expectoration in the streets."[1] It was the reaction, in a more general sense, of business men whose interests were not directly threatened, but who had more confidence in their own administrative ability than in that of Government with its eighteenth-century habits of aristocratic corruption and leisureliness.

[1] *Hansard*, vol. cvii, p. 195, 11 July 1849 (Foster).

Criticisms of the Board's measures were frequently made in terms from the political vocabulary of a passing age, when every official was a place-holder, and every place a piece of patronage to be dispensed by the Secretary to the Treasury. Not till the introduction of competitive examinations for the Civil Service was the sting taken out of this argument. All these groups had specific and conscious motives for resisting the Board. There were others who shouted with them, whose motives were less explicit, whose hatred of Gwydyr House could hardly be defined in words; who were moved obscurely to oppose to its hard utilitarianism a sentimental clinging to the old ways, and to meet its brisk efficiency with the inertia of comfort-loving, routine-keeping men. Long ago Lord John Russell had warned Chadwick: "There is one thing always to be kept in mind. We are endeavouring to improve our institutions. Hitherto they have been lax, careless, wasteful, injudicious in an extreme; but the country governed itself, and was blind to its own faults. We are busy in introducing system, method, science, economy, regularity, and discipline. But we must beware not to lose the co-operation of the country. They will not bear a Prussian Minister, to regulate their domestic affairs. So that some faults must be indulged for the sake of carrying improvement in the mass."[1]

It was by coincidence merely that the attack developed during the brief régime of the Derby Government. Whatever party had been in power—Whigs, or Tories, or Radicals for that matter—the principles of Gwydyr House were offensive to them all; and any Government not stiffened by the courage of conviction which moved Chadwick and Shaftesbury and Southwood Smith would have hesitated to defend a group of men who, through bad fortune and misunderstanding, through the misrepresentations of others and their own faulty judgment, had long overdrawn the credit of public confidence which had been extended to them under the terrors of an epidemic. In Gwydyr House there was, indeed, a gleam of hope when the Tories ousted the Whigs. Wood, Hayter, and George Lewis must go. Above all, it meant a change at the Woods and Forests, and surely no new President could show less good will and understanding than the outgoing Seymour. Perhaps, thought Chadwick, the Derby Ministry could be per-

[1] Russell to E. C., 9 October 1836.

Y

suaded to go into the question of the Treasury's constitutional right to exercise a dispensing power and scrap an Act which Parliament had approved but which the Treasury regarded with disfavour.

These hopes were soon disappointed. Lord John Manners, the Board's new chief, though he did not display the rancour of Lord Seymour, made it plain that he intended to do no more than carry out the plans which his predecessor had been maturing. On 29 April 1852 Shaftesbury moved a resolution in the Lords, "that the sanitary state of the Metropolis requires the immediate interposition of Her Majesty's Government."[1] It was a test motion, designed to draw the Tories into the open, to discover if they had any intention of taking action against the reviving companies. These, of course, were "truisms," replied Derby, when Shaftesbury had reached the end of his depressing narrative.

"Now, if it were a *tabula rasa* that Parliament had to deal with —if the vast interests of existing companies had not to be consulted, which had been found a practical difficulty in the way of all legislation that had been attempted—he had no doubt it would be better and more efficacious that there should be one single authority charged with the administration of the water and the removal of all offensive matter, than vest the separate powers of water supply and sewerage in separate bodies, thereby losing the unity of action that appertained to a single authority. But there was great difficulty in deciding what that central authority should be. The practice of Continental Governments might be quoted; but other Governments were much more free to act for the benefit of the population than a Government subject to popular influences and control, and which had to study not only the interests, but the views and feelings, of those for whom they legislated. He did not dispute the advantages of cleanliness, and he agreed with the most reverend Prelate (Archbishop of Canterbury) that cleanliness and decency were the handmaids of morality and religion. But it was not by Act of Parliament that you could compel people to be moral, decent, or clean; and in many cases legislation to enforce those objects would be opposed by the persons for whose real and permanent interests they were legislating. (Shaftesbury: No, no!)"[2]

[1] *Hansard*, vol. cxx, pp. 1283-98.   [2] Ibid., p. 1305.

Balancing the interests of the water companies against those of the population of London, Derby in a speech of remarkable frankness thus came down in favour of the former; and he then went on to stress the objectionable features of centralisation, to discount the popular demand for sanitary improvements, to disparage Shaftesbury's statistics, and to assert in conclusion that beyond a certain point the Government could not go in interfering with the internal affairs of the people—altogether, in fact, to act to perfection the part of a Prime Minister who was casting round to find justification for doing nothing. Chadwick had no doubt that Derby's information came from the subordinate officers of the Treasury, who in their turn were probably primed by shareholders in the water companies.[1] The indignation of the reformers was well voiced by Dr. John Roberton, an old ally from the days of the battle on behalf of the railway labourers of the Summit Tunnel. "Is not the sanitary state of the stables of the Gentry minded?" he demanded. "Don't their racers get plenty of pure water? have not they well ventilated stables and room enough to rest their bodies and stretch their limbs? Doubtless they have: and when the mass of mankind comes to be as much valued as racers My Lords and others will help on Sanitary Reform."[2]

A few weeks later Lord John Manners introduced a Bill to repeal the Interments Act of 1850. The proper remedy, he observed, was not the principle of monopoly and centralisation, which had failed to work despite the great and almost extravagant powers confided to the General Board, but the "more constitutional, simple, and less objectionable method, by which from time immemorial the parochial authorities had been entrusted with the burial of the dead."[3] Thus, by his Metropolitan Burials Bill, the Home Secretary was empowered to close any burial grounds proved to be obnoxious, and the parishes were enabled, singly or in combination, to provide new grounds or to contract with the trading cemeteries. Chadwick could only conclude that his new chief had not read the evidence of the trial and failure of the very measures which he now proposed. What use

---

[1] E. C. to ? (probably Delane), 29 April 1852.
[2] Dr. John Roberton to E. C., 3 May 1852.
[3] *Hansard*, vol. cxxii, pp. 872, 874, 17 June 1852.

would these powers be in the hands of the parish politicians, the men who had permitted the abuses to flourish unchecked, resisting amendment with all the obstinacy of ignorance and prejudice? Under the rule of the vestrymen of Marylebone and St. Pancras, the Officer of Health, on whom pivoted the whole arrangements for advice and regulation, could find no place. It was illusory to expect parishes—or even Unions, which could never be induced to combine to establish district schools—to co-operate of their own accord to acquire a cemetery, a possibility "as remote as their union to construct of themselves a locomotive."[1] One of the parish clergy, he heard, had stated that "a good and sufficient chapel" for a parochial cemetery could be built of rubble for £1,000.[2] Rubble! What a falling off from the architectural splendour of Chadwick's National Cemetery!

In the same month (June 1852) a Bill empowering the London Necropolis and National Mausoleum Company to purchase 2,000 acres of Woking Common on which to lay out a cemetery, was approved by the Commons, after the chairman of the Select Committee had remarked that all parties admitted the powers possessed by the General Board "had been tried without effect, and that, if this Bill were not carried, it would be perfectly hopeless to expect any remedy from the Board of Health."[3] Lord John Manners agreed, welcoming a measure which he thought calculated to remove the evils complained of; and his approval was echoed by Lord Seymour. To Chadwick it was obvious that the Bill was the scheme "of vulgar projectors and a vulgar architect," a building speculation disguised as a public measure, which included amongst its proposals pit burial for paupers, the use of railway arches as mortuaries, and the transport of corpses in the common horse-boxes of the railway.[4] Yet the Government had given the Bill their benediction—was it because "the present Solicitor-General Sir Richard Bethel was deeply engaged in this speculation, his brother in law Mr. Abrahams being the architect?"[5]

In the course of the debates on the interments question Lord

---

[1] E. C. to Russell, n.d.   [2] E. C. to the Bishop of London, 31 January 1852.
[3] *Hansard*, vol. cxxi, p. 892, 21 May 1852.
[4] E. C., "Objections to the Necropolis Bill," MS., n.d.
[5] E. C. to ? (Russell), n.d.

Seymour in alliance with the metropolitan members delivered a sharp attack on the principles, constitution, and personnel of the General Board. Even the inoffensive Southwood Smith did not escape, and one member asked why he should continue to draw his salary now that the Act under which he was appointed had been repealed; all he had done was to go to Paris and assist in the writing of ten thousand letters.[1]

"There was considerable inconvenience in the constitution of the Board itself," Lord Seymour told the Commons on 21 June. "Although he, when President of the Board, was responsible to Parliament for the proceedings of that Board, yet when he attended the Board and made a proposal, it was seldom he could get a seconder, for Mr. Chadwick and Dr. Southwood Smith, forming the majority of the Board, carried the question against him. He had told the Government that it was impossible to go on in that way. He thought it would be far better if some Lord of the Treasury were to assist Mr. Chadwick, so that the Government might have some possibility of controlling the Board, and preventing the inconvenience and delay of business which now repeatedly occurred."[2]

The impression Seymour conveyed of himself playing the Dormouse to Chadwick's Mad Hatter and Southwood Smith's March Hare was, of course, quite unfounded. It was not the first time in his relations with the General Board that he had revealed that he possessed an ingeniously constructive memory. He now drew for an appreciative House a picture of himself wrestling with two sullenly stubborn colleagues, and finally giving up attendance at a Board where he could only make a useless gesture of protest. Seymour must be confusing them with some other Board, wrote Shaftesbury blandly. Surely he had not forgotten that out of the 237 meetings held during his tenure of office, he had attended only three; that once only was any resistance offered; and that was by Shaftesbury, not by Dr. Smith or Mr. Chadwick? That occasion was, of course, on 30 January 1851, when Seymour had startled the Board by proposing that they should take over two of the cemeteries and enter into competition with the remainder of the trading companies; and it was the Board not

---

[1] T. Duncombe: *Hansard*, vol. cxxii, p. 1082, 21 June 1852.
[2] *Hansard*, vol. cxxii, p. 1081.

Seymour whose representations had finally prevailed with the Treasury, short-lived though the victory was. Shaftesbury, who felt a justifiable annoyance at the suggestion implied in Seymour's speech that only Chadwick and the Doctor conducted the business, pointed out with some acerbity that he had been absent from one only of the Boards at which Seymour had made an appearance, and that out of the total number held during Seymour's period of office he had attended 101.[1] *The Times* report was not quite correct, Seymour hastened to explain. What he had said was that he remembered attending the Board at the end of 1850 or beginning of 1851, and making a proposal which was not seconded, and which consequently dropped. Finding himself in this position he felt disinclined to attend the Board—even if he had the time. "I do not believe that I stated that I met with frequent opposition at the Board, but I may have said that my views were frequently opposed to those of the Board, and I said I considered the constitution of the Board defective as an executive department, because differences, which were honestly entertained on both sides, led to delay and repeated correspondence with the Treasury."[2] Thus, on Seymour's own showing, the resistance he encountered from his colleagues had now dwindled to a single instance of conflict of views, and this had apparently proved sufficient to "disincline" him to attend the Board. Forwarding copies of the letters to Lord Carlisle, Chadwick implored him that before the question arose of renewing the Board's term of office, a committee of inquiry should be held to investigate all such charges, so that the measure should not be left to the mercy of the Treasury.[3] But Seymour was never challenged in public, and he never modified the original version of his charge against his former colleagues, which was to be revived again as a weapon in the final grand assault on the General Board.

Meanwhile, on the water question, the Government had with equal decision turned its back on Gwydyr House. Shortly before the fall of the Whigs, Lord Seymour introduced a Bill for metropolitan water supply. He did not believe it possible, he declared, for a Government commission to superintend such a function; to create a municipal corporation, however, would mean delay,

[1] Shaftesbury to Seymour, 22 June 1852.
[2] Seymour to Shaftesbury, 24 June 1852.   [3] E. C. to Carlisle, 26 June 1852.

and it would probably be inefficient, in any case; a combination of the companies, again, might be the means to economy, but it was not Parliament's duty to require it.[1] In this way he disposed, one by one, of the schemes of Chadwick, the parochialists, and Sir William Clay, leaving as the most practicable solution—since securities must be given to the consumer which would not entail any undue exertion by the Government—the proposal that the companies should be left as they were, subject only to certain conditions as to quality, distribution, and rate of charge. His Bill, which no less clearly represented the ideas of Sir John Johnstone than the Bill of the previous year represented those of Sir William Clay, was inherited a month later by Lord John Manners, who promptly sent it, with a batch of other Bills from the water companies, to a Select Committee. Here, after two months at a cost of £1,000 a day in retainers for a score of counsel and Parliamentary agents, the Government Bill was hammered into a shape which the companies found possible to accept. On 7 June a surprised House was requested to go into Committee on the measure, the Government having taken the Second Reading at so late an hour that the principles of the Bill had not so far come under discussion.[2] Both Mowatt and Lord Ebrington delivered damaging attacks upon the Bill, but it mustered ample support in a House which included eighty-six shareholders of the water companies;[3] and eventually it reached the Lords so late in the session, as Shaftesbury complained, that they had to pass it without knowing more of it than if it were a Chaldee manuscript.[4]

The Metropolitan Water Supply Act of 1852[5] obliged those companies which drew their water from the Thames to remove their intakes to some place above Teddington Lock, beyond the influence of the tide which daily agitated and re-agitated the sewage of the capital. The companies were given till 31 August 1855 (the Chelsea Company a year longer) to do this. They were also obliged to cover in their reservoirs, and to filter all water intended for domestic use; and it was stipulated that within five years a constant supply must be laid on by every company. The

[1] *Hansard*, vol. cxix, pp. 218–19, 6 February 1852.
[2] Ibid., vol. cxxii, pp. 839–72, 17 June 1852.
[3] The figure given by Joseph Hume: *Hansard*, vol. cxx, p. 84, 25 March 1852.
[4] *Hansard*, vol. cxxii, p. 1267, 24 June 1852.   [5] 15 & 16 Vict., c. 84.

Government had, in fact, been as gentle as possible in putting the curb on the companies. Lord Ebrington alleged that the Select Committee had refused to hear his evidence, and that the truth had emerged only when the companies' experts disagreed amongst themselves.[1] The schedule of uniform rates and charges, which Sir John Johnstone had said would amount to a confiscation of the companies' property, had been quietly dropped, together with the clauses which were intended to compel competition between the companies. To Chadwick this second Home Office Bill displayed "an offhand ignorant and supercilious contempt" for the needs of the population and for his own labours to relieve them, and it appeared less objectionable than the first in one respect only: it did not guarantee to the companies a monopoly of bad supplies at three times the price for which good supplies could be obtained from the sources he had indicated.[2] It exhibited no attempt by its framers to view water supply and drainage as a unified problem, and it did nothing to end the bad old practices of the past, such as the additional charges for water-closets and baths which acted as taxes on health and cleanliness. It obliged some of the companies to seek new intakes; but their source was still the Thames, hard with lime and fouled by the refuse of the towns through which it ran—and Chadwick's Surrey springs were once more disregarded.

It is hardly possible, after reading the story of Chadwick's struggle to give London a wholesome and universal water supply, not to conclude that a splendid chance had been missed. If his recommendations had been acted upon and the companies had been bought out in 1851, the ratepayers of London would have saved themselves fifty years of discomfort and ill health, and some £40,000,000 of compensation which in 1902 was thrown as a back-breaking burden of debt on the Metropolitan Water Board. The solution of the "practical men," of Seymour and Wood, of Derby and Manners, proved no solution at all. Fourteen years later, when cholera raged for twenty-three weeks in London and killed 5,548, it was revealed that the East London Water Company continued, in contravention of the fourth section of the 1852

[1] *Hansard*, vol. cxxii, p. 856, 17 June 1852.
[2] "Notes of heads of remonstrance on the Metropolitan Water Bill," MS., n.d.

Act, to distribute water which had not been passed through filter
beds; and though the provisions of the 1852 measure were repeated and strengthened by the Metropolis Water Act of 1871, it
was not till 1899 that Londoners were receiving the promised
constant supply.

The history of the metropolitan water companies affords the
classic example of a great vested interest, rooted so strongly among
the governing classes, with its friends in the Press and the departments of State, its spokesmen in the Government, and its silent
battalions of shareholders in the House of Commons, that it was
enabled to hold out for generations in the face of all the evidence,
until the mounting exasperation of the public forced it to a
capitulation—on its own terms. How many politicians and civil
servants, Chadwick wondered, were drawing dividends and
directors' fees from works which the Board of Health had condemned as inefficient and unhealthy? "The new Secretary at
War: the Right Hon. R. Vernon Smith who brought forward one
of the New River Company's bills: inherited shares in it. His
father was the chairman of the New River Company, and really
wrote the report of one of the Committees on the water question.
The present solicitor to the Treasury Mr. Reynolds is a Director
of the West Middlesex Water Company. Several clerks of the
House of Commons I am told are holders of water shares. The
public offices are beset with them, and with shareholders in other
companies."[1] In Parliament the Board's measures came under
discussion in "an atmosphere of shareholders." The aura of
influence of a great body of capital extended far beyond the circle
of those with direct pecuniary interests. "The Minister may be
told this is great property, 'capital' invested for an important
public object; you cannot sacrifice it in families; the House will
not support you. You can never carry such a measure."[2] The
railways in Germany, he heard, charged little more than one-
third of the English fares, and yet returned a profit of 6 per cent,
the reason being that, since they were State-owned, they were
exempt from the influence of shareholders in the chambers and
Government departments. How much better than in England
where it was thought no disgrace for shareholders like Sir William

[1] E. C. to G. Goldsmith (editor of the *Globe*), 7 February 1852.
[2] E. C. to ? (Delane), n.d.

Clay or Sir John Johnstone to vote on questions in which they had a financial interest![1]

He detected sinister figures like these behind every interest disturbed by the Board. The chairman of one of the two cemetery companies against which they had first taken proceedings was father to an under-secretary of State; the chairman of the other had an under-secretary as nephew. Chadwick was indignant, therefore, but not surprised, when he discovered that these companies "had information long before we received it, that a hostile course would be taken against us."[2] Then there were the great slum landlords. The Marquis of Salisbury, the Lord Privy Seal, opposed the application of the Public Health Act to Hertford, where whole rows of houses belonging to him had not a single privy. Lord Lonsdale, ground landlord of Whitehaven, successfully resisted the introduction of the Act into the town, which the Board estimated would cost £22,000 to put in a sound sanitary condition; though it was said that he found twice that sum to back an opera company. In the closing months of 1852 these two noblemen showed themselves as the most active opponents of the Board in the Upper House. The outstanding example of another type of critic was Toulmin Smith, theorist of Local Self-Government and defender of the vestry and court leet, who thrust himself forward as the spokesman of various parties opposed to the Board. The Corporation of the City of London had spent £300 in circulating his pamphlets. The Town Commissioners of Bristol had paid him £80 for lecturing against the Public Health Act. He had acted as counsel for the Hampstead Water Company before the 1851 Committee, and had been briefed to promote a Local Act for Birmingham to counter the application for the Public Health Act. Thus, Chadwick summed it up, in the newspapers and on public platforms, retained advocates assumed the guise of impartial judges, and in Parliament shareholders and shareholders' agents appeared as impartial public representatives.[3]

The defeat of the Derby Government in the elections of the summer of 1852 caused little rejoicing in Gwydyr House.

[1] E. C. to G. Goldsmith, 7 February 1852.
[2] E. C. to J. T. Delane, 1 November 1851.   [3] E. C. to ? , 28 July 1851.

"I quietly dread the effect of changes, and negotiations, and office hunting and leaving, at this particular juncture," observed Shaftesbury. "We have not a moment to lose. The next three months are, 'I speak as a man,' inestimably valuable; and if we let slip that time for preparation, we may be utterly ruined.

"Yet what shall we gain by a return to our old Masters? Seymour will be no better than John Manners, as John Manners proved to be no better than Seymour. D'Israeli, to all intents and purposes, is equal to Charles Wood; and Hamilton is vastly superior to Hayter. Walpole, to be sure, and Salisbury and Lonsdale are sad specimens of knowledge and will in sanitary matters. Yet, all I have said, are nearly alike. Public men know nothing, want to know nothing, hate to be told anything, which does not openly and directly affect their political position and safety."[1]

At this time (July–August 1852) Shaftesbury was on the Continent, recuperating from the effects of overstrain, and his letters to Chadwick uncover the frustration and bitterness left by the disasters of the past session. "It is needless to tell you of the heat here," he wrote from Ems, "for I understand the weather is fiercer, if possible, in London. . . . I have sat and pictured, to myself, the sufferings of *our* clients in their crowded alleys, Courts, Lanes, and houses of the Metropolis, with poisonous and deadly water, until I have become more sorrowful than, perhaps, they are themselves! I cannot well describe to you the pain of my disappointment, actual and *prospective*; *for I see* that our enemies, these 'Sons of Zervinat' will prove too strong for us. It comes between me and my 'cure' (this is the local term), I do not receive half as much benefit as I should do, were our hopes accomplished. . . ."[2]

It was with appreciative envy that Chadwick, and still more Shaftesbury, watched the progress of Louis Napoleon's social reforms, with their swift clean strokes of unrestricted, beneficent power. He was "laying about him furiously in Paris," noted Shaftesbury, where "he has proclaimed war against all courts, alleys, lanes, and culs de sac." "The Galignani of yesterday contained a programme of improvements which made my hair stand on end. Every working man that lives will on seeing these results shout 'vive la Despotisme'; 'à bas les gouvernements libres!'

[1] Shaftesbury to E. C., 18 July 1852.   [2] Shaftesbury to E. C., 16 July 1852.

Why our Vestries, Boards of Guardians, paving Boards, and all
the apparatus of what is called 'local' and 'Self' government,
have only been so many obstacles in the way of physical and Social
amelioration."[1] When Emil Chevalier came as a special Commissioner in August 1852 to examine the lodging-houses and model
dwellings of London, Chadwick sent him, in the company of
Count Cavour, on a tour of some of the worst districts. They
agreed, he wrote to Shaftesbury, that the Lodging House Act was
working very well, and were favourably impressed by the model
dwelling-houses; but they were "in horrors" at the neglected
condition of the slum population.[2]

"Your letter filled me with grief and shame," replied Shaftesbury. " 'The thing,' as old Job said, 'that I greatly feared, is
come upon me'; and the Sin and sensuality of Protestant, free,
and wealthy England towards the mass of the civil population,
will be shown up to the whole world, and then contrasted with
the paternal care of Papist, despotic, impoverished France!

"To avert such an issue, and to stand well in a day of account,
you and I and many others have laboured long, but have been
reluctantly and feebly backed in the beginning; and we shall be
nobly and angrily opposed in the end.

"This day I have been to Frankfort on business—the City is
broad, clean, and very handsome—but the Stinks (whence they
come I know not) were prodigious. Cesspool-breezes were blow-
ing from all points of the Compass; and I felt, I regret to say,
something akin to a malicious comfort that some other places,
beside London, had their own abominations."[3]

Barnstaple rejected Lord Ebrington, "our only stay in the
House of Commons,"[4] in the elections of 1852, hatred of the
Public Health Act coming to the aid of the customary electoral
weapons of bribery and treating.[5] Looking over the new Government, Chadwick could see only one face which seemed to promise
hope and a rescue from frustration; it was that of Palmerston,
the Home Secretary, whose caustic marginalia and insolent little
notes were said to have kept the sluggish patricians of the Foreign
Office in a state of unexampled activity. Here was a fellow-

[1] Shaftesbury to E. C., 18 July 1852.   [2] E. C. to Shaftesbury, 7 August 1852.
[3] Shaftesbury to E. C., 12 August 1852.   [4] Shaftesbury to E. C., 16 July 1852.
[5] Earl Fortescue to E. C., 13 November 1853.

warrior against cant and routine, and one, moreover, related by marriage to Lord Shaftesbury, for whom he had a curious respect. Palmerston for his part listened more sympathetically than his predecessors at the Home Office to the views of the General Board; and at a public dinner at Lewes, after Lord Ducie had lamented the shortage of farm manures, he delivered, to the ponderous amusement of *The Times*, a eulogy of the untapped treasures of town guano, based apparently on some vague recollections of Chadwick's theories.[1]

The new President of the Board was not Lord Seymour, as Shaftesbury had feared, but Sir William Molesworth, yet another President who preferred to preside at a distance, and to act in embarrassing independence without consulting his colleagues. His first move was to declare that he would not insert in a Confirming Bill any town where a majority of the ratepayers appeared to be against it. This, Chadwick pointed out, amounted to a reversal of the provision in the Public Health Act giving the Board the power to intervene in any place proved to suffer from excessive mortality. It would deprive the subject, moreover, of the common law right to pure air and the means of healthy existence; no local majority could assume the authority to determine that a minority or even a single individual should be so deprived, and should die in consequence. Such a power would be a sovereign power, and an arbitrary one; it would give local bodies the right "if not of the gallows literally of the pit. . . ."[2]

So 1852 closed, with the Board brooding over two major defeats in the capital, with Shaftesbury low in spirits and Chadwick beginning to sound his friends about the possibilities of employment in the Home Office. When Robert Rawlinson read a paper on town drainage at the Institute of Civil Engineers in December, not one voice was raised in his support.[3] The mention of Chadwick's name one day in the Court of Common Council precipitated "a perfect outburst of fury."[4] There were few men alive, he thought, "so little loved and so intensely hated; and whose official position is so precarious."[5]

[1] *Times*, 19 July 1852.
[2] E. C. to Russell, n.d.
[3] E. C. to F. O. Ward, 15 December 1852.
[4] E. C. to Andrew Boardman, n.d.   [5] Ibid.

The year 1853 brought with it no lessening of the gloom. Its opening weeks were clouded by the unfortunate Croydon inquiry. Hawkesley and his friends grew increasingly clamorous. Before a Lords' Committee Toulmin Smith, acting on behalf of the slum landlords of Hertford, the Marquis of Salisbury and Baron Dimsdale, routed one of the Board's Inspectors.[1] Above all, hostile elements in the localities were enormously encouraged and strengthened by the course of events in London, where Chadwick's schemes collapsed in the final disaster of an open quarrel between the General Board and the Metropolitan Commission of Sewers.

When the first Metropolitan Commission of Sewers succumbed to its internal disorders in September 1849, it had been succeeded by a smaller body of thirteen members, selected mainly for their scientific and technical knowledge, and including Sir John Burgoyne from the Board of Ordnance, prominent railway engineers such as Robert Stephenson and J. M. Rendel, and a number of officers from the Royal Engineers. Alarming stories presently came to Chadwick's ears. The great Mr. Rendel had been heard to use such expressions as "Sanitary Humbug," and had scoffed at the whole subject of sanitary improvement; it was quite sufficient, he contended, for the Commission to carry sewers down the centre of the streets, leaving the owners to drain into them or not, as they thought fit.[2] Chadwick's trial works were brought to a stop. The eminent engineers attended only intermittently to their unpaid public duties, and the business of the Commission was frequently held up for lack of a quorum. Their one considerable achievement was the notorious Victoria Street sewer, on which, after estimating that it would cost £13,854, they spent £33,000; part of it fell into ruins almost immediately, necessitating an additional large outlay for repairs.[3] As Londoners watched their rates mounting, while their streets and houses remained as foul as ever, *The Times* and Sir Benjamin Hall were presently as loud in complaint of the new Commission as

[1] *Minutes of Evidence taken before the Select Committee of the House of Lords on the General Board of Health (No. 3) Bill*; *P.P.*, 1852–3, vol. xxxi, p. 231 (Lords).

[2] E. C. to Carlisle, 1 November 1849.

[3] *Reports and Communications by the Board of Health to the Home Secretary on the Drainage of the Metropolis*; *P.P.*, 1854, vol. lxi, pp. 3–4.

they had been of the old.[1] By pressure on its more amenable
members and by representations to the Government, Chadwick
endeavoured to maintain his control over the course of affairs at
Greek Street. His anxiety increased as they drew further and
further away from his influence. On the general theory of town
drainage, and on the particular question of the drainage of
London, the views of Chadwick and his Inspectors clashed with
those of Bazalgette, the Superintending Engineer of the Commission, and Cubitt and Stephenson, their Consulting Engineers.
"As to pipes he would not touch one," Stephenson had once
declared. "He hated the very name of them, and felt inclined
never to mention the word again."[2] In November 1852 the stone-
ware pipes, which had been laid down three years before in
Church Lane and Carrier Street, St. Giles, by the first Metropolitan Commission of Sewers, were pulled up and replaced by brick
drains, Bazalgette giving as his reasons the number of stoppages,
the cost of removing obstructions, and the risk of opening the
ground for examination under old and badly built houses.[3] This
report had a marked effect on those who did not know all the
circumstances—that the failure had occurred in a block of buildings with a deficient water supply, mostly common lodging-houses
occupied by the lowest type of Irish labourers; and that these
forty-eight houses amounted to a very small fraction of the 27,000
in London which by now were being drained by 346 miles of
pipes.[4] Another damaging document put out from Greek Street
was a report on "Past Failures and Present Condition of Pipe
Sewers," in which Bazalgette, after examining 122 pipe-sewers,
found that some were completely choked, 23 were cracked or
broken, and 113 contained deposit, in 66 ranging from $2\frac{1}{2}$ to 7
inches in depth.[5] It was thus not long before the officers of the
Sewers Commission were being invoked as authorities by those
who wished, from whatever motives, to resist or discredit the
General Board of Health.

[1] See, for example, Hall's attack, *Hansard*, vol. cxvi, pp. 1063–71, 16 May
1851.
[2] *Communications from the General Board of Health, and reports of Superintending
Inspectors in respect to the operation of Pipe Sewers*; P.P., 1854–5, vol. xlv, p. 49.
[3] *Pipe and Tunnel Sewers, Reports of Mr. Bazalgette relating to*; P.P., 1852–3,
vol. xcvi, pp. 9–11.
[4] P.P., 1854–5, vol. xlv, p. 5.   [5] P.P., 1852–3, vol. xcvi, p. 12.

By August 1853 Chadwick could contain himself no longer, and Southwood Smith joined him in a letter to Lord Palmerston protesting against the wastefulness and erroneous principles of the works which the Sewers Commissioners were planning to execute. Bazalgette proposed to spend two million pounds on laying down another thousand miles of brick sewers, an "expenditure in worse than waste," and the main lines of intercepting sewer which he contemplated would cost a further three millions. For one-third of this amount, self-cleansing pipes could be installed. Furthermore, by adopting Austin's methods for the drainage of the metropolis, not only would the pollution of the Thames be avoided, as Bazalgette intended, but at the same time another great object would be secured which he had sacrificed— the sewage would be saved for disposal as manure.[1] The letter did not stop Bazalgette's preparations, but in the controversy which followed Palmerston showed himself a good friend to the General Board. In November 1853 he pointedly sent the Sewers Commission copies of reports he had received from a number of the Local Boards, "to show the cheapness and efficiency of the tubular system."[2] Bazalgette took up the challenge, and made a personal inspection of the places in question. He satisfied himself that the cost of pipe drains was considerably greater than the General Board had stated, that in four out of the five towns he had visited there had been notable failures, and that none of them had as yet possessed pipes long enough to give them a fair trial.[3] In reply the General Board submitted reports from the engineers responsible for the works under judgment. These censured Bazalgette for conducting so hasty and superficial an examination, and showed that at Rugby pipes had worked satisfactorily for a period of two years and at St. Thomas's, Exeter, for two and a half; that at Barnard Castle only one defect had been found in three miles of pipes; and that at Tottenham, Bazalgette, in order to give a "general idea" of the charges resulting from the new system had quoted one bill for £40—neglecting to point out that this was incurred by the owner of one of the largest houses in

[1] *Reports and Communications by the Board of Health to the Home Secretary on the Drainage of the Metropolis*; *P.P.*, 1854, vol. lxi, pp. 5–6.

[2] Ibid., p. 139.

[3] Ibid., pp. 184–204: *Report upon the Drainage and Water Supply of Rugby, Sandgate, Tottenham, St. Thomas's, Exeter, and Barnard Castle*, 13 February 1854.

the town, who had put in eight cocks, four water-closets, 212 feet of private drains and apparatus for watering his carriage and flower garden.[1]

There we must leave the controversy, which poured its subsidiary stream of hate into the flood which overwhelmed Chadwick in July 1854. In the localities Bazalgette's reports were gratuitously circulated by the enemies of the Board to inoculate local opinion against the persuasive arguments of the Inspectors. At a public meeting at Weymouth, for example, an opponent rose to ask Austin, "What guarantee can the General Board offer us at Weymouth against such fatal consequences as these" (flourishing the diagrams of stopped pipes published by the Metropolitan Commission of Sewers), "if we adopt pipe drainage, and what course would they advise?"[2] Members of Parliament read Bazalgette's reports on the pipe sewers of the metropolis, and looked at the eleven pages of diagrams which supported them, showing alarming cross-sections of pipes choked black with sediment, and the impression spread that the majority of pipe drains beneath London were cracked and oozing filth or were blocked by the retained ordure. It had a powerful effect when Chadwick's fate was in the balance in the vital debates of 1854. As F. O. Ward told him: "I referred to Bazalgette's lithographs as having mainly contributed to the strong impression in the House of Commons which led to your retirement:—*and Sir John Shelley confirmed that statement*, referring to one particular lithograph (of a pipe from Mr. Rich's premises) shown as quite blocked up in Bazalgette's report, and which he particularly remembered as the subject of jokes about the *rich* state of the pipe: whereas, on turning to Grant's report, this very pipe proves among the poorest—being in fact completely *clear*."[3]

[1] *Communications from the General Board of Health, and reports of Superintending Inspectors in respect to the operation of Pipe Sewers*; P.P., 1854–5, vol. xlv, pp. 58, 88, 99.
[2] Ibid., p. 15.   [3] F. O. Ward to E. C., 25 April 1855.

Z

CHAPTER XVI

ACHIEVEMENTS, 1848–1854

As the Board entered upon the last twelve months permitted to them by the Public Health Act, they began to weigh anxiously the chances that their mandate would be renewed by Parliament. A despondent letter from Shaftesbury, taking the cure at Ems in the summer recess of 1853, showed that he faced the coming session with gloomy foreboding. He had been cut to the quick when Palmerston withdrew support for his Mendicancy Bill, and he saw in its rejection a sign of his waning influence.

"The House, it is said, refused to listen; this, if it be so, is a sad omen for any future exertions; I have not time before me, as I had twenty years ago when I moved the factory bill; nor have I the same struggle and fire to endure disappointments. Punch and the Times have done their best for me; but my friends, it seems are weaker, and my enemies stronger, than either or both together!

"I am sadly dispirited; and I shall have no heart left either to attempt, or imagine anything more. And, at last, when our rulers give the coup de grace to the Board of Health, I shall feel, like Othello, that my occupation is gone."[1]

They must make a defensive statement, he wrote later the same month; "but it will be to no purpose as an effort to ward off a capital sentence. That our dissolution is resolved on, I cannot doubt; the very fact of the combination against us of the Metropolitan members and the Subordinates of the Treasury would make our position very difficult to a bold and just Ministry; it will render our overthrow and oppression too certain and almost agreeable to a Government that is neither one nor the other." "Why should the Subalterns at the Treasury be jealous of me and my Lodging House Act?" he went on. "I am no Candidate for place, or pension, or political favour. God knows I have had

[1] Shaftesbury to E. C., 3 August 1853.

trouble enough for nothing; abundance of 'monkey's allowance, more kicks than half-pence.' Is it Mr. Wilson? but what is the use of asking *who*? the name of our enemies is 'Legion.'"[1]

With this feeling that they were ringed round by a multitude of open foes, and that an even more numerous host worked secretly for their destruction, the Board drew up at the end of 1853 the apologia for their five years of activity.[2] It was a more modest and inoffensive document than Chadwick had intended it to be, but its only concession to the opposition was to omit some of his more truculent passages. Chadwick was less resigned to defeat than was Shaftesbury, and less convinced that defeat was inevitable. Once when he had mentioned to Lord John Russell some encouraging facts about their progress, the Prime Minister had asked why the Board "did not ding them into people's ears: they needed to be saturated with them."[3] There, thought Chadwick, was the fundamental reason for the general distrust with which the Board were now regarded: the ignorance of their achievements which permitted the misrepresentations of their enemies to pass unchallenged. He hoped to enlist sympathy by a plain factual account of what the Board had done, and a reasoned explanation of the position they had taken up on certain controversial questions.

First, then, there were the figures which summarised the Board's work in executing the Public Health Act. By the end of 1853 284 towns had applied for the Board's intervention. The Inspectors had examined and reported on 243 of them; and 182, with a total population of 2,100,000, had been brought under the Act. In 126 of these towns surveys had been completed, or were then in progress. For 70 places plans of public works, founded on the surveys, had been prepared. In 31 towns, including Gloucester, Salisbury, Ely, Dover, Preston, Lancaster, Penzance, Wigan, and Chelmsford, plans for an entirely new set of combined works had been approved by the Board, and mortgages to the amount of £467,000 sanctioned for their execution. In the other 39 partial plans, providing for new sewers to combine with exist-

[1] Shaftesbury to E. C., 28 August 1853.
[2] *Report of the General Board of Health on the administration of the Public Health Act, and the Nuisances Removal and Diseases Prevention Acts, from 1848 to 1854*; P.P., 1854, vol. xxxv, p. 1.
[3] E. C. to Russell, n.d. (1851).

ing waterworks, for an extension of the water supply, or for other improvements contemplated by the Act, had been examined and approved, and a further £589,000 in mortgages had been sanctioned for these purposes. In thirteen towns, including Rugby, Tottenham, Alnwick, Morpeth, Hitchin, Ormskirk, Barnard Castle, Ottery St. Mary, Ashby-de-la-Zouche, Launceston, Croydon, and St. Thomas's, Exeter, the public works for drainage and water supply were finished and in operation; and in all except Croydon they were reported to be working satisfactorily. In the coming year the Board expected similar works to be completed in another thirty-five towns. The Report did not mention that this list was shorter than they had hoped to present, and that one main reason why it was not longer was the shortcomings of the Board of Ordnance, who had greatly exceeded in time and cost their original estimates for surveying the towns brought under the Act.[1] Even so, considering the means at their command and the burden of their other commitments, they had done well. They had been engaged at the same time in their ill-fated metropolitan ventures, none the less laborious and protracted because they were ill-fated; half a dozen Inspectors were all the staff they had been able to employ on the local inquiries; and they had spent less than £64,000 (more than a third of which was repayable by the Local Boards) in their five years of service, a figure well within their Parliamentary vote.

So much for the extent of their operations. But had the Public Health Act brought benefit to the towns where it had been introduced? On this point the Board could admit no doubt. By the Act a place could, for little more than a hundred pounds, arm itself with powers which, if sought by Local Bills, might cost several thousands. It could, calling on the expert counsel of the Board's Inspectors, equip itself with a system of public works which were novel in design, cheap to construct, and efficient in operation, bringing the means of health and cleanliness down to a weekly charge of a few pence. But greater than the economy of money which resulted was the economy of life. In selected groups of the working class, placed under favourable sanitary conditions, the annual death rate had declined from 30 to 13 per thousand. If the death rate throughout the kingdom

[1] Minutes, 26 March 1851, 10 June 1853. E. C. to Burgoyne, 20 June 1853.

stood at the same level, 25,000 lives would be saved annually in London, and 170,000 in England and Wales; and the average age at death, now twenty-nine, would be raised above forty-eight. In these practical exercises in social arithmetic the Board set a plain target before administrators: to close the gap between an actual mortality of 30 per thousand and a "natural" or "inevitable" mortality of 13 per thousand or less.

These were the benefits which sanitary reform held out for the future. But they could be obtained only if certain administrative principles were recognised and acted upon. In the first place, it must be acknowledged that defence against zymotic disease was not a matter which could safely be left to the will and resource of the individual; the chief preventive measures, large-scale works for municipal and domestic drainage and water supply, could be generally and systematically introduced only by a public board. Secondly, it could not be expected that even a local public board should carry out unaided works of a special nature. To overcome the inertia of local opinion and to supply the deficiencies of local knowledge, there must be a central department with wide initiatory and supervisory powers. The flag of centralisation was thus nailed firmly to the mast. And by its side the Board ran up another, no less detested: that of municipal enterprise. Recanting earlier statements, based upon the Health of Towns report, which asserted the superiority of trading water companies in efficiency and economy, they commended for imitation the examples of public management by town councils and Local Boards which in recent years had come under their notice. The reformers of Gwydyr House thus identified themselves with two unpopular propositions: that local representative bodies were not competent to administer without central aid and supervision all matters which affected their districts; and that profit-making bodies were not invariably the best instruments for rendering service to society. Against these doctrines would certainly be ranged the advocates of local self-government, who were many, and of private enterprise, who were even more numerous.

From the localities, where in nearly 250 towns the sanitary condition had been laid bare by the Inspectors and in half of them the first steps at least had been taken towards improvement, the general picture was one of steady and accelerating progress. The picture had its shadows—local blundering, for example, of which Croydon was the most notorious instance. There had been differences of opinion with forty or fifty of the Local Boards. But resentment was aroused by the novelty not the extent of the General Board's control, which was of course far less than that of a modern department. The bit was galling because it was new, not because it was excessively sharp. Of the 182 Local Boards, only six were set down as hostile by Gwydyr House; and the reasons are worth noting:

"Two of these local boards, under the influence of small owners of the description of property requiring amendment, manifested their determination not to execute the Act, by an attempt to dismiss their surveyors, with a view to the entire breaking up of the boards, an attempt which we were bound to resist, because we could not sanction the removal of those officers without just and legal cause. With reference to two other hostile boards, plans of works were proposed which we could not sanction, on the grounds that the works themselves were not the most efficient and that they were unduly expensive. On our withholding our sanction to these works, the parties interested in them made loud complaints of uncalled-for interference. In another town, in which the engineer employed has been at variance with the General Board, it was found necessary, on examination of the proposed works, to insist on a reduction of 24 per cent on the gross sum, for which the sanction for a mortgage of the rates was sought. The performance of this duty was followed on the part of the engineer and others by Parliamentary opposition and complaint.

"We are aware of no instance in which we have experienced hostility, but on some similar ground."[1]

Against this advance the Board had to set the total failure of their efforts in the metropolis. Regretfully they glanced once more at the Water Supply and Interment schemes, denying that it was any intrinsic weakness in their conception which had brought them to nothing, and reasserting that faith in the principles of planned service and public ownership which formed their essence. Enough has been said already about these measures. There was much else touched upon in the Report—all the multi-

[1] *Report of the General Board of Health on the administration of the Public Health Act . . . from 1848 to 1854*, p. 53.

farious activities of a brisk and capable department, continually looking for fresh opportunities to exercise its powers and for fresh pretexts to widen them. They had advised Sir Charles Wood to abolish the Window Duties;[1] supplied Lord Palmerston with ammunition for his campaign against the smoke nuisance,[2] considered what regulations might prevent the sale of unwholesome or adulterated articles of food.[3] Of these minor occupations of the Board three call for more than the incidental notice they have so far been given in this study—their attempt to encourage the erection of improved working-class houses by local authorities and progressive landlords; their Act for the regulation of common lodging-houses; and their two reports on Quarantine.

A mass of memoranda remains to show that in the last months of the Board's existence Chadwick was busy on the clauses of a General Building Bill, which would have been the first attempt to extend to the whole country the norms of sanitary construction. This was not, however, the first attempt of the Board to "Christianise," as Shaftesbury phrased it,[4] the domestic condition of the working classes. What might be done in this direction had been demonstrated in practice by the Metropolitan Society for Improving the Dwellings of the Industrious Classes, who had built in the Old Pancras Road and Mile End New Town two blocks of model lodging-houses, in which the mortality rate had dropped to 13·6 per thousand.[5] To encourage the establishment of similar lodging-houses Ashley introduced a Bill into the Commons in April 1851.[6] It was a permissive measure, on the lines of the earlier Baths and Washhouses Act, making available to boroughs and parishes with a population over ten thousand powers to erect lodging-houses, the cost being borne upon the rates.[7] The Act was still-born. No local authority took advantage of its provisions; and it is chiefly interesting as an example of the

[1] E. C. to Sir Charles Wood, 1 April 1851.

[2] *Letter from the General Board of Health to the Home Secretary on Smoke Consumption* P.P., 1854, vol. lxi, p. 533.

[3] Minutes, 27 November 1849, 12 May and 21 June 1853.

[4] *Hansard*, vol. cxv, p. 1268, 8 April 1851.

[5] Southwood Smith, *Results of Sanitary Improvement, illustrated by the operations of the Metropolitan Society for Improving the Dwellings of the Industrious Classes*; Charles Knight, London, 1854.

[6] *Hansard*, vol. cxv, pp. 1258–76, 8 April 1851.

[7] 14 & 15 Vict. c. 34.

General Board's policy of encouraging the enterprise of public bodies.

The main reason for its failure, we may judge, lay in the inhibitions of the ratepayer, who was not prepared to risk a loss on a municipal building programme, and whose fears were reflected in the caution and lack of initiative of the local authorities. Model houses were all very well, but could they produce a reasonable return of profit? The same doubt restrained the improving landlord. "No doubt nothing can be more desirable than to provide good houses for the Poor, but I do not see my way in it," Lord Ellenborough once told Chadwick. ". . . No Agricultural Labourer can afford to pay in rent more than one shilling a week, and I cannot build a really good Cottage for less than £80 or even £90. In the last two years I have expended from £1,000 to £1,200 on cottages and I am sure I do not get more than 2 per cent. In Towns no Speculator will build without getting at least 6 per cent, and he ought to have that."[1] This, in Chadwick's view, was the crux of the housing problem. It was essential to show that sound and sanitary building need not involve a lowered profit, that good business might be as powerful a motive as high principles for erecting model cottages. "The desideratum for the working classes is to bring science and capital to bear on the construction of their houses: the only way to improve them and at the same time to make them cheaper is to make them a manufacture."[2] This meant, in the first place, experiment with new materials and methods of construction, with fire-brick grates, tubular chimneys, tile roofs, and hollow brick walls and floors. It meant, secondly, the enlistment of large capital, to make possible the economies of mass production. Chadwick was thus always on the watch for the progressive landlord who might be talked into trying out his ideas; a man like James Matheson, for example, who was about to spend some of the fortune he had made in India on improving the town of Stornoway.[3] He was delighted, again, when Colonel Phipps, the Prince Consort's secretary, informed him in December 1848 that Albert was considering how to improve the labourers' houses on his property,

[1] Lord Ellenborough to E. C., 11 August 1848.
[2] E. C. to T. Bamfield, 6 January 1845.
[3] E. C. to James Matheson, 18 March 1845.

and within a fortnight he submitted a lengthy paper on materials and building methods. The model cottages erected under the patronage of the Prince for the Exhibition of 1851 owed much to Chadwick's advice; and he was convinced that by building them in large numbers similar or better cottages might be put up at half or two-thirds the cost, and still give a return of 7 per cent.[1]

A second Bill was introduced by Shaftesbury in the 1851 session, aimed, not at the dwellings of the stationary population, but at the doss-houses which accommodated from night to night the shifting thousands of homeless vagrants.[2] The common lodging-houses, maintained, as Dr. Ferriar had said, by the "keepers of fever beds," were the foci of contagious disease in the district. Here for twopence or threepence a night bed and board were found for the thieves and prostitutes of the neighbourhood, and the various classes of the fraternity of tramps—hawkers of matches and laces, travelling tinkers and umbrella repairers, ballad-singers and beggars "on the downright." Mingling with these colourful but disreputable characters were the migrant labourers, seeking work and driven into this company for want of suitable shelter elsewhere. "Last night I spent entirely in going through all the lodging-houses and brothels in the town," Lyon Playfair once wrote to Chadwick. "I began at twelve and finished at half-past four, so I saw a prodigious quantity. Such sights! frequently fourteen in a room, women and men lying stark naked together!"[3] The remedy, Chadwick had urged in the *Sanitary Report*, was to oblige all lodging-house keepers to take out a licence, and to subject their establishments to inspection by the medical officer of the Poor Law Union.[4] The demand for public control was taken up by the Inspectors in their local reports. Carlisle, observed Robert Rawlinson, had seventy-two lodging-houses, one huge forcing-bed for the generation of vice in all its forms; it was in vain to erect workhouses, gaols, and hospitals, or to establish penal colonies for the punishment, reformation, or suppression of vice, if these places, the fountain-head of all that was depraved, were

---

[1] Phipps to E. C., 8 December 1848; E. C. to Phipps, 23 December 1848, 14 May 1851, 3 November 1851.

[2] *Hansard*, vol. cxvii, p. 1123, 24 June 1851; vol. cxviii, pp. 325–37, 8 July 1851. 14 & 15 Vict. c. 28.

[3] L. Playfair to E. C., n.d., *c.* 1843–4; probably referring to Sheffield.

[4] *Sanitary Report*, 1842, p. 365.

left unregulated.[1] Hence in 1851 a Bill "was made up for Lord Shaftesbury who got it passed, and whose name it bears."[2] It was an undeniable success. By the middle of 1854 Chadwick could point to a remarkable diminution in the number of fever cases reported from the lodging-houses of London. Out of a population of 30,000 in the 1,400 or 1,500 houses under inspection, there had been only ten cases of fever, whereas it had formerly been common to have as many as twenty cases in one quarter from a single lodging-house.[3]

Of all the Board's work none has been so completely forgotten as their reports on Quarantine;[4] yet Chadwick maintained that if they had rendered no other service than the publication of those reports, their appointment would have been fully justified.[5] There is something to be said for this view. Based though they were on a false epidemiology, the reports issued in practical recommendations of the greatest value to the health and well-being of the seafaring population. The evidence the Board had collected, Chadwick believed, proved beyond doubt that the plague, cholera, and yellow fever all fell into the category of diseases which were bred amidst filth and overcrowding, and which might therefore be prevented in the proportion that these localising conditions were removed. He passed on to conclude that the contagionist theory was utterly discredited, and with it the quarantine system erected upon it. As well raise a barrier against the wind as expect to keep out the epidemic atmosphere which brought the pestilence by military guards at the frontier and warships at the approaches to the seaport towns. The true defence was not quarantine but cleanliness. A glance into the forecastle of most merchant ships would reveal at once why the outbreak of an epidemic was so often associated with the landing of the mariner. The seamen of the world's greatest maritime power lived in floating cellar-dwellings, more noisome and des-

---

[1] *Report on Carlisle*, pp. 56–7.   [2] E. C. to M. Verge, n.d. (1890).
[3] *Reports made to the Home Secretary by the Assistant Commissioner of Police, upon the operation of the Common Lodging-houses Act*; *P.P.*, 1852–3, vol. lxxviii, p. 525; 1854, xxxv, p. 115. *Papers received by the Board of Health, exhibiting the operation of the Act*, 1852–3, vol. lxxviii, p. 553.
[4] *Report on Quarantine*; *P.P.*, 1849, vol. xxiv, p. 137. *Second Report on Quarantine: Yellow Fever*, 1852, vol. xx, p. 117.
[5] E. C. to T. Thornely, 17 July 1854.

tructive of health than any in a Liverpool back street; and the effect showed itself in the statistics of mortality, which gave this "important and comparatively defenceless class of the community" a working life shorter by far than that of any other class of labourers. The Board therefore proposed the dissolution of the existing quarantine establishments, and their replacement by sanitary regulations. A ship in harbour should be brought within the scope of the Nuisances Removal and Diseases Prevention Acts, and subjected to the same precautionary measures as a house on shore. In case of sickness the captain should be obliged to bring a medical officer aboard, who should take charge, and order the cleansing and purification of the ship, the diminution of overcrowding, and the removal of the sick. During the epidemic of 1848–9 the Board issued instructions to this effect, in the face of sturdy protests from Sir William Pym, the Director-General of Quarantine at the Privy Council Office.[1]

If quarantine was useless to defend the population from disease, there seemed no reason why its obstructions to commerce should be allowed to continue. Frequently the detention of a cargo for three or four weeks involved a loss as great as the whole cost of its transport to England; perishables such as fruit rotted in the holds; the price of cotton goods went up 15 per cent. Manchester had long been thinking along these lines; and when the British Government decided that it was time steps were taken to liberalise the quarantine system, it was perhaps due less to the General Board than to the Manchester Chamber of Commerce, convinced, as Dr. Sutherland put it, that "sanitary reform and free commerce are synonymous terms, and that filth and restrictions will in future go together."[2]

Spain, Portugal, and the Italian states still clung superstitiously to the old-style quarantine, but in the United States, France, and Austria faith in its efficacy was waning, and the French Government received strong support when it summoned a Quarantine Conference to Paris in July 1851. Dr. John Sutherland, the Board's ablest and most persuasive medical officer, attended as the chief British representative. By the third week of the Con-

---

[1] "Special Notification to Captains of Merchant Ships, Steamers and Colliers"; London Gazette, 1 December 1848, pp. 4386–9.
[2] J. Sutherland to E. C., 31 December 1851.

ference Sutherland was reporting to Chadwick that he had won over the most influential contagionist in Italy, the representative of Naples, and the delegates were condemning lazarettos root and branch as doing more harm than good in their present state.[1] As they sat at the Affaires Etrangères discussing Sutherland's proposals for hygienic reforms in the Turkish Empire, they heard the discharge of cannon and musketry as the people of Paris manned the barricades in defence of the Republic; a terrified official rushed in crying that all was lost, and the sentries at the outer doors disappeared ("always a sign of great danger," remarked Sutherland drily), but the delegates, declining the offer of a guard from the Cabinet, continued undaunted to discuss pratique and Bills of Health while a battle raged in the streets three or four hundred yards away.[2] The Conference resulted in a victory for Chadwick's hygienic principles, if not for his anti-contagionist views. Quarantine remained, but much of its ancient barbarity and unreason would in future be swept away. Vessels were to be subject to the examination and certification of a port medical officer, who would in effect be the equivalent of the urban officer of health. All governments were instructed to attend to the hygiene of their ships and the sanitary condition of their seaports.[3] The die-hard Pym obstinately refused to accept the recommendations of the Conference, declaring that it was impossible to furnish every ship with a bill of health. Absolute nonsense, cried Sutherland; "I wish we had one hour of Sir Robert Peel or Lord Palmerston to sweep the whole buzz of objections away."[4] Half a century was to elapse before the quarantine system was finally settled on scientific principles, and the penal interdict of earlier times replaced by the modern procedure of notification and medical inspection, disinfection, and inoculation. In the early stages of that development the Board's reports had a considerable and beneficial influence. Translated into French and Italian, they

---

[1] J. Sutherland to E. C., 23 October 1851.
[2] J. Sutherland to E. C., 8 December 1851.   [3] J. Sutherland to E. C., 5 December 1851.
[4] J. Sutherland to E. C., 4 August 1852. The Minutes of the Conference were printed by the French Government, but not made public. For an account of its proceedings, see "The International Quarantine Conference of Paris in 1851–2," by Gavin Milroy (one of the Board's Medical Inspectors), in *Transactions of the Society for the Promotion of Social Science*, 1859, pp. 605–12.

circulated on the Continent and in all the maritime towns of the Levant and of North and South America, directing the attention of governments to the floating slums of the forecastle, and teaching that clean ships and regular medical inspections were better protection against the spread of infection than naval squadrons or a cordon of troops.

The Board's defence of their policy seems to have caused not the slightest ripple on the surface of opinion. Since Chadwick's *Sanitary Report* of 1842 the propagandist efforts of the reformers had shown steadily diminishing returns as the popular mind became saturated with horrors and hardened by reiterated shocks. This latest production of his, flattest and most pedestrian of all sanitary manifestos, fell dead from the press.

Who amongst the friends of the Board was capable of shaking public opinion out of the sluggish unconcern into which it had relapsed after the subsidence of the cholera panic? There were a few names of national weight and influence, but the political leaders of the public health movement were mostly amiable nonentities. The public health movement suffered from its bores. The House rapidly emptied whenever R. A. Slaney introduced his favourite motion for a committee to report on practical plans for the improvement of the working classes; and his talk of sickness benefits, old age pensions, and savings banks was met by Ministerial stonewalling or the retort of some private member that "he wished the people not to depend upon Government."[1] W. A. Mackinnon lectured the House regularly and conscientiously on the evils of smoke and Smithfield Market and intramural interment, but even his friends shook their heads over the results. "Mr. Mackinnon never succeeds. They say he has no tact," Dr. Holland remarked sadly to Chadwick. "He has a great knack at failing."[2] It was a restive team that Chadwick sought to harness to his plans. Shaftesbury and Ebrington and Southwood Smith moved under his control; but others did not respond so readily to his command. Lord Carlisle was too pliant to be relied

[1] *Hansard*, vol. cix, pp. 359–75, 5 March 1850 (Trelawney).
[2] P. H. Holland to E. C., 22 March and 22 July 1846.

upon. Joseph Hume, again, as the great advocate of retrenchment, co-operated willingly in urging model act procedure in place of costly Local Bills; but he looked with misgiving on Chadwick's engineering estimates and the proposed creation of a paid local bureaucracy throughout the country.

Chadwick himself frowned upon the organisation of a "sanitary party." Such talk would divert attention from measures to men, would show "how few they are and *how young they are.*"[1] Had it not been a trick of Leslie and Byng at the Sewers Commission, when they could pick no holes in the measures themselves, to attempt to discredit them as the work of "Chadwick's party"?— by which stratagem they detached those members who prided themselves on their independence of viewpoint and freedom from party ties, and, moreover, convinced Walter of *The Times* that the measures were the product of cliques and cabals. A sense of professional decorum also deterred Chadwick from becoming the centre of a body of political agitators. As a public officer, he declared, he must belong to no party. The General Board had quasi-judicial duties to perform, and so, though they might receive support from any party, they could not themselves belong to one. Inspectors under attack were ordered by Chadwick to keep away from meetings of the Sanitary Association. He endeavoured himself to maintain a proper distance from this propagandist body; he was even reluctant to appear at their dinners, but was overruled "on the grounds of purism" by Shaftesbury and Carlisle.[2]

Seeking the reasons why the Board fell in 1854, we note first then that their well-wishers were badly led and weakly organised. Chadwick's own explanation for the disasters which befell the Board is given in one of the most self-revealing letters he ever wrote. Addressed to an American relative in the closing months of 1852, it describes his preparations for a strategic retreat, and tries to lay bare the reasons why that retreat might soon be forced upon him. It is the letter of a very lonely man, maintaining his courage and strength of purpose still unbroken, but feeling keenly the thwarting of great objects and the ingratitude of powerful men.

"Our Board is terminable next year; powerful parties are

[1] E. C. to Lord ? (Ebrington), 6 August 1852.   [2] Ibid.

labouring to prevent its renewal, and most probably they will prevent its renewal under any conditions on which I can be employed. The new elections have lost us one powerful friend, and have added one or two very certain enemies.

"Under these circumstances I should be obliged, if you would warn my father's family of the uncertainty of the continuance of any assistance from me. I have felt myself obliged to give similar warnings here.

"I have long considered it prudent to reduce my establishment and expenditure; but I have never got a clear months time to look about me and to do the work, which if done at all must be done by myself for I get no assistance on which I can depend. . . . I am moreover much observed by the enemies of our measures and it is as hazardous as changing the position of an outnumbered army in the presence of an enemy; and I have felt that it is highly dangerous to give an appearance of retreat, or display want of confidence in the cause.

"I write to you fully because you are the only one related to me who are likely to take a public as well as private interest in my work.

"There is a prima facie case against me of imprudence, and mismeasurement of forces in bringing against myself personally and the cause, so many enemies, but I knowingly entered the field against very large odds, much has been gained, and eminently large results have only been lost by small chances, such as the unexpected deaths of the late Earls of Carlisle and Shaftesbury removing the two most powerful allies from the House of Commons. In other respects the cause which deserved to be fortunate has been unfortunate. There has been, in some instances foul dealing against it, to an extent which has been unexampled which no more required to be calculated upon than the revival of the practices of dark ages such as poisoning and assassination. In some respects, I have felt that our measures are in advance of the time; the science of prevention is a new one: vast sums are spent in the charity of alleviation: the sanitary association can with difficulty obtain subscriptions of a few hundreds. I have a firm reliance that much that I have done, and hope to have strength, and to be left in peace to lay out, will be found available and profitable in other times, and in the hands of other men.

"Some ground has been lost for the want of sufficient exposition; but for that I could get no time. The works you will receive from me, on the drainage of towns, and the application of the refuse of towns, have all had to be worked out by myself including the elementary principles of engineering applicable; and the consultations which from courtesy have been very extensive have been one source of obstruction. The least pleasant part of my retrospect up to this point has been the general failure of acts of generosity, or of confidence. If I were to go over the ground again, I would exact more: insist more on the exclusive direction of my own measures, have made entire clearances of staffs habituated to measures which require change, have pressed my claims for results obtained immediately on the ministers or on the public for recognition and have had shorter accounts, have overlooked less frequently opportunities of personal vindication. . . ."[1]

The great odds against the reformers, treachery in unexpected quarters, a public opinion slow to grasp the significance of preventive administration, the incalculable malice of fortune—so much Chadwick clearly sees. How far was he himself to blame? Why should the name of Chadwick, associated as it was with great measures for the improvement of health and morals, so grate upon the public ear? That he was so hated was a distasteful fact which he faced unflinchingly, but, conscious of his own high purpose, he was honestly bewildered that it was so. But there were some facets of his character of which he was less aware. He could not know of the irritation caused by the constant nagging of that voice, always making unpleasant truths unpleasantly obvious, and by that cocksure manner, impatient of all opposition, with which he sustained his arguments. In the process of editing and revising by his colleagues, Chadwick's reports were weeded of their querulous personalities and the cruder manifestations of his robust belief that his opponents must be either fools or rogues, but his manuscript drafts and private correspondence supply innumerable examples. McCulloch reprimanded the Board for the expense of their reports—was it not because those reports had more than once overturned his opinions as a political economist?[2]

[1] E. C. to Andrew Boardman, n.d.
[2] E. C. to ? (Lord Brougham), 1 June 1849.

William Napier's creditors closed in on him and forced him to flee to Brussels—and the shortness of credit allowed to the explorer of the Surrey sand springs led Chadwick to suspect some foul intrigue by a hard-water interest.[1] Professor Liebig thought that in so wet a country as England liquid manure must be washed out of the soil and wasted—but then Liebig was the patentee of a solid manure. Professors Graham, Miller, and Hoffman presented a report to the Government against the soft Farnham water, and in favour of Clark's process for softening water by chemical means —were they not chemists?[2] There never was a man more suspicious of his antagonists' motives than Chadwick, more convinced that their objections sprang from a materialist root, a trading profit, a family connection or some snug little place. Whenever he moved towards an accommodation, he never left any doubt that he felt he was striking a pact with evil things, with greed and ignorance and prejudice. Justified though his suspicions only too often were, they gave Chadwick a stiffness of temper which was of no aid to him in conducting the diplomacy of Gwydyr House.

If anything could restore the Board's popularity, it was an epidemic. Fear was their most powerful and dependable ally; and, mingled with the anxiety with which they scanned the weekly mortality returns, there was perhaps a repressed hope that they would be called upon, as Shaftesbury put it, to "resume our old 'aggressions'."[3] Twice already, in July 1850 and September 1852, they had informed the Government that they believed the country was in imminent danger of a return of the cholera;[4] but neither the Whigs on the first occasion, nor the Tories on the second, could be persuaded that it was necessary to put the Diseases Prevention Act into operation, together with the additional powers which the Board were demanding on the strength of their experience in 1848–9. In September 1853, however, the cholera appeared unmistakably in Hamburg, and in a day or so it broke out again in its old haunts in Newcastle and Gateshead. In the first fifteen days of the outbreak 214 deaths were reported

[1] E. C. to F. O. Ward, 1 July 1851.   [2] E. C. to F. O. Ward, June 1851.
[3] Shaftesbury to E. C., 26 August 1852.
[4] Minutes, 19 July 1850, 13 December 1852.

2A

from Newcastle, and 1,371 before September was out. The Board's "Choleraic heroes,"[1] John Sutherland, R. D. Grainger, and Hector Gavin, were promptly on the scene. Fearing that their enemies would attempt to elbow them out of the administration of the Diseases Prevention Act, Shaftesbury wrote privately to Palmerston. At the same time he entreated Chadwick, "Be very respectful for be assured that the slightest expression will be magnified into a crime by men who are resolved to remove us from our places, and tarnish us in reputation." "Let me counsel you," he wrote again, "to take the most *conciliatory* tone with the Boards of Guardians, the Treasury, and all authorities; one ground of our unpopularity is, as I have been told, that we were too dictatorial. I know that it was necessary to be so to overcome resistance; but let us be as forbearing as possible."[2]

Chadwick found that he had not misplaced his trust in Palmerston, who held the soundest of views on the value of cleanliness and the supineness of local authorities. The Home Secretary advised the Treasury to let the Board have such additional medical assistants as they considered necessary, and called for a list of nuisances in London to enable him to decide whether they might be made the subjects of indictment.[3] Whether it was due to Palmerston's support, or to Chadwick's studied restraint, or simply to the chastening fear of a threat so speedily renewed, the atmosphere which surrounded the Board in this latest epidemic was better than in 1848–9. The Board's relations with the College of Physicians, the Scottish Law Officers, the Customs, the Board of Trade, the Poor Law Board and the Metropolitan Commission of Sewers, were handled with the greatest caution; and Inspectors who went round to warn the Guardians of St. Olave's and Greenwich of the impending attack reported an eager desire to co-operate and a readiness to admit that "in 1849 things were left too late, and that the pestilence was fairly down upon them, before they took proper measures."[4] But the Board's powers remained what they had been three years before; the same ignorance and incompetence ruled in the localities; and the filth that had been cleared away during the earlier visitation had long

[1] Shaftesbury to E. C., 22 September 1853.
[2] Shaftsbury to E. C., 28 August, 17 September 1853.
[3] Minutes, 24 September, 10 October 1853.   [4] Ibid., 30 September 1853.

since returned with all the inevitability of a natural process.

"We have had the scourge you predicted, and as you predicted," the Town Clerk of Gateshead told Rawlinson. "The cholera has been true to its character. The dispensary Surgeon told me that he could have stood on a gallery in Martin Dunn's premises in Hillgate, alluded to in the Gateshead Report, and have pitched four beans into four rooms, each containing a cholera corpse. . . . The plague spot is this—when a sanitary improvement is proposed, it is discussed with reference, not to its necessity, but its expense: and if expensive, however necessary, it is shelved. This has been the case in Gateshead and what are the consequences? Our tradesmen, wholesale and retail, have lost thousands, their customers being afraid to enter the town—even with supplies—and enormous expense has been incurred in tending and feeding the sick and burying the dead— a grievous permanent charge upon the rates for the support of the widows and orphans who have lost their breadwinners—*and the work is yet to do*." "A movement is on foot for an inquiry," went on Rawlinson, "and I trust it will be granted, in order that the saddle may be placed on the right horse—and the absolute necessity for granting larger powers to the General Board of Health may be made fully apparent. The powers of that Board are crippled from a miserable apprehension of interference with vested rights and local authorities, and the General Board is blamed for not exercising powers denied them."[1]

The General Board called for a public investigation. The epidemic at Newcastle, they asserted, had been aggravated by causes which might have been prevented if the local authorities had exercised a proper regard for their Common Law obligations as well as their statutory duties with respect to the public health.[2] It was alleged that the introduction of complete works in the town would probably have interfered with the interests of a trading water company, whose shareholders got themselves elected to the Town Council in order to obstruct the exercise of the sanitary powers conferred by the Newcastle Local Act. Similarly at Gateshead a number of owners of small tenements had been elected to oppose the Public Health Act; and at Luton the owner

[1] R. Rawlinson to E. C., 22 October 1853.
[2] Minutes, 8 November 1853.

of some houses in which fifteen deaths had occurred was a member of the Local Board.[1]

So great was the indignation amongst the working classes of Newcastle that there was some fear that they would rise and pull down the houses which were the seats of the pestilence—and which, wrote an angry Inspector, all ought to be bombarded.[2] The unrest amongst the Newcastle population, the allegations of incompetence against the local authorities, and the rumours of negligence on the part of the water company, could not be ignored in the dangerously inflammable atmosphere of an epidemic, and the Government therefore appointed a Commission of Inquiry, which included John Simon, Joseph Hume, and J. F. Bateman. The Commissioners demonstrated, with nearly six hundred pages of evidence,[3] that Newcastle possessed all the unwholesomeness of an ancient walled town, together with added evils of comparatively modern origin. They described the cellar-dwellings, the back-to-back cottages, the increased overcrowding which had resulted when the York and Berwick Railway had been driven through the town; and stated that five-sixths of the houses lacked water-closets or any other form of fæcal house-drainage, and two-fifths were entirely without drains of any kind, even for carrying off the rain. They revealed that the Town Council had neglected to put into force its powers under the recent Local Act until the day after the outbreak reached its climax, and had acted then only upon the instigation of the Inspector of the General Board. They gave it as their opinion that in view of the "great sanitary capabilities of Newcastle," its death rate, which had averaged 28·6 over the previous fifteen years, was nearly double the natural or necessary mortality, and that a thousand or twelve hundred lives were unnecessarily sacrificed there every year. But the Commissioners could not prove that the condition of the town had declined in the four years since 1849, when it had escaped very lightly; nor that its administration was more neglectful than that of a dozen other industrial towns which had no cholera cases at all. In 1853–4 as in 1848–9 the real cause of cholera remained

---

[1] Minutes, 7 December 1853.

[2] E. C. to ? , 28 September 1853.

[3] *Report of the Commissioners on the Causes of the Outbreak of Cholera in the Towns of Newcastle-upon-Tyne, Gateshead, and Tynemouth*; *P.P.*, 1854, vol xxxv, p. 131.

a mystery;[1] and the medical profession was no more agreed upon its treatment, the suggestions published in the Press including the use of ice, castor oil, laughing-gas, charcoal, and mustard poultices and hot mint tea.[2]

By November 1853 the outbreak on the Tyne had burned itself out. A few months later the disease appeared in the capital. But before the London epidemic reached its height, Chadwick and his colleagues had fallen from power. Not even the fear of cholera could drive out the hatred which by now surrounded the General Board of Health.

[1] Snow had put forward his theory of water transmission in 1849 in his pamphlet, *On the Mode of Communication of Cholera*, a second edition of which was published in 1854; but forty years later, as may be seen from the sceptical comments of Creighton in his *History of Epidemics in Britain* (1894), the theory was still fighting for general acceptance.

[2] *Times*, 15 August, 17 August, 25 August, 6 September, 13 October 1853.

CHAPTER XVII

THE FALL OF THE BOARD

"I HAVE now been engaged more than twenty-two years uninter-
mittently for ten or twelve hours a day, with little recess or holiday
except on the occasion of ill health in successive extraordinary
services," Chadwick told Palmerston, as the Board approached
the end of the term of office allowed by the 1848 Act.[1] He was
paying now the price of that unrelaxing labour. As he entered
upon the last half-year of his official career, his reserves of
strength, though not of spirit, were seriously lowered by sickness.
He had not completely shaken off the effects of a fever which he
had caught in the spring of the previous year, on one of his visits
of local inspection; and he was further weakened by dyspepsia,
brought on by irregular hours and habits, combined with his un-
resting mental exertion and anxiety. His medical adviser had
warned him that he must soon seek relief from the excessive
burden he was shouldering. But as yet Chadwick had no thought
that the coming struggle in Parliament would result in his being
thrust into a perpetual and unwilling retirement. The General
Board, he knew, would be in some jeopardy; there would be harsh
things said about himself; and *The Times*, the anti-centralisers,
the water companies and slum landlords, the bone-boilers and
all his other enemies, would take down their weapons for the
attack. But he rested his faith in a powerful and well-disposed
Home Secretary—and also, because he was a simple man, in the
merits of six years of valuable and conscientious labour. A few
months' rest; then two years more at Gwydyr House; and after
that he might pick up and unravel some other thread of the social
tangle, education, perhaps, or police, or factory regulation. With
some such programme in his mind, he faced with fair confidence
the debates which were to decide his future.

[1] E. C. to Palmerston, 31 May 1854.

358

It was Palmerston's intention to introduce a Bill to extend the Public Health Act for a further two years. In view of the weakness which had revealed itself in the past six years, however, the administrative machinery at the centre was to be changed. As he explained, on the Second Reading of his Public Health Act Amendment Bill, to all intents and purposes the Board was an independent body, not controlled by any department, nor represented by a responsible organ in Parliament. At present it was no more bound to obey the orders of the Home Secretary than was the Navy Board or the Victualling Department. He proposed therefore to make it a branch of the Home Office, giving the Secretary of State the power to appoint and remove its members and to issue orders and directions to them.[1] Thus, by putting the the Board under ministerial control he hoped to remove the ground for the charges of arbitrary and irresponsible conduct; and by bringing the department under the protective wing of the Home Secretary to give it effective means of defending itself in the Commons.

This arrangement, it became clear at once, would not satisfy the critics of the Board. Judging that the Home Secretary would exercise no real control over the Board and would hold no real responsibility for its actions, they demanded that the department should be reconstructed on the lines of the Poor Law Board, with a new Minister, a President of the Board of Health, at its head. It was a sound solution, pointing the way to a healthy constitutional development of the new department; and in this respect the critics were right, as Chadwick from the first had been wrong. But the debates of 1854 did not turn solely upon this point. In pursuing their object the advocates of a Ministry of Health poured undiscriminating abuse upon the men and measures of the General Board. Their victory would mean the end of the defective administrative structure set up in 1848; but it would also mean the expulsion of the three reformers of Gwydyr House and a general condemnation of their policy. Chadwick saw only too much reason to distrust a scheme the chief sponsor of which was Lord Seymour, behind whom were ranged the representatives of the manifold interests attacked by the Board. Was it to increase the efficiency of sanitary administration that the proposal was

[1] *Hansard*, vol. cxxxv, pp. 973-4, 31 July 1854.

made—or to call a halt to the activity of himself and his colleagues? As he remarked to Russell, the change at the Poor Law Board, which was pointed to as a favourable precedent, was thought to work well because no complaints were heard; but though there was somewhat more of quiet in the House, it was at the expense of progress in the office.[1]

It was a determined and brilliant attack which Lord Seymour launched in the Commons. Into two speeches, compact with ridicule and contempt, he contrived to compress all the criticisms which at one time or another had been levelled at the Board, garnishing his argument with personal details which gave it a convincing ring of authenticity. These speeches, delivered as they were with the authority of a former President of the Board, blasted their hopes, threw consternation amongst their friends, and swept the waverers into the division lobbies against the Bill. No stronger proof was needed of the want of someone to represent the views of the Board in Parliament than the way in which the ex-President misrepresented them almost without contradiction in these final debates.[2]

The first attack came on 6 July, on the Board's supply vote, a motion by Palmerston for £11,855 to defray their expenses for the next financial year (to 31 March 1855). Lord Seymour at once objected to the grant of money for the maintenance of a body whose actions, far from forwarding sanitary measures, had served only to make them unpopular, since under its rule they were brought in, not by the free will of the people, but by the despotic interference of the Central Board. Sir William Molesworth had quite properly refused to consider himself responsible for the proceedings of a Board of which he was only an individual member, whose opinion might be overruled by his colleagues. Seymour himself, when he was President, had sent a communication to the Board, after consulting with the other members of the Government, indicating the course he thought they should adopt; they had told him that his proposition was not seconded—"that the members of the Board knew nothing of what the Government might wish; they only knew that, at their Board, the proposal was not seconded, and it consequently fell to the ground." Was that the way to conduct public business? Were they to vote

[1] E. C. to Russell, 27 July 1854.   [2] See Appendix, p. 376.

money for a Board which thus set the Government at defiance? "The only way to bring these gentlemen to reason was just to stop their salaries." Seymour next turned his scorn upon the Inspectors and their local reports. He had himself visited one town just after such a report had been sent in, and after testing by personal examination the statements made in it, he did not hesitate to declare that a more exaggerated report he had never read. The Inspector invariably recommended that the town he had examined should be brought under the Board of Health; in return the Board stated that the Inspector, having devised a very beautiful system of drainage, had better be allowed to carry it out; and if the town did not adopt this advice and employ the Inspector, it encountered such hindrances and difficulties that it soon bitterly repented its decision. "The fact was, that the inspector brought in the Board, and then the Board brought in the inspector." After a dig at the Board's engineering theories ("utterly denied by the best engineers of the metropolis"), he described the report which they had published in their defence as "almost an indecent thing to have been sent out by a Government establishment," being full of conclusions "arrived at by the Board of Health, but denied by everybody else." He ended by remarking how complaints of the Poor Law administration had ceased once Chadwick had been removed.[1]

Seymour was heartily seconded by Sir Benjamin Hall, the member for Marylebone, who thought that the best thing the Government could do would be to give Chadwick and Southwood Smith their money and dismiss them. "The Chief Commissioners, in succession, had found it impracticable to control the mischievous vagaries and extravagances of these two persons, and the only remedy was to get rid of them altogether." And Chadwick in particular, who, after being removed from the Poor Law Commission for his "rules of atrocious stringency," had "concocted a pamphlet" on sanitary subjects, on the strength of which he had manoeuvred himself into power at the Board of Health. "He himself was quite at a loss to know what services this man had rendered to the community."[2]

It was now very plain that Palmerston was to have no easy passage for his Amendment Bill, which he introduced on 10 July.

[1] *Hansard*, vol. cxxxiv, pp. 1298–1300.   [2] Ibid., pp. 1301–7.

During the days that followed the opposition interests mobilised their strength, and, in the ignorance or indifference of the mass of the Commons, the critics increasingly dominated the debates. Almost to a man, Chadwick informed Russell, he knew the causes of the Board's unpopularity with "the minority called the house." That member, for example, who rose to denounce their proceedings as interference with self-government, was a factory owner, whose chimney poured forth soot on all about him.[1] "The lobby was crowded, with the water engineers at the head of whom was Hawksley, and with Parliamentary agents, and with parliamentary counsel canvassing against the measure," he told F. O. Ward on his return from the House on 18 July. "Only one petition was heard against the measure: on the other side we had to lament that there was none for." Ill-health unfitted Chadwick for the strain of combat. Weak as he was, however, he mustered his energies to repel the attack, pouring out hastily drafted notes of appeal to his Parliamentary acquaintances. Unfortunately the session was near its close, and few of his political friends were in town. There was Lord Lansdowne, for example, who might make an effective reply to the Poor Law cry which had been raised; but Lansdowne was off to Stoke Park, whence his testimony, if it came at all, must come too late.[2] Scarcely a man with political influence had paid attention to the subject, and there was no time now to coach them in even the elements of public health administration. Desperately Chadwick looked round for a spokesman in the Commons. He appealed to Sir George Pechell, the member for Brighton, to refute the charge that he had made the Poor Law unpopular and had been dismissed from that office in consequence, reminding Pechell that in the Andover debates of 1846 he had supported the vote of censure on the Commissioners.[3] The Board would be entitled to public support, he suggested to the Wolverhampton member, T. Thornely, if it had done nothing more than produce the reports which demonstrated to the medical authorities of the Continent the futility of quarantine with its obstructions to commerce which cost England alone upwards of two millions a year.[4] The bitter personal hostility he

[1] E. C., "Parliamentary Presidentship. Notes of a draught letter to Lord John Russell on the new Public Health Board arrangements," MS., n.d.
[2] Lansdowne to E. C., n.d.   [3] E. C. to Sir George Pechell, 12 July 1854.
[4] E. C. to T. Thornely, 17 July 1854.

had aroused, he reminded Hume, was due largely to the complete practical demonstration he had made of Hume's own proposals for reducing the expense of private bills.[1] To E. B. Lytton he wrote: "You have known me at intervals for a very long period, and whatsoever weaknesses I may have I trust you will believe I could not have acted in so foolish a manner as to set at defiance a Government, and prevent my chief from attending to perform the duties of his office and move illegal coercion or violence towards towns. But if you were to believe I really had done anything deserving of dismissal, I trust that you and your friends will not set the example of a condemnation by acclamation, that you will give us the benefit of the lowest criminals, and ask to have the offences distinctly stated, and proved, and to allow the accused to answer before a Committee if no other competent tribunal. . . . It is declared however that we are universally condemned: that on account of our proceedings the public and the house condemns us. Now the house is I really believe a few members and the public Mr. Walter of the Times, the views of whose engineer I could not promote."[2]

Save an occasional polite acknowledgment, Chadwick had little to show for these attempts to touch the public conscience of his correspondents. He relied too much on arguments in detail, which might convince a man on one point, or convict him of an error in fact, but could not convert him to a principle. While, with his passion for legal exactitude, he was worrying how he could tell members of Parliament what really happened at the Board of Health on that fateful 30 January 1851, they were concerned about such general questions as the limits of central control. There was Newdegate, for example, who thought it at best a sometimes necessary evil; it destroyed self-reliance, and prevented capable individuals from exercising in their localities that amount of independent authority which afforded the only inducement to persons of the middle classes to act upon principles more generous than those of mere self-interest. In short, centralisation meant a loss of public spirit; and so, Newdegate informed S. H. Gael, he found it impossible to speak in support of Mr. Chadwick, the arch-centraliser.[3]

[1] E. C. to J. Hume, 23 July 1854.   [2] E. C. to E. B. Lytton, n.d.
[3] N. Newdegate to S. H. Gael, 24 July 1854.

What particularly exasperated Chadwick was the charge that the Board had made themselves unpopular by their interference and tyranny—the Board, who had always been ready to assist the newly formed local authorities with all the technical skill and information at their command. It hardly showed want of confidence, he suggested to the member for Droylsden, when his constituents asked that Mr. Chadwick should go down and give them advice in person on their works.[1] He sent appeals to the more progressive Local Boards, to Woolwich, Hull, Penzance, York, Preston, and Lancaster, urging them to make known to their members and Lord Palmerston the friendly and helpful nature of their relations with the central Board.[2] He received a sheaf of testimonials in reply. "Where would our Sanitary affairs have been had you remained quiescent or willing to accommodate yourself to ignorance and prejudice?" asked the Rev. J. Clay of Preston indignantly; and he wrote a few days later to tell Palmerston his opinion that "by acting, to the best of our power, on the suggestions and advice of the General Board—we have—under Providence—hitherto escaped that terrible disease which has severely visited some Towns remarkable for their resistance to the recommendations of the General Board."[3] The letters were comforting, but they had little echo in the Commons, where more attention was paid to the member for Totnes or the member for Marylebone than to some small-town engineer or the obscure chairman of a provincial Board. There were upwards of a hundred members, Chadwick estimated, who knew that, so far as their own constituencies were concerned, the charges of coercion were false, yet said not a word to vindicate the General Board. Lancaster, Barnard Castle, Ormskirk, Penzance, Wakefield, Woolwich, wrote strongly to refute the accusation;[4] but Chadwick was hurt at the silence of most of the Local Boards. He heard later that

---

[1] E. C. to Charles Hindley, 9 July 1854.

[2] E. C. to William Dunn, 14 July 1854; Rev. Henry Brown, 20 July; E. H. Rodd, 21 July; George Leeman, 22 July.

[3] Rev. J. Clay to E. C., 12 July 1854; to Palmerston, 22 July 1854.

[4] William Dunn (Lancaster) to E. C., 13 July 1854; J. A. Kershaw (Ormskirk) to Lord ? (Palmerston), 20 July; Thomas Darke (Penzance) to E. C., 22 July; George Tanday (Wakefield) to E. C., 26 July 1854; George Brown (Barnard Castle) to E. C., 12 July 1854; Henry Brown (Woolwich) to E. C., 27 July 1854.

fourteen of them, and probably more, had spontaneously adopted resolutions and sent them to the Home Office.[1]

As the end of July approached, Palmerston faced the possibility that he might lose his Amendment Bill. One sacrifice might save the Board, he thought—Chadwick's head. When the suggestion reached Shaftesbury's ears he wrote at once to offer his resignation, telling Palmerston that he must be held equally responsible for the conduct of the Board.[2] With a majority of new members on the Board, suggested Shaftesbury, the hostility of the public might abate somewhat, and Palmerston might then be able to retain the services of Southwood Smith during the cholera epidemic. But the Doctor loyally followed his colleagues, being reluctant, as Chadwick told Russell, to act with persons whose views and habits were unknown to him.[3] When Palmerston rose, therefore, on the Second Reading of his Amendment Bill on 31 July, he held in his hands the resignations of all three members of the Board. Whether or not they took effect would depend upon the outcome of the debate.

Lord Seymour now delivered his second and more damaging attack.[4] He dismissed in slighting terms the Board's work over the past six years. For London they had recommended "such a supply of water as could be scraped out of the sand of the Surrey hills"; the Metropolitan Commission of Sewers had resigned in a body rather than adopt Chadwick's tubular drains; the Board's reports, printed by the thousand, merely embodied the preconceived views of three or four prejudiced men. The Metropolitan Interments Act aroused his particular contempt. They had spent eighteen months and much money in collecting information, "or what purported to be information," on the interments question, the upshot of which was that no one was to die but the Board were empowered to pounce upon the body. "All the ordinary feelings of mankind were to be set aside, all the tender emotions of relations to be trampled upon, all the decency of mourning, all the sanctity of grief to be superseded, in order that the Board of Health might get their funeral fee." That the Act had passed was largely owing to the popularity of Sir George Grey, who had

[1] E. C. to F. O. Ward, 18 July 1855.
[2] Shaftesbury to Palmerston, 27 July 1854.
[3] E. C. to Russell, 29 July 1854.   [4] *Hansard*, vol. cxxxv, pp. 980–94.

asked him personally to see that it should come into operation without delay. At much personal inconvenience, therefore, he had remained in town that autumn, and had taken no vacation whatever, apart from a few days at a time, and these were spent in visiting places to which the Act was to be applied. A fortnight after Dr. Smith's appointment, he called on the Board. "He asked them, 'Well, gentlemen, have you got into order? and if so, what are you going to do? Have you made up your minds as to what shall be your first step?' 'Oh, yes,' said these gentlemen, 'we have made up our minds what we shall do.' 'What is that?' 'Well, we're going to Paris' . . . and the Board accordingly went to Paris, taking their secretary with them to write their letters and pay their bills." On their return he had objected to the employment of Paxton and Dr. Braun, and had felt his objection justified when the Exchequer had remonstrated with the Board for entering upon expensive arrangements without Treasury sanction. He had not attended all the meetings of his colleagues, who were in the habit of holding Boards every day some three or four minutes in duration. But he had gone to Gwydyr House on 30 January 1851 to tell them what steps the Treasury thought they should take to carry out the Interments Act. The Board read him a seven-page letter, in which they argued the point with the Treasury; and they then told him that his proposal was not seconded. True, Lord Shaftesbury had since denied that this was what had occurred; but "Lord Shaftesbury, speaking upon his honour, spoke, it was to be remembered, upon the information of the secretary—not having been himself present on the occasion—whereas he (Lord Seymour), having been present, spoke from his own recollection." After this episode he had stayed away, having "found by experience that it was to no purpose that he attended a Board where he was systematically overborne, while he could occupy his time to really useful public purposes in his own office."

Turning next to the Board's conduct in the localities, he asserted that it was against the principles of the constitution for a petition from one-tenth of the ratepayers of a district to bind the rest. Moreover, opponents in the locality had no power to test the genuineness of the signatures, and, in fact, the Inspectors refused to allow the inhabitants to see the petition. "The jobbing of the

Board of Health presented an amount of dirt which must be very startling to the clean party in question. . . . The whole thing was perfectly monstrous. Some engineer whom no one else would employ, or some medical man whom nobody would consult, would be anxious to have the Health of Towns Act applied to his district; he would then get a few signatures, and would send up his impartial suggestion that a particular place could not get on without the interposition of the Board; the Board, jumping at the suggestion, would forthwith send down one of its elect inspectors, equally craving employment, who would, on arrival at the luckless place of his destination, place himself in communication with the doctor or engineering adviser, who being the person who had communicated with the Board, would thus have acquired a *locus standi*; the united pair would then consult with the surveyor of the local board, whose opinion, seeing that he could only be removed by the central Board, would be sure to take only one direction, and, by this combination of powers, the principle of self-government was utterly violated under the constitution of the Board."

It is interesting to speculate on the working of Seymour's mind when he made these assertions, each with its small portion of fact economically admixed with a large amount of obliquity and suppression. In his limitations and assumptions Seymour is a type of a large and influential class, who, then and since, opposed the progress of social reform. The wildness of his accusations and the demonstrable inaccuracy of many of his statements lay him open to the gravest charges; but to explain his performance there is no need to postulate any deliberate falsehood, any planned and cold-blooded murder of the truth. It was not perhaps that he consciously cut and selected facts to suit his purposes, but rather that the facts were bent and patterned by the pull of a strong mind set in decided courses. The whole tenor of his thought was opposed to the Board of Health and what it stood for. A long process of conditioning by personal contacts in family and political relations had bred in him an aversion—so far removed from the sphere of reason that it might be termed instinctive—to the idea of interference with the business of the governing classes, whether that business was in the form of commercial undertaking or of local and central administration. He hated State intervention, "the interfering with everything and everybody," as he called it, and at Gwydyr House he found himself associated with men who looked on such intervention as a duty. It was intervention, moreover, in matters whose importance he lacked the knowledge and the sympathy to appreciate in full. The technicalities of sanitation, the subject matter of sanitary investigation, were foreign to him; and, because foreign, diverting. He could scarcely repress his derision at the thought of a Board solemnly discussing the dimensions of earthenware sewer pipes or the construction of Reception Houses for the corpses of the poor. And, finally, he detested the members of the Board. They were enthusiasts. They stuck out for principles when they could have had an easier time by listening to the Treasury. Like one of the worldly-wise at a revivalist meeting, he was bored by their lecturing, resentful of their assumption of moral superiority, uneasy in the presence of their earnestness.

There was no one in the Commons sufficiently informed and sufficiently convinced to stand up to Seymour's onslaught. Many who heard him must have believed, like historians of a later generation, that he "spoke with authority because he had at one time been an ex-officio member of the Board."[1] Sir William Molesworth, the Board's official spokesman, did not open his mouth in their defence; and, if he had been willing, he knew nothing about the subject. When Shaftesbury rose to make his reply in the Lords, it was many hours later, after he had had time to see the reports in *The Times*. After Seymour's first attack he pointed out that Seymour had put in no more than seven appearances altogether at Gwydyr House, and that it was on the sixth of these that he made his proposition about metropolitan interments;[2] the impression given by Seymour that he had been driven away by the constant opposition of Chadwick and Southwood Smith was thus shown to rest on the slenderest foundation. The Lords gave him a sympathetic hearing when, after Seymour's second speech, he declared that there was hardly an assertion in it which might not be met by as flat a contradiction;[3] but it had little effect on the Commons when he quoted the letter in which Seymour had stated that he would be unable to attend the Board

[1] J. L. and B. Hammond, *Lord Shaftesbury*, p. 166.
[2] *Hansard*, vol. cxxxv, pp. 236–8, 14 July 1854.   [3] See Appendix.

without neglecting his duties at the Woods and Forests; or when
he showed that the average attendances at the Board were not
three or four minutes, but five, six, or seven hours, even ten
during the cholera, and that his hard-pressed colleagues were
obliged to take some of their papers home at night.[1]

The crucial debate of 31 July, therefore, was a victory for
Lord Seymour. A storm of hate and indignation burst over
Chadwick's head. Before the fury of that general condemnation
even his friends hesitated or were silent. His great public services
were forgotten in an unreasoning gesture of revulsion. He was
the bureaucrat and centraliser, who had sought to confine the
liberties of the individual within the strait-jacket of a system; the
ambitious careerist, perpetually intriguing for greater power and
crushing without pity all who opposed his will. The legend was
now complete.[2] And though his friends might comfort him with
the reminder that Wellington had become a national hero after
being pelted in the street,[3] so long as Chadwick lived his character
and ideas would never be entirely freed from the taint of that
suspicion.[4]

---

[1] *Hansard*, vol. cxxxv, pp. 1079–83, 1 August 1854.

[2] The classic version is that given in the anonymous *Engineers and Officials*,
1856:
"In a word, Mr. Edwin Chadwick suggested the original inquiries; settled
the plan of operations; marshalled, selected, and digested evidence; grew from
secretary into a commissioner; issued rules, regulations, and maxims; chose his
colleagues, his servants, and his witnesses, and in his official capacity, under
the mantle of the Board, tried, condemned, and sentenced his opponents; and
recommended the Board, that is to say, himself, for further powers, privileges,
and honours. Never has the expedient of reiteration been so vigorously and
unscrupulously used, page after page, volume after volume, pamphlet after
pamphlet, speech after speech; the same reckless assertions are supported by
the same fallacious evidence, selected and cooked for the occasion, and the
same certain conclusions are arrived at, that is to say, that every city, town,
and village may obtain universal health and a large income from the sale of
sewerage on one sole condition—unquestioning, blind, passive obedience to the
ukase, decree, bull, or proclamation of the autocrat, pope, grand lama of
sanitary reform, Edwin Chadwick, lawyer and commissioner. . . . He was
determined that the British world should be clean, and live a century, but on
one condition only—that they consented to purchase the real patent Chadwickian soap, the Chadwickian officially-gathered soft water, and the true
impermeable telescopic earthenware pipe, and when they did die, were
interred by his official undertakers in the Chadwickian necropolis."

[3] William Stuart to E. C., 19 August 1854.

[4] When, two years later, a public subscription was being raised for
Southwood Smith, the originators (Dr. Waller Lewis and R. D. Grainger)

On the following day Sir William Molesworth introduced a Public Health Bill, to constitute a new health department on the same lines as the Poor Law Board, comprising a President with a secretary and under-secretary. Edwin Chadwick was to be pensioned off with £1,000 a year.[1] In his letter of resignation to Palmerston, Shaftesbury had voiced with some bitterness his regret that their six years of intense labour, "productive, as will, hereafter, be seen, of great benefit to the country," had been rewarded with so much suspicion and calumny.[2] Chadwick was even more bitter. To endure the insults of the House of Commons was hard enough; they were made no more bearable by the thought of facing the future with an income cut by one-third—when if he had held an office abolished on account of its inutility he would have retired, like the Masters in Chancery, on a full salary. But the blow fell heaviest on the unoffending and uncomplaining Southwood Smith, now sixty-six years of age, who, "without fault proved and indeed after extraordinary and successful labour is dismissed a ruined man without any compensation whatsoever."[3]

It would be some comfort if the Board fell into good hands. Lyon Playfair would be a great acquisition, Chadwick suggested, and the Inspectors would welcome him as secretary or chief executive officer.[4] But the Government had decided that the capitulation was to be complete, and that to silence the critics they must be taken into partnership. Chadwick read with horror the announcement that the President was to be Sir Benjamin Hall, the voice of the Marylebone vestry, and the secretary Tom Taylor, the man who wrote lampoons for *Punch* when he should have been drafting bye-laws. It was "a huge imposture"—a President engaged ten hours a day in Parliament, occupied with the calls of society and his constituency, entirely ignorant of the business and with little time or opportunity to remedy his ignorance; he

---

decided to keep Chadwick's name off the Committee lest it "ruin the whole proceedings." "Moreover," Chadwick told Sir John Easthope (n.d. 1856), "they were of opinion that it was essential to the measure that it should be kept clear of the General Board of Health."

[1] *Hansard*, vol. cxxxv, pp. 1138–42, 1 August 1854.
[2] Shaftesbury to Palmerston, 27 July 1854.
[3] E. C. to ? , 7 August 1854. He was later awarded a pension of £300.
[4] E. C. to ? (Palmerston or Russell), 4 August 1854.

would inevitably be the "mere puppet of an intriguing secretary," whose knowledge was shallow and whose interests lay outside the department. For a time Chadwick thought wildly of a dramatic intervention in the forthcoming election contest in Marylebone, and even roughed out an address to the ratepayers, asking them to consider the strictures passed by the Lords on Hall's speech, and then go to the polls and give their votes as they would give a verdict before the country. He was denied this pleasure of seeing the usurper humbled by the judgment of the Marylebone voters, but fate dealt him satisfaction of a different sort. Very shortly after his appointment, as he watched the machinery Chadwick had designed and the men Chadwick had trained going to work in the cholera epidemic, Hall was confiding to one of the Inspectors that he was astonished to find how much there was to be done, and how much his derided predecessors had done; no three men, he observed, could possibly have worked harder.[1] "So far as I can judge," Dr. Sutherland told Chadwick, "the President seems quite disposed to make himself completely master of the sanitary subject, to avail himself of every means of information, and to take his place in the House at the beginning of next session, as a Reformer, resting his position on his own knowledge and observation, and ready to face any opponents who may appear. I may state in confidence, that both Mr. Austin and I are rather afraid of his going too fast, and raising the interests against him. It has indeed happened with him, as with every other person, who has taken any pains in the way of enquiry, that he is astonished at the magnitude of the evils with which he has to contend, while his sympathies appear to be all engaged in their removal."[2] And presently the "London Engineering Clique" was showing itself as dissatisfied with the new President as with the old Commissioners.[3]

Shaftesbury had found a fit text for the Board and their officers when they assembled for their parting dinner, in the shadow of public opprobrium and still smarting from the Parliamentary boot. "We are troubled on every side yet not distressed; we are

[1] E. C. to F. O. Ward, 26 April 1855.
[2] J. Sutherland to E. C., 11 September 1854.
[3] J. Sutherland to E. C., 18 October 1854.

perplexed but not in despair, persecuted but not forsaken, cast down but not destroyed."

What thoughts passed through Chadwick's mind as he listened to Shaftesbury at that final banquet? Darkened with the bitterness of those last few weeks, they must yet have contained much to console and satisfy. A rest and a thousand a year had never been better earned. In the twenty-two years since Nassau Senior had introduced him into the public service, he had been engaged continuously in the diagnosis of social disease and the prescription of legislative remedies. He had been a major influence on three Royal Commissions of the first importance, and produced a series. of State papers unequalled for the clarity and force of the administrative intelligence they displayed. Since its beginning he had been the heart and brain of the public health movement. His foresight had equipped the Registrar-General with authority to draw up the national balance sheet of sickness and death. From the Poor Law office he had guided the nation-wide inquest which paved the way for legislation. He had been the first to see as a whole the problems of municipal engineering, the interdependence of drainage, water supply, and sewage disposal. By the impact of his reports and the personal influence he had exerted on politicians and the leaders of outside opinion, he had in ten years educated the law-making classes to appreciate the issues at stake, and forced the first Public Health Act on the statute book. From Gwydyr House, with an inadequate Act, he had done what he could; and it is just to say that in his single-minded pursuit of the public welfare, and the fertility of his projects for social betterment, he had done more than any other man of his time would have had the courage, the ability, and the toughness to attempt.

Throughout these years the motive principle of his social philosophy was the "Sanitary Idea," the conviction that the wretchedness and ill-health laid bare by his investigations were preventable; while the characteristic element in his administrative theories was the assertion that this could be done by Government, the perception that the organised power of the State was a tool which could be sharpened and applied to the shaping of the social environment. To the men of his day his exposition of distasteful facts, with a brutal insensitiveness to the feelings of the respectable interests concerned, was like surgery without anæsthetics. And the remedies he prescribed—the inspection of factories and mines, the regulation of building, the control of noxious trades, the recognition of employers' liability for workmen's accidents, the public ownership of railways and water supplies, the extension of Whitehall's authority into the localities—together constituted a confining system of rules and restraints which freedom-loving capitalists and Corporations regarded with horror, and for which they could find no greater condemnation than to trace it back to its un-English origins. On these questions the balance of opinion has radically shifted, and it has shifted in favour of Chadwick. A generation accustomed to Government intervention on a scale he never dreamed of will find little to shock in his centralising theories and will ascribe the outcry against the General Board of Health less to the violence of a doctrinaire department than to the restiveness of local authorities under an unfamiliar curb. In an age of municipalised gas and water and transport, of nationalised railways and coal-mines, of Ministries of Health, Labour, and National Insurance, of public Boards administering services as diverse as broadcasting and airways, the voices of the champions of *laissez faire* and private enterprise speak with diminished assurance and authority. It has been Chadwick's misfortune, however, that he has continued to be seen through the eyes of hostile contemporaries and judged by their standards. His reputation would rank higher if later historians had examined their witnesses and allies more closely, and asked whether in fact a George Lewis or a Lord Seymour stood for a more enlightened and humanitarian administration. Chadwick has been further unfortunate in that, of all his work, it is the Poor Law which is best remembered and which his name first calls to mind. It is not generally realised, first, that the maimed and partial measure of 1834 embodied only part of the broader schemes of preventive administration he had begun to plan; and secondly, that his years as a subordinate at Somerset House formed a less valuable episode in his career than his years as the controlling mind of the General Board of Health. For this reason, perhaps, he arouses in the authors of the "Minority Report on the Poor Law" of 1909 an antagonism one would not expect from the authors of the "London Programme" of 1892.

He lived thirty-six years after his retirement, busy, useful years, in which he played a prominent part in spreading the gospel of sanitary and administrative reform. We catch characteristic glimpses of him from time to time—quietly informing the Aberdeen Town Council that the normal death rate of their city was 14 not 24 per thousand; instructing Louis Napoleon in the virtues of sewer manure, and telling Bismarck how to spend the millions of the French indemnity by improving the towns of Germany; giving evidence to the Newcastle Commission on the effects of physical training in the half-time schools; contesting without success the University of London seat and three or four others; playing with new-fangled notions, overhead railways, the American writing machine, tricycles for policemen, ventilation towers for the great towns. He talked and wrote without rest, addressing the British Association on the benefits of competitive examinations, and the Social Science Association on the military lessons of 1870, and discussing at the soirées of the Society of Arts anything from irrigation in India to the best methods of constructing a school; turning out correspondence and pamphlets inexhaustibly, letters to *The Times* to urge an omnibus monopoly for the metropolis, memoranda to Mr. Gladstone on the advantages of a uniform cheap telegraph service, papers for Florence Nightingale on the health of the army in India. And near the end, when he was very old and forgotten, and his political friends were all dead or as forgotten as himself, we find him trying to persuade Lord Salisbury to get him a peerage. The Chairman of the Metropolitan Board of Works went to the Lords, he complained, but there was no official recognition of the services of the greatest of the sanitary reformers. Not till a few months before his death was he granted his delayed and disproportionate honour. "Had he killed in battle as many as he saved by sanitation, he would have had equestrian statues by the dozen put up to his memory."[1]

We leave him as the writer of *The Times* obituary remembered him at the Athenæum, his "benevolent and leonine face, wrinkled with the lines of thought, and surmounted by the black skull cap" —his features wearing "an expression of severe complacency."[2] And why should he not be complacent? His countrymen had

[1] *Daily News*, 7 July 1890.   [2] *Times*, 7 July 1890.

good reason to thank him. He had played the chief part in founding a new and beneficent department of Government. More than any other individual he had been responsible for civilising the life of the great towns. Owing nothing to wealth or birth, by sheer indefatigable industry and ability he fought his way to a unique place in British administration. He did not enter a field of Government activity where he did not introduce some fertile idea or strengthen, with observation and experience, some proposition already advanced. It is true that while he was in Whitehall everything he touched seemed to crumble in his strong, clumsy hands into inertia and frustration and failure. In part that was due to his personal defects. To the end he remained an immense, tireless dynamo which it was difficult to harness. But his failures were the result less of his faults than his virtues—the courage that did not fear to challenge accepted principles, and the devotion to public duty which would not compromise with overmighty interests. It was the recompense for many disappointments, and the reward for his unquenchable optimism, that he should live to see the current of the age turn with him, and his enemies at the last confounded.

APPENDIX

LORD SEYMOUR'S SPEECHES, 6 JULY AND 31 JULY 1854
(pp. 360–1, 365–7 above)

CHADWICK drew up a number of memoranda rebutting Seymour's allegations point by point. A few examples will serve to illustrate Seymour's standards of controversy.

Seymour: "He had himself visited a town immediately after a Report of that kind [*sc.* a local report by an Engineering Inspector] had been sent in, and having taken the Report in his hand and tested by personal examination the statements which were made in it, he had no hesitation in declaring that a more exaggerated Report he had never read."[1]

Chadwick: "On this representation it is proper to state that Lord Seymour never communicated anything of the kind in his place at the Board, to enable them to make inquiry into the facts, or to enable the particular inspector to adduce anything he may have to shew in his justification. The Board submit that it is a grievous abuse after an opportunity has been possessed of making them where they might have been properly investigated to make such statements where the parties accused have no power of answering. Although reports upon examinations of towns are locally published; and subjected generally to local scrutiny and opposition they are unaware of any instance, where before select committees of the House or otherwise any such charge as that made by Lord Seymour has been substantiated."

Seymour: "All the ordinary feelings of mankind were to be set aside, all the tender emotions of relations to be trampled upon, all the decency of mourning, all the sanctity of grief to be superseded, in order that the Board of Health might get their funeral fee."[2]

[1] *Hansard*, vol. cxxxiv, p. 1299, 6 July 1854.
[2] Ibid., vol. cxxxv, p. 982, 31 July 1854.

Chadwick: "Now if ever there was an official investigation in which the ordinary feelings of mankind previously overlooked the decency of mourning and the sanctity of grief were considered, it will be acknowledged on the examination of the reports on the subject by impartial persons to be the Metropolitan scheme of extramural sepulture.

"A great living writer speaks of that report emphatically as an honour to humanity. The measure by which Lord Seymour superseded it was one which after the feelings of mankind and the peculiar sufferings of the poor had been displayed and provided for sets them aside scornfully and tramples upon them. . . ."

Seymour: Sir George Grey had requested him to put the Interments Act into operation without delay; he had therefore remained in town that autumn to carry out his right honourable Friend's wishes.[1]

Chadwick: "Now the whole of this is at variance with the truth. He declared at the first and at all times that he could not attend; he moreover avowed to the Members of the Board that his rule was never to act until he was obliged, and then to do as little as he could. He acted in accordance with this declaration, and not in accordance with his promise to Sir George Grey to expedite the matter; he did not attend the deliberations of the Board, he made no offer to take part in them, though it was his right as well as his duty to do so."

Seymour: "After Dr. Smith had been a fortnight in office, he went to the Board to hear what they proposed and were prepared to do. He asked them, 'Well, gentlemen, have you got into order? and if so, what are you going to do? Have you made up your minds as to what shall be your first step?' 'Oh, yes,' said these gentlemen, 'we have made up our minds what we shall do.' 'What is that?' 'Well, we're going to Paris' . . . and the Board accordingly went to Paris, taking their secretary with them to write their letters and pay their bills."[2]

Chadwick: "It was not the first step of the Board, and he was never told that it was the first step. The first steps were taken immediately the Royal assent was given, and they are stated in

[1] *Hansard*, vol. cxxxv, p. 985.   [2] Ibid., p. 986.

page 1 of the printed Minutes laid before Parliament. Whilst the large measures therein recited, and in other Minutes from the 5th of August to the 4th of September were in progress, it was requisite to make other preparations for the work in hand.

". . . To collect information upon which to lay down a plan in outline for legislation is one thing; to get information to fill up the plan in detail for subsequent practical execution is another and even more important step. . . . The Board considered it necessary that they as well as their chief officers, who were charged with the executive measures should see with their own eyes the practical working of a change of system which had been in operation for a number of years in the largest capital in Europe, and they had moreover important questions to determine which they considered might be the most economically determined on the spot. . . ."

Seymour: He had objected to the employment of Paxton and Dr. Braun.[1]

Chadwick: The Board had thought of seeking Paxton's advice on the vegetation and layout of their National Cemetery; and had consulted Dr. Braun in order to avoid those violations of taste in monumental decoration which made some burial grounds 'mere stone quarries.' "This recourse to the highest available talent is sneered at by Lord Seymour who speaks as if the subject in hand were common churchyards, as if moreover in his view they required no special care."

Seymour: "He had attended the Board on 30 January 1851, and proposed that they should adopt the Treasury's plan for bringing the Interments Act into operation. The Board resisted his suggestion and told him that his proposal was not seconded."[2]

Chadwick: "This statement is so couched as to imply a misrepresentation to the house; namely, that the Board were about to proceed with the execution of a new scheme new and unauthorised by the Government, and unsanctioned by Parliament, whereas the grounds for their measure had been submitted with all the evidence to the Government and to the public. . . . In the Act provision was made for the purchase of the whole of the trading

[1] *Hansard,* vol. cxxxv, p. 986.   [2] Ibid., p. 987.

cemeteries. The duty which remained to be performed was to comply with the provisions of the statute. . . . The course which his Lordship thought fit to take whether at the instance of the Chancellor of the Exchequer or upon his own suggestion was against the known intent of the statute. On the grounds stated in the letter to the Treasury . . . the plan proposed by Lord Seymour was absurd in itself and on the consideration of those grounds was rejected by the Treasury who after several months of time [and] money had been lost and evil had been protracted by Lord Seymour's opposition agreed to the Board proceeding with the measure according to their original report. . . ."

Seymour: "Lord Shaftesbury, speaking upon his honour, spoke, it was to be remembered, upon the information of the secretary— not having been himself present on the occasion—whereas he [Lord Seymour] having been present, spoke from his own recollection."[1]

Chadwick: "We declare most solemnly that we were present at a Board held on the 30th of January 1851 the day on which it is recorded in the Minutes that Lord Seymour attended and made a motion that was not seconded, and we further declare that Lord Shaftesbury was present and made the proposition which was adopted. On our remembrance being called early to Lord Seymour's allegation, that he had been *told* that his motion had not been seconded, we declare that he was not so told by us or by Lord Shaftesbury in our presence on that occasion, nor do we believe that he was so told on any other occasion whatsoever.

"On no occasion did it happen to Mr. Chadwick or Dr. Southwood Smith to move to set aside any propositions made by Lord Seymour. They on all occasions endeavoured to treat him with the respect due to his office and position, whilst they had to pass over gratuitously offensive behaviour on his part towards themselves which in one instance Lord Shaftesbury considered ought not to be passed over, and made it the subject of a remonstrant correspondence and resolution."

[1] Ibid., p. 987.

BIBLIOGRAPHY

A. MANUSCRIPT SOURCES

(1) THE CHADWICK MANUSCRIPTS

Chadwick kept copies or rough drafts of most of his papers, and these are now deposited in the library of University College, London. Besides letters, memoranda, and drafts of speeches, the collection includes most of his pamphlets and proof sheets of many of the articles he contributed to newspapers and various sanitary and administrative journals.

The papers contain very little material bearing on his early career; there is practically nothing, for example, about his relations with Bentham. From the period of the Factory Commission onwards, however, the serious gaps are few, and the material relating to the sanitary movement and the General Board of Health is particularly full and valuable.

Unless otherwise indicated, all letters and papers quoted in this book are from the collection at University College. The original spelling and punctuation have been preserved.

(2) AT THE PUBLIC RECORD OFFICE

The Ministry of Health papers deposited at the P.R.O. contain:

(a) Minute Books of the Poor Law Commission (M.H.1), 35 vols., from August 1834 to July 1842.

(b) Rough Minute Books (M.H.2), 37 vols., from August 1834 to June 1847.
   Appendices to Minutes (M.H.3), 3 vols., from 1835 to 1846.
   Extracts from Minutes (M.H.4), 2 vols., from July 1839 to December 1841.

(c) Minutes of Proceedings of the Commissioners for Inquiring into the State of Large Towns (M.H.7), 1 vol., 1843 to 1845.

(d) Minute Books of the General Board of Health (M.H.5), 12 vols., from 22 November 1848 to 21 February 1856.
   Rough Minute Books (M.H.6), 20 vols., from 26 September 1848 to 3 March 1858.

The Minutes of the Poor Law Commission were used by the Webbs. For the defects of these Minutes, see Chadwick's comments in his

380

evidence to the Select Committee on District Asylums (*P.P.*, 1846, vol. vii, pp. 86–8, 364–75). There seems to be room for a re-examination of these records, with the assistance of the material in the Chadwick MSS., which brings out and illustrates the issues underlying the colourless entries in the Minute Books.

(3) AT COUNTY HALL, WESTMINSTER.

The Record Room at County Hall (Room B.21) holds all the minutes and other papers of the several district Commissions of Sewers, and of the Metropolitan Commission which replaced them in December 1847. The following were found particularly useful:

(*a*) "Metropolitan Commission of Sewers. Orders of Court" (i.e. Minutes), vol i, 6 December 1847 to 4 January 1849. Printed. Vol. ii, 10 January 1849 to 4 October 1849. Manuscript. Thirty-one vols. altogether, to 31 December 1855.

(*b*) "M.C.S. Minutes of the General Purposes Committee," vols. i–v, from 9 December 1847 to 18 December 1849. Twenty-nine vols. altogether, to 27 November 1855.

(*c*) The correspondence, petitions, MS. reports, etc., relating to (*a*) and (*b*) are to be found in:
"Original Papers. Court and General Purposes Committee," vols. i–v, from December 1847 to 4 January 1849. The series then continues as "M.C.S. Court Papers," vols vi–lxvii, from 10 January 1849 to 31 December 1855.

(*d*) Proceedings of Committees:
"M.C.S. Trial Works Committee. Minutes and Report Book," 1 vol., from 6 March 1849 to 8 October 1849.
"M.C.S. Works Committee. Trial Works Committee. Sewage Manure Committee. Original Papers," 2 vols., from 22 January 1849 to 8 October 1849.
"Metropolitan Sewers. Works Committee. Minutes," 1 vol., from 22 January 1849 to 4 June 1849.
"Ordnance Survey Committee. Minute and Report Book," 1 vol., from 21 March 1849 to 1 August 1849.
"Metropolitan Sewers. Finance Committee. Minutes," 1 vol., from 29 January 1849 to 9 October 1849.
"Minute and Report Book. Bye-laws Committee," 1 vol., from 9 February 1849 to 2 October 1849.
"M.C.S. General Committee. Special Committee Tooting. Bye-laws Committee. Sewage Manure Committee. Ordnance Survey Committee. Original Papers," 1 vol., from January 1849 to July 1849.

"Metropolitan Sewers. Sub-Committee on Disposal of Refuse, 13 February to 8 March 1849. Sewage Manure Committee, 19 March to 8 October 1849," 1 vol.

(e) Printed papers, reports of surveyors, etc., are contained in:
"Metropolitan Commission of Sewers. Papers ordered to be printed, 1848–49," 1 vol.
"M.C.S. Reports, etc., 1849," 2 vols.

(4) MISCELLANEOUS

There are a few letters in the Bentham Manuscripts at University College, London, and in the following collections at the British Museum: Correspondence and papers of the family of Bentham; Letters to Francis Place; Macvey Napier Papers; Correspondence of C. Babbage; Liverpool Papers; Original Letters to Charles Griffin; Non-scientific Correspondence of Sir Richard Owen; Miscellaneous Papers; Peel Papers. Many of these are duplicated in the Chadwick Manuscripts.

At the National Library of Wales:
The Papers of Nassau Senior.

B. A SELECTION OF THE MORE IMPORTANT PAMPHLETS, ARTICLES AND SPEECHES BY EDWIN CHADWICK

The following list should be regarded as representative rather than exhaustive, though it probably contains the most valuable of Chadwick's writings. Many others are to be found in the transactions of such bodies as the British Association, the Association for the Promotion of Social Science, the Statistical Society, the Society of Arts, and the Sanitary Institute of Great Britain.

"Life Assurances," *Westminster Review*, vol. ix, pp. 384–421, February 1828. Reprinted, with additional notes, Charles Knight, London, 1836.

"Preventive Police," *London Review*, vol. i, pp. 252–308, 1830.

"Centralization. Public Charities in France," *London Review*, vol. i, pp. 536–65, 1830.

"Real Incendiaries and Promoters of Crime," *Examiner*, 20 February 1831, pp. 114–16.

"Taxes on Knowledge," *Westminster Review*, vol. xv, pp. 238–67, July 1831.

"On the Principles and Progress of the Poor Law Amendment Act," *Edinburgh Review*, vol. lxiii, pp. 487–537, July 1836. Reprinted 1837.

"On the best modes of representing accurately, by statistical returns, the duration of life, and the pressure and progress of the causes of mortality amongst different classes of the community, and amongst the populations of different districts and countries," *Journal of Statistical Society*, vol. vii, pp. 1–40, April 1844.

"Papers (by John Roberton, Robert Rawlinson and Edwin Chadwick) read before the Statistical Society of Manchester on the demoralisation and injuries occasioned by the want of proper regulations of labourers engaged in the construction and working of railways, etc.," ed. E.C. Charles Knight, London 1846.

"Health of Towns. Report of the speeches of Edwin Chadwick, Esq., Dr. Southwood Smith . . . and others at a meeting . . . to promote a subscription in behalf of the widow and children of Dr. J. R. Lynch," Chapman, Elcoate and Co., London, 1847.

"Sewer Manure," Report to Metropolitan Sewers Commission, 1849.

"A Letter to the Right Hon. Viscount Palmerston, etc., on the improvement of the sanitary condition of the army at home and in the field," Eyre and Spottiswoode, 1855.

"On improvements in machinery and in manufacturing processes, as affecting the condition of the labourer," address to Philanthropic Congress at Brussels, *Journal of Society of Arts*, vol. iv, pp. 803–7, 14 November 1856.

"Address to the electors of Southampton," 1857.

"The Economical, Social, Educational and Political Importance of Open Competitive Examinations for admission to the public service," to British Association, 1857, *Journal of Statistical Society*, vol. xxi, pp. 18–51, 1858.

"On the application of sanitary science to the protection of the Indian Army," *Transactions of National Association for the Promotion of Social Science*, 1858, pp. 487–504.

"The progress of the principle of competitive examination for admission into the public service," to British Association, 1858, *Journal of Statistical Society*, vol. xxii, pp. 44–75, 1859.

"Results of different principles of legislation and administration in Europe; of competition for the field, as compared with competition within the field of service," *Journal of Statistical Society*, vol. xxii, pp. 381–420, 1859.

"The chief methods of preparation for legislation especially as applicable to the reform of Parliament," to Society for Promoting the Amendment of the Law, Charles Knight, 1859. Republished in *Fraser's Magazine*, vol. lxxv, pp. 673–90, May 1867.

"On the Physiological as well as Psychological Limits to mental labour," *Transactions of British Association*, 1860.

"Public Health," *Transactions of Social Science Association*, 1860, pp. 574–606.

"Post Office Savings Banks," *Journal of Statistical Society*, vol. xxiv, pp. 519–22, 1861.

"The subject matters and methods of competitive examinations for the public service," to British Association, 1862, *Journal of Statistical Society*, vol. xxvi, pp. 72–7, 1863.

"The comparative results of the chief principles of the Poor Law administration in England and Ireland, as compared with that of Scotland," *Transactions of Social Science Association*, 1863, pp. 712–25.

"The present state of economy and trade," *Transactions of Social Science Association*, 1864, pp. 69–105.

"The loss of life and property by shipwrecks," *Transactions of Social Science Association*, 1865, pp. 77–101.

"The Economic Principles of a reform of the legislation and administration for the conveyance of passengers and goods on railways," Longmans, London, 1865.

"The Government Purchase of Railways," *Journal of Society of Arts*, vol. xiv, pp. 198–207, 9 February 1866.

"What action, if any, ought the Government to take with regard to railways?" *Transactions of Social Science Association*, 1867, pp. 593–605.

"University of London Election: Address to members of Convocation. With a letter from J. S. Mill," 1867.

"On Standing Armies," London, 1868.

"National Elementary Education. An Address," 1868.

"Les Unions Ouvrières en Angleterre au point de vue criminelle," Paris, 1868.

"The election for the Kilmarnock Burghs. Statement in relation thereto," 1868.

"Movement for International Economy of Military Expenditure," *Journal of Statistical Society*, vol. xxxii, pp. 456–8, 1869.

"The Military and Naval Force derivable from the introduction of military drill, and gymnastic exercises, as part of a national system of education in all elementary schools," Royal United Service Institution, May 1870.

"National Education. Letter thereon to the Lord President of the Council," London, 1870.

"The sanitary and economic advantages of smooth and impermeable street surfaces," *Transactions of Social Science Association*, 1871, pp. 489–501.

"The chief economical principles for consideration in relation to National as against Standing Armies, as displayed in the present war on the Continent," *Transactions of Social Science Association*, 1870, pp. 500–16.

"Memorandum on plan and estimate for drainage of Cawnpore," 1871.

"Lettre sur l'instruction obligatoire en France, adressée par E.C. à M. Mignet," Académie des Sciences Morales et Politiques, Orleans, 17 November 1871.

"On the jurisprudence of chargeability for sanitary works and for poor rates, police rates, and other branches of local administration," London, 1873.

"What are the best means of drawing together the interests of the United Kingdom, of India, and of the Colonies?" *Transactions of Social Science Association*, 1874, pp. 850–69.

"The system of the water supply of the metropolis," *Sanitary Record*, vol. iv, pp. 243–8, 8 April 1876.

"Address on Public Health," *Transactions of Social Science Association*, 1877, pp. 74–121. Reprinted, Spottiswoode and Co., London, 1877.

"Sanitary Condition of Aberdeen," *Transactions of Social Science Association*, 1877, pp. 582–91.

"The Sanitation of a County," *Sanitary Record*, vol. viii, pp. 257–62, 26 April 1878.

"National Water Supply," *Journal of Society of Arts*, vol. xxvi, pp. 767–774, 5 July 1878.

"The need of reforms in the administrative organisation of the sanitary service, with special reference to the appointment of Medical Officers of Health," to Sanitary Institute of Great Britain, 1878, *Sanitary Register*, October 1878, pp. 5–19.

"The Requisite Attributions of a Minister of Health," to International Congress of Hygiene, Paris, 4 August 1878, *Sanitarian*, vol. vii, pp. 59–67, February 1879.

"Address as President to International Association for the Promotion of Means for Improving the Supplies of Drinking Water to Populations," delivered at Amsterdam, September 1879, G. Norman and Son, London, 1879.

"On the Norma of sanitation in the school stages of life," *Transactions of Sanitary Institute*, vol. i, pp. 271–9, 1879.

"Letter from Mr. Edwin Chadwick, on the application of sanitary science to the reduction of infantile mortality among the wage classes in Croydon," *Transactions of Sanitary Institute*, vol. i, pp. 310–14, 1879.

"Circulation or stagnation: being the translation of a paper by F. O. Ward on the arterial and venous system for the sanitation of towns, with a statement of the progress made since then for its completion by Edwin Chadwick, C.B.," *Transactions of Sanitary Institute*, vol. ii, pp. 259–87, 1880.

"The Census of 1881," *Journal of Society of Arts*, vol. xxviii, pp. 717–23, 16 July 1880.

"Employers' Liability for accidents to workpeople," *Fraser's Magazine*, New Series vol. xxiii, pp. 680–92, May 1881.

"National Education. On the rise and progress of the half-time principle for mixed physical and mental training, as the foundation of a national system of education," Charles Knight and Co., London, 1881.

"Progress of sanitation: in preventive as compared with that in curative science," *Transactions of Social Science Association*, 1881, pp. 625–649.

"The Prevention of Epidemics," to Brighton Health Congress, December 1882, *Sanitary Record*, New Series vol. iii, pp. 270–7, 15 January 1882.

"Position of Sanitation in England," to Association of Public Sanitary Inspectors, June 1884, *Sanitary Engineering*, vol. viii, pp. 482–5, 13 June 1884.

"On the evils of disunity in central and local administration, especially with relation to the metropolis, and also on the new centralisation for the people, together with improvements in codification and in legislative procedure," Longmans, London, 1885.

"Commentaries on the report of the Royal Commission on Metropolitan Sewage Discharge, and on the combined and the separate systems of town drainage," Longmans, London, 1885.

"Sanitary review of the session," to Association of Public Sanitary Inspectors, May 1885, *Sanitary Engineering*, vol. x, pp. 296–8, 8 May 1885.

"Ventilation with air from superior couches in place of inferior couches," *Sanitarian*, vol. xv, pp. 11–15, July 1885.

"Sanitary Sewage and Water Supply," *Transactions of Sanitary Institute*, vol. ix, pp. 343–8, 1887.

"Sanitary Conditions of Water Supplies," *Transactions of Sanitary Institute*, vol. ix, pp. 348–51, 1887.

"Elementary Education Question and the Half-time System," Longmans, 1887.

"Progress of sanitation, civil and military, to the year 1888," to Association of Public Sanitary Inspectors, 1888, *Journal of Society of Arts*, vol. xxvi, pp. 1029–34, 7 September 1888.

"General History of Principles of Sanitation," Cassell and Co., London, 1889.

"Present Condition of Sanitary Science," to Association of Public Sanitary Inspectors, *Sanitarian*, vol. xii, pp. 385–95, May 1889.

"Competitive Examination," London, 1890.

C. OFFICAL REPORTS DRAFTED WHOLLY OR PARTLY BY CHADWICK

First Report from Commissioners appointed to collect information . . . relative to employment of children in factories, 1833, vol. xx, p. 1.

Second Report, 1833, vol. xxi. p. 1.

Supplementary Reports, 1834, vol. xix, p. 253, vol. xx, p. 1.

Report from Commissioners for inquiring into the administration and practical operation of the Poor Laws, 1834, vol. xxvii, p. 1.

Appendix (A) Parts II, III, IV: "Evidence collected by Edwin Chadwick; Rural Questions," 1834, vol xxix, p. 1.

Chadwick's report on London and Berkshire was reprinted in *Extracts from the information received by His Majesty's Commissioners, as to the administration and operation of the Poor Laws*, London, 1833 (pp. 201–339).

First Report of Commissioners appointed to inquire into the best means of establishing an efficient constabulary force in the counties of England and Wales, 1839, vol. xix, p. 1.

Report of the Poor Law Commissioners to the Secretary of State, on an inquiry into the sanitary condition of the labouring population of Great Britain, 1842, vol. xxvi, p. 1 (House of Lords).

District Reports, 1842, vol. xxvii, p. 1 (House of Lords).

Report on Scotland, 1842, vol. xxviii, p. 1 (House of Lords).

Supplementary Report on the result of a special inquiry into the practice of interment in towns, 1843, vol. xii, p. 395.

First Report of Commissioners for inquiring into the state of large towns and populous districts, 1844, vol. xvii, p. 1.

Second Report, 1845, vol. xviii, pp. 1, 299.

First Report of Commissioners appointed to inquire whether any and what special means may be requisite for the improvement of the health of the metropolis, 1847–8, vol. xxxii, pp. 1, 57.

Second Report, 1847–8, vol. xxxii, p. 253.

Third Report, 1847–8, vol. xxxii, p. 339.

The Reports of the General Board of Health are included in Section E below.

Of the Annual Reports of the Poor Law Commission, Chadwick's

388 BIBLIOGRAPHY

influence is most visible in the First (1835), Fourth (1838) and Fifth (1839).

D. EVIDENCE GIVEN BY CHADWICK BEFORE ROYAL COMMISSIONS AND PARLIAMENTARY COMMITTEES

Select Committee on Metropolitan Police, 1828, vol. vi, p. 1. Chadwick was apparently not summoned as a witness; but the paper at Appendix F, pp. 322–5, is probably his: "Outline of the advantages which would result from extending the circulation of the *Police Gazette*; apprehension of offenders; recovery of stolen property; prevention of crime."

Select Committee on Intoxication among the Labouring Classes, 1834, vol. viii, p. 315; 11 June 1834, pp. 29–40.

Select Committee on the Highways Act, 1837–8, vol. xxiii, p. 325; 5 March 1838, pp. 11–25; 7 March, pp. 34–46.

Select Committee on District Asylums for the Houseless Poor in the Metropolis, 1846, vol. vii, p. 1; 27 February 1846, pp. 86–8; 5 May 1846, pp. 364–75.

Select Committee on Local Acts, 1846, vol. xii, p. 1; 28 May 1846, pp. 21–41.

Select Committee on Railway Labourers, 1846, vol. xiii, p. 411; 16 June 1846, pp. 146–54.

Select Committee on Sewage Manure, 1846, vol. x, p. 535; 26 June 1846, pp. 106–20.

Select Committee on the administration of the Poor Law in the Andover Union, 1846, vol. v, Part I, p. 1; Part II, p. 1; 25 July 1846, pp. 549–68; 28 July, pp. 869–92; 29 July, pp. 893–909; 30 July, pp. 912–26; 927–33, 934–6; 11 August, pp. 1106–7; 15 August pp. 1274–92, 1310–11.

Select Committee on the Law of Settlement, 1847, vol. xi, p. 1, etc. *Fourth Report,* 1847, vol. xi, p. 201; 4 March, 1847, pp. 1–18; 9 March, pp. 18–40; 11 March, pp. 40–63; 16 March, pp. 64–95.

Select Committee (Lords) to consider the subject of Printing Papers for the House of Lords, 1854, vol. xxi, p. 135 (House of Lords); 30 May 1854, pp. 25–30, 35–7.

Papers relating to Re-organisation of Civil Service, 1854–5, vol. xx, p. 1. Chadwick's paper, 1 August 1854, pp. 136–227.

Select Committee on operation of Corrupt Practices Prevention Act, 1854, 1860, vol. x, p. 1; 15 March 1860, pp. 153–67.

Two Papers submitted to Commission (on Popular Education) by Mr. Chadwick, as to half-time teaching and military and naval drill, and on time and cost of popular education on large and small scale, 1862, vol. xliii, p. 1. *Further return, being letter to Mr. Senior, explanatory of former paper, ibid.*, p. 91.

Select Committee on Metropolitan Local Government, 1866, vol. xiii, p. 171. *Second Report*, 1866, vol. xiii, p. 317; 23 July, pp. 223–31.

Select Committee on employment of steam on Tramways, 1877, vol. xvi, p. 445; 22 March 1877, pp. 108–14.

E. PARLIAMENTARY AND DEPARTMENTAL PAPERS

(1) 1831–47: PUBLIC HEALTH, POOR LAW, FACTORY ACT, PRIVATE BILLS

Select Committee on Bill to regulate the labour of children in mines and factories, 1831–2, vol. xv, p. 1.

Instructions from the Central Board of Factory Commissioners to the District and Medical Commissioners, 1833, vol. xxxi, p. 349.

Extracts from Reports made to the Poor Law Commissioners on the subject of the education of the poor, 1833, vol. cccxxiv, p. 657 (House of Lords).

Reports from the Factory Inspectors on the effects of the educational provisions of the Factories Act, 1839, vol. xlii, p. 353.

Select Committee (Lords) on the supply of water to the metropolis, 1840, vol. xxii, p. 715 (House of Lords).

Select Committee on health of towns, 1840, vol. xi, p. 277.

Select Committee on building regulations and the improvement of boroughs, 1842, vol. x, p. 161.

Select Committee on interments in towns, 1842, vol. x, p. 349.

Letters from R. H. Greig and H. Ashworth to E. Chadwick; also, correspondence and return relative to the removal of labourers from agricultural districts to manufacturing districts, 1843, vol. xlv, p. 119.

Select Committee on medical relief to the sick poor, 1844, vol. ix, p. 1. *Second Report*, 1844, vol. ix, p. 31. *Third Report*, 1844, vol. ix, p. 93.

Resolutions relative to Private Bills, 1845, vol xxxvi, pp. 1, 3.

Instructions to Surveying Officers appointed by the Commissioners of Woods and Forests to institute preliminary inquiries, under 9 & 10 Vict., c. 106, in cases of application for Acts for the formation of cemeteries, 1847, vol. xxxiii, p. 87.

Letters from the Poor Law Commissioners to the Secretary of State respecting the transaction of the business of the Commission, 1847, vol. xlix, p. 1.

(2) 1848–54: REPORTS, RETURNS AND OTHER PAPERS RELATING TO THE GENERAL BOARD OF HEALTH

(a) Administration of Public Health and Nuisances Acts

Report on the measures adopted for the execution of the Nuisances Removal and Diseases Prevention Act, and the Public Health Act, up to July 1849, 1849, vol. xxiv, p. 1.

Minutes of information collected in respect to the drainage of the lands forming the sites of towns, to road drainage, and the facilitation of the drainage of suburban lands, 1852, vol. xix, p. 1.

Minutes of information collected with reference to works for the removal of soil water, or drainage of dwelling-houses and public edifices, and for the sewerage and cleansing of the sites of towns, 1852, vol. xix, p. 307.

Minutes of information collected on the practical application of sewer water and town manures to agricultural production, 1852, vol. xix, p. 133.

Copies of the correspondence between the General Board of Health and the Metropolitan Sanitary Association, on the subject of amendments in the Nuisances Removal Act, 1852, vol. xvii, p. 285 (House of Lords).

Reports on an inquiry relative to prevalence of disease at Croydon, and to plan of sewerage, 1852–3, vol. xcvi, p. 35. *Further Reports from Board of Health,* ibid., p. 221. *Statement of preliminary inquiry, etc.,* ibid., p. 117.

*Minutes of Evidence taken before the Select Committee of the House of Lords on the Bill " to confirm certain Provisional Orders of the General Board of Health for Hertford, Accrington, Bangor and Uxbridge, etc., "*1852–3, vol. xxxi, p. 231 (House of Lords).

Report on state of works of drainage and sewerage, etc. (at Croydon) by Thomas Wicksteed, 1854, vol. lxi, p. 347.

Copies of all correspondence, memorials and reports, in reference to the application of the Public Health Act to the township of Barton-upon-Irwell, 1854, vol. lxi, p. 1.

Report on administration of the Public Health Act, and Nuisances Removal and Diseases Prevention Acts, from 1848 to 1854, 1854, vol. xxxv, p. 1.

Details of the receipt and expenditure of the Board, the persons in their employment, the number and names of places from which applications were made, the method of applying the Act, the amounts of the mortgages secured on local rates, the average cost of the works, etc., may be found in the following returns:

1850, vol. xxxiii, p. 335.
1850, vol. xxxiii, p. 591.
1851, vol. xliii, p. 321.
1852, vol. liii, p. 1.
1852–3, vol. xcvi. p. 1.
1854–5, vol. liii, p. 19.
1857 (Sess. 2), vol. xli, p. 3.
1867, vol. lix, p. 141.

Orders in Council for the application of the Public Health Act were published in the *London Gazette*, as were also the Notifications in respect to the Nuisances Removal and Diseases Prevention Act. Specimens of the Provisional Orders are given in *P.P.*, 1850, vol. xx,

p. 321 (House of Lords): "Provisional Orders for the application of the Public Health Act to Stratford-upon-Avon, Dartford, Newport (Mon.), Brecon, Harrow, Derby, Dover, Chelmsford and York."

The collection of Chadwick's pamphlets in the British Museum contains some 140 of the local reports by the Inspectors of the General Board.

(b) Cholera, 1848–9 and 1853–4

Report to the Poor Law Commission on the capabilities of the Metropolitan Workhouses for the reception and treatment of cholera cases, 1847–8, vol. li, p. 431.

Report of the General Board of Health on the epidemic cholera of 1848 and 1849, 1850, vol. xxi, p. 3.

Despatches and other documents relating to the outbreak of the cholera in the island of Jamaica, 1851, vol. xxxvi, p. 561.

Memorandum addressed to Viscount Palmerston, Her Majesty's Secretary of State for the Home Department, on behalf of a deputation which waited on him, on 27th February 1854, for the purpose of urging the necessity of preparations against the apprehended return of the cholera, 1854, vol. xix, p. 43 (House of Lords).

Letter from Dr. H. Gavin, Medical Superintending Inspector, General Board of Health, showing benefits resulting from house-to-house visitation in Newcastle, Dundee and Glasgow, 1854, vol. lxi, p. 109.

Report of Commissioners on causes of outbreak of cholera in towns of Newcastle-upon-Tyne, Gateshead and Tynemouth, 1854, vol. xxxv, p. 131.

(c) Metropolitan Interments Act

Report on a general scheme for extra-mural sepulture, 1850, vol. xxi, p. 573.

Report to the General Board of Health, by Dr. Sutherland, on the practice of intramural interments in the metropolis, 1850, vol. xxxix, Part I, p. 153 (House of Lords).

Number of interments that have taken place in the churchyard and vaults of the church of St. Margaret's (Westminster), 1840 to 1849, 1850, vol. xxxiii, p. 369.

Report "on the circumstances attending the revolting practices that have been said to occur in the St. Giles's cemetery in the parish of St. Pancras" by H. Austin and R. Rawlinson, 1850, vol. xxxix, Part I, p. 1 (House of Lords).

Report of preliminary proceedings under the Metropolitan Interment Act from 5th August to 31st December 1850, 1851, vol. xxiii, p. 429.

Second Annual Report of the General Board of Health, under sec. 73 of the Metropolitan Interment Act, 1852, vol. xx, p. 97.

Minutes of the Board of Health relating to the Metropolitan Interments Act since August 1850; and correspondence relative to the purchase of cemeteries, and the Abbey Wood Estate, 1852, vol. liii, p. 37.

Expenditure under the Act is shown in the following returns:

1851, vol. xxiii, p. 429.

1852, vol. liii, p. 227.

1852, vol. liii, p. 1.

(d) *Metropolitan Water Supply Bill.*

Report by the General Board of Health on the supply of water to the metropolis, 1850, vol. xxii, p. 1.

Extract Minute from the proceedings of the General Board of Health, 7 February 1850, respecting supply of water to the metropolis by proposed new companies, 1850, vol. xxii, p. 965.

Letter from the General Board of Health to the Secretary of State, dated 5th July 1850, transmitting a Minute of the Board with reference to the River Lea Trust Bill and the New River Company Bill, 1850, vol. xx, p. 351 (House of Lords).

Report on the proposed gathering grounds for the supply of the metropolis from the soft water springs of the Surrey sands, by the Hon. William Napier, 1851, vol. xxiii, p. 61.

Report by Mr. Rammell, an Inspector of the Board of Health, on the soft water springs in the Surrey sands, etc., 1851, vol. xxiii, p. 137.

Report of the Commissioners on the chemical quality of the supply of water to the metropolis, 1851, vol. xxiii, p. 401.

Select Committee on the Metropolis Water Bill, 1851, vol. xv, p. 1.

Select Committee on the Metropolis Water Supply Bill, and the Chelsea Water-works Bill, 1852, vol. xii, p. 1.

Further minutes of evidence relative to the New River, East London Waterworks, and Lee River Trust Bills, and the Wandle Water and Sewage Bill, 1852, vol. xii, p. 221.

Further minutes of evidence relative to the East London, Southwark and Vauxhall, Grand Junction, West Middlesex and London (Watford) Spring Water Companies' Bills, 1852, vol. xii, p. 561.

Select Committee of the House of Lords on the Metropolitan Water Supply, 1852, vol. xxi, p. 339 (House of Lords).

Return of gaugings, reports and communications in relation to the sources of the soft-water springs in the Surrey or other sands for the supply of the metropolis, received by the General Board of Health since the presentation of their Report on the supply of water to the metropolis, 1852, vol. xxxi, p. 515 (House of Lords).

(e) Relations with the Metropolitan Commission of Sewers

Statement transmitted by Mr. John Leslie, to the Secretary of State for the Home Department, complaining of the constitution and administration of the Commission of Westminster Sewers, etc. 1847, vol. lvii, p. 123.

Letter from the Chairman of the Metropolitan Commission of Sewers to the Secretary of State, transmitting a report on the transactions of the Commissioners during the year 1850, 1851, vol. xlviii, p. 75.

Reports of Mr. Bazalgette relating to Pipe and Tunnel Sewers, 1852–3, vol. xcvi, p. 511.

Select Committee on Great London Drainage Bill, 1852–3, vol. xxvi, p. 387.

Reports and Communications by Board of Health to Home Secretary on the drainage of the metropolis, 1854, vol. lxi, p. 113.

Communication from General Board of Health, and reports of Superintending Inspectors, in respect to operation of pipe sewers, 1854–5, vol. xlv, p. 295.

Reports of District Engineers on working of pipe sewers, 1854–5, vol. liii, p. 173.

(f) Miscellaneous Activities

Letter, dated 19 March 1849, from the Board of Health to the Treasury on the advantages of printing official reports in the octavo, instead of the folio form, 1849, vol. xlv, p. 21.

Report of the General Board of Health on Quarantine, 1849, vol. xxiv, p. 137.

Report of Dr. Arthur Farre and Mr. Grainger to the General Board of Health, on Thirty-eight metropolitan workhouses, 1850, vol. xxi, p. 737.

Report to the Board of Health in reference to the sanitary condition of Agar Town, St. Pancras, and other parts of the metropolis, 1851, vol. xxiii, p. 1.

Report on a general scheme of extra-mural sepulture for country towns, 1851 vol. xxiii, p. 177.

Second Report on Quarantine: Yellow Fever, 1852, vol. xx, p. 117.

Reports made to the Home Secretary by the Assistant Commissioner of Police on the operation of the Common Lodging-Houses Act, 1851, 1852–3, vol. lxxviii, p. 525; 1854, vol. xxxv, p. 115.

Papers received by Board of Health, exhibiting operation of Common Lodging-Houses Act, 1852–3, vol. lxxviii, p. 553.

Letter from the General Board of Health to the Home Secretary on smoke consumption, 1854, vol. lxi, p. 533.

F. A SELECTION OF BOOKS

(1) BIOGRAPHIES OF CHADWICK

The memoir prefixed to *The Health of Nations* (2 vols., 1887), written by Sir Benjamin Ward Richardson from information communicated by Chadwick himself, is the most authoritative source for Chadwick's personal and family history. It is unfortunately brief and very reticent.

The Board of Health is dismissed in one page, and the mildness of the narrative points to the exercise of a strong censorship by Richardson. The survey of Chadwick's works which follows is largely an uncritical précis, but it contains a few comments by Chadwick himself. An abridged version in one volume, *National Health*, was published in 1890.

Richardson's memoir may be compared with the articles in the *North British Review*, vol. xiii, pp. 40–84, 1850 (by Professor Masson), and *The Sanitarian*, vol. v, pp. 176–82, April 1877, both of which incorporate material supplied by Chadwick himself.

Maurice Marston's *Sir Edwin Chadwick* (1925) is a popular account, of little weight, and based largely on Richardson. *Edwin Chadwick and the Early Public Health Movement in England*, by Dorsey D. Jones (University of Iowa Studies in the Social Sciences, vol. ix, No. 3, 1931) is a more scholarly work, but its sources are limited to the more accessible of the printed materials.

Also:

R. A. Lewis, "Edwin Chadwick and the Railway Labourers," *Economic History Review*, Second Series, vol. iii, No. 1, pp. 107–18, 1950.

"Edwin Chadwick and the Administrative Reform Movement, 1854–56," *University of Birmingham Historical Journal*, vol. ii, No. 2, pp. 178–200, 1951.

Portraits of Chadwick are given in Richardson and Marston (both late, æt. *c.* 70); J. A. Dolmege, *Towards National Health*, 1931, æt. *c.* 45; and, with B. W. Richardson and Professor R. Owen, "A Scientific Triad," in the *Pictorial World* for 29 May 1890. There is a bust of Chadwick in the library of University College, London.

(2) MEMOIRS AND LETTERS OF CONTEMPORARIES

Since sanitary measures were at the very margin of political interest, very little can be derived from the biographies and printed papers of the leading political figures of the time.

E. Hodder's *Life and Work of the Seventh Earl of Shaftesbury* (1886) contains some valuable extracts from Shaftesbury's diary, but is very discreet on controversial issues. Chadwick had to be restrained by Richardson from bursting into print to attack this book, presumably on account of its omissions and the emphasis it lays on Shaftesbury's work at the Board of Health at the expense of his colleagues.

Dr. Southwood Smith (1899) by the Doctor's granddaughter, C. L. Lewes, is a guileless essay in hero-worship, which regards him as the originator and chief figure in the public health agitation, barely mentioning Chadwick. Though its documentary value is slight, however, it succeeds in conveying an impression of Southwood Smith's charm of character. See also F. Howell, *Sanitary Reform and Services of Dr. Southwood Smith in connection therewith* (pamphlet, 1855).

For the Earl of Carlisle there is little except the *D.N.B.* article by G. F. Russell Barker and the essay by Harriet Martineau in *Biographical Sketches* (4th ed., 1876).

The Letters, Remains, and Memoirs of Edward Adolphus Seymour, Twelfth Duke of Somerset, K.G., ed. W. H. Mallock and Lady Gwendolen Ramsden (1893), is quite useless, Chadwick and the Board of Health being nowhere mentioned. There is a sketch of Seymour's life in *The Seymour Family*, by A. Audrey Locke (1911).

For G. C. Lewis there are the *Letters*, edited by Sir Gilbert Frankland Lewis (1870), and the essay by W. Bagehot in his *Biographical Studies* (1881). A memoir of George Nicholls, by H. G. Willink, is prefixed to vol. i of the 1898 edition of his *English Poor Law*.

Also:

M. Bowley, *Nassau Senior and Classical Economics*, 1937.

J. Bowring, *Memoirs of Jeremy Bentham*, 1843.

H. Cole, *Fifty Years of Public Work*, 1894.

E. B. de Fonblanque, *Life and Letters of Albany Fonblanque*, 1874.

Mrs. Grote, *The Personal Life of George Grote*, 1873.

M. Greenwood, *The Medical Dictator, and other Biographical Studies*, 1936 (for William Farr).

W. Hale-White, *Great Doctors of the Nineteenth Century*, 1935 (for John Simon and Neil Arnott).

J. L. and B. Hammond, *Lord Shaftesbury*, 1923.

N. A. Humphreys, *Vital Statistics: a memorial volume of selections from the reports and writings of William Farr*, 1885.

R. E. Leader, *Life and Letters of J. A. Roebuck*, 1897.

J. G. Lockhart, *Viscount Halifax, 1839–1885*, 1935 (for Sir Charles Wood).

A. Newsholme, Lecture on William Farr, *Economica*, Nov. 1923.

R. Owen, *Life of Richard Owen*, 1894.

W. Reid, *Memoirs and Correspondence of Lyon Playfair*, 1899.

B. W. Richardson, *Disciples of Æsculapius*, 1900 (for Thomas Wakley and John Snow).

F. Smith, *Life and Work of Sir J. Kay-Shuttleworth*, 1923.

(3) The Public Health Movement

Sir John Simon's *English Sanitary Institutions* (1890) is the fullest and best account, written by an authority who knew and respected the leaders of the movement and very largely shared their theories. *The*

Public Health Agitation, 1833–48, by B. L. Hutchins (1909), reprints a series of lectures delivered at the London School of Economics, and contains short but useful studies of Southwood Smith and Chadwick. *The Story of English Public Health*, by Sir Malcolm Morris (1919), is admittedly based on Simon. A more recent study, *Towards National Health*, by J. A. Dolmege (1931) pushes the story back into earlier centuries.

The work of earlier reformers is described in M. C. Buer, *Health, Wealth, and Population in the early days of the Industrial Revolution*, 1926; M. D. George, *London Life in the Eighteenth Century*, 1925; G. T. Griffith, *Population Problems of the Age of Malthus*, 1926.

Also:

Sir George Newman, *The Rise of Preventive Medicine*, 1932.

    The Building of a Nation's Health, 1939.

    Health and Social Evolution, 1931.

Sir A. Newsholme, *Elements of Vital Statistics*, 1889 (contains examples of Chadwick's statistical blunders).

    Ministry of Health, 1925.

H.M.S.O., *The Story of the General Registry Office* (centenary volume, 1937).

The best introduction to the medical theories of the time is probably given by the two classics of epidemiology, John Snow's *On the Mode of Communication of Cholera*, 1849 (reprint of second edition of 1854, entitled *Snow on Cholera*, New York, 1936) and William Budd's *Typhoid Fever*, 1874 (reprinted ,New York, 1931). Southwood Smith's views are stated in his *Philosophy of Health* (1835).

Also:

C. Creighton, *History of Epidemics in Britain*, 1894.

F. H. Garrison, *An Introduction to the History of Medicine*, 1914.

E. W. Goodall, *A Short History of Infectious Epidemic Diseases*, 1934.

M. Greenwood, *Epidemiology, Historical and Experimental*, 1932.

D. J. Guthrie, *History of Medicine*, 1945.

H. H. Scott, *Some Notable Epidemics*, 1934.

H. E. Sigerist, *Man and Medicine*, 1932.

C. Singer, *A Short History of Medicine*, 1928.

H. Zinsser, *Rats, Lice, and History*, 1935.

(4) ADMINISTRATIVE AND ECONOMIC HISTORY

E. Cannan, *History of Local Rates in England*, 1896.

C. T. Carr, *Concerning English Administrative Law*, 1941.

J. H. Clapham, *Economic History of Modern Britain*, 1930.

F. Clifford, *History of Private Bill Legislation*, 1885.

E. W. Cohen, *The Growth of the British Civil Service*, 1941.

S. Dowell, *History of Taxation and Taxes in England from the Earliest Times to the year 1885*, 1888.

H. Finer, *The British Civil Service*, revised edition 1937.

G. L. Gomme, *London in the Reign of Victoria*, 1898.

B. K. Gray, *Philanthropy and the State*, 1908.

H. R. G. Greaves, *The Civil Service in the Changing State*, 1947.

E. Halévy, *History of the English People*, 1924–7.

J. L. and B. Hammond, *Age of the Chartists*, 1930.

B. L. Hutchins and J. A. Harrison, *History of Factory Legislation*, 1911.

H. Jephson, *The Sanitary Evolution of London*, 1907.

H. J. Laski, W. I. Jennings, and W. A. Robson (ed.), *A Century of Municipal Progress*, 1935.

R. Moses, *History of the Civil Service*, 1914.

G. Nicholls, *History of the English Poor Law*, 1854.

A. Redford, *History of Local Government in Manchester*, 1939.

A. H. Robson, *The Education of Children engaged in Industry, 1833–1876*, 1931.

G. Slater, *Poverty and the State*, 1930.

K. Smellie, *A Hundred Years of English Government*, 1937.

F. H. Spencer, *Municipal Origins*, 1911.

S. and B. Webb, *Statutory Authorities*.
  English Poor Law History (vols. 4 and 7–9 of *English Local Government*, 1906–29).

W. H. Wickwar, *The Public Services*, 1938.

O. C. Williams, *Historical Development of Private Bill Procedure and Standing Orders in the House of Commons*, vol. i, 1948.

A. Wilson and H. Levy, *Workmen's Compensation*, 1939.
  Burial Reform and Funeral Costs, 1938.

G. PAMPHLETS

The great majority of Chadwick's collection of pamphlets, covering all his multifarious interests, poor law, public health, education, police, agriculture, etc., are deposited in the British Museum. They fill 535 volumes, under the Press mark C.T.

Part of Chadwick's library, 274 books and 43 pamphlets, was given to the Manchester Public Libraries in 1891 by his son, Osbert Chadwick.

INDEX